OUR FACE FROM FISH TO MAN.

1. Devonian shark; 2. Upper Devonian air-breathing, lobe-finned fish; 3. Lower Carboniferous amphibian; 4. Permo-Carboniferous reptile; 5. Triassic mammal-like reptile; 6. Cretaceous mammal; 7. Lemuroid primate; 8. Recent Old World monkey; 9. Chimpanzee; 10. Tasmanian; 11. Roman athlete.

For details see p. xiii.

OUR FACE
FROM FISH TO MAN

*A Portrait Gallery of Our Ancient Ancestors
and Kinsfolk together with a Concise
History of Our Best Features*

BY

WILLIAM K. GREGORY

Professor of Vertebrate Palæontology, Columbia University;
Associate in Anthropology and Curator of the Depart-
ments of Ichthyology and Comparative Anatomy,
American Museum of Natural History; Member
of the National Academy of Sciences, etc.

WITH A FOREWORD BY
WILLIAM BEEBE

With 119 *Illustrations*

(Facsimile of the 1929 edition)

HAFNER PUBLISHING COMPANY
New York and London
1967

Originally published 1929
Reprinted 1967

Printed and published by
HAFNER PUBLISHING COMPANY, INC.
31 East 10th Street
New York, N.Y. 10003

Library of Congress Catalogue Card Number 63-14246

TO

HENRY FAIRFIELD OSBORN

FOREWORD

BY WILLIAM BEEBE

A FOREWORD to a volume such as the present one of Dr. Gregory's is as superfluous as would be the retention of the third eye, the Cyclopean one, of our ancestors, in the center of our forehead today. No more wonderful subject for a volume could be imagined than the evolution of the human face, and no more competent author than William K. Gregory. The result seems to me eminently satisfactory.

If the reader's interest is real but cursory, let him do nothing but look at the illustrations. They will ensure a thousand percent interest to every walk along Fifth Avenue or Regent Street. If pressure of other interests permits only an hour's perusal, or complete lack of natural history knowledge requires facts to be strained through the mesh of popular language, read but the preface and the first few paragraphs of each chapter. Taken as a whole this is not a "popular" book in

iii

the sense of a superficial one. The details of evolution of our eyes, ears, nostrils, mouth—these are too delicate, too intricate for words of one syllable. Yet to read and understand this volume requires no more concentrated attention than the remembrance of the highest diamond in the ninth trick, or to what Steel Preferred fell in the Autumn of 1914.

I advise no Fundamentalist or Anti-Evolutionist to read it, for if he have no sense of humor he will not understand it, and if he have, his belief will be like Dunsany's King who "was as though he never had been." If with Bergson we believe that the origin of laughter was cruelty, then an S. P. C. to something should be formed to prevent the spectacle of a Fundamentalist's face functioning with the third eyelid of a bird, the ear-point of a deer, the honorable scars of most ancient gills, and with his lip-lifting muscles in full action as he sneers at truth. A moment's thought of these few characters presents a new viewpoint on what we are wont to call the "lower" animals, for if our third eyelid were more than a degenerate flap we, like an eagle, could look straight at the sun; if our ears could straighten and turn as once, the lives of

FOREWORD

pedestrians would be safer; if the ghosts of gills were still functional, drowning would be impossible, and if the fang-revealing sneer showed less degenerate canines, we might have a more physically wholesome fear of cavilers against the doctrine of Evolution.

The impregnable array of facts gleaned through the centuries of man's intellectual supremacy proves beyond all question the gradual rise toward human perfection of the various components of the face, and this confirms our precious organs of sense as most noble gateways of the human mind and soul. Kindness, gentleness, tactfulness, patience, can flow out through only these channels. It is a worthy thing to have written a book about them; it is a fortunate chance to be able to read it.

PREFACE

According to popular standards of civilized peoples, men of one's own race and tongue were called "men," "warriors," "heroes," but people of other races were "barbarians," "unholy ones," "foreign devils." The founder of one's own clan was often considered to be the son of a deity, while the barbarians were the descendants of monkeys or other wild animals. Or the first man was created perfect, in the image of God. One's own family, of course, was fairly true to type but sin had played havoc with the features of other races. To believe all this was comforting to one's own "face" in a world where the inferiority complex occasionally haunted even kings.

Imagine then the effect of telling one-hundred-percent Americans that they are not the descendants of the god-like Adam but are sons and daughters of *Dryopithecus*, or of some nearly allied genus of anthropoid apes that lived in the Miocene age,—and that before that they had long tails and ate grubs and beetles!

If the reader is curious to know the worst he will find it in these pages. There even his own great-grandfather—a Jove-like patriarch with ample beard, piercing eyes and an aquiline nose—will be subjected to unsparing analysis. It will be shown how much the proud old gentleman was indebted to a long line of freebooting forbears that struggled for a precarious living in the sea, on muddy flats, on the uplands or in the trees—æons before Adam delved or Eve span. In detail it will even be charged that the real founder of the family was not the powerful settler to whom the king gave a grant of land extending far back from the river, but a poor mud-sucking protochordate of pre-Silurian times; that when in some far-off dismal swamp a putrid prize was snatched by scaly forms, their facial masks already bore *our* eyes and nose and mouth.

Accordingly this little book can hardly expect much popularity either in Tennessee, where the very idea of evolution is anathema, or in the metropolitan strongholds where pithecophobia is still prevalent and man's complete superiority to the

PREFACE

all too man-like apes is somewhat nervously stressed.

Nor can the author hope for much favor from the public, that wants only results and is willing to spend a billion dollars annually on cosmetics and safety razors. For this book does not pretend to tell how to improve one's face but only how and why one has one.

At best then it can only hold a magic mirror up to proud man and bid him contemplate his own image—a composite of an infinitely receding series of faces,—human, prehuman, anthropoid, long-snouted, lizard-like,—stretching back into the shadows of endless time.

CONTENTS

PAGE

FOREWORD iii

PREFACE vii

PART I.   PORTRAIT GALLERY OF OUR ANCIENT
RELATIVES AND ANCESTORS

THE VALUE OF A FACE 3

THE BEGINNINGS OF OUR FACE . . . 4

THE SHARK'S FACE AND OURS . . . 12

THE MASK-FACE OF OUR GILLED ANCESTORS . 20

OUR ANCESTORS COME OUT OF THE WATER . 27

WHAT WE OWE TO THE EARLY REPTILES . 32

THE ONE-PIECE JAW REPLACES THE COMPLEX
TYPE 36

OUR MASK-FACE BECOMES MOBILE . . 40

OUR LONG-SNOUTED ANCESTORS CROWD OUT
THE DINOSAURS 45

BETTER FACES COME IN WITH LIFE IN THE
TREE-TOPS 52

THE ALMOST HUMAN FACE APPEARS . . 64

AT LAST THE "PERFECT" FACE . . . 70

PART II. CONCISE HISTORY OF OUR BEST FEATURES

THE BONY FRAMEWORK OF THE GOD-LIKE MASK 83

FISH-TRAPS AND FACES 92

xi

CONTENTS

PAGE

THE FIRST MOUTHS 92

THE BEGINNINGS OF TEETH . . . 97

THE PRIMARY JAWS 102

THE RISE OF THE SECONDARY JAWS AND THEIR
TEETH 106

ORIGIN OF THE MAMMALIAN PALATE . . 118

EVOLUTION OF THE TONGUE AND RELATED
STRUCTURES 123

ORIGIN AND EVOLUTION OF THE HUMAN LIPS 129

LATER STAGES IN THE HISTORY OF THE TEETH 134

CONCLUSIONS 152

HISTORY OF THE NOSE 153

OPTICAL PHOTOGRAPHY AND ITS RESULTS . 173

THE HUMAN EYES AS INSTRUMENTS OF PRECISION 173

THE EYES OF INVERTEBRATES . . . 173

ORIGIN OF THE PAIRED EYES OF VERTEBRATES 182

ORIGIN OF THE HUMAN EYES . . . 188

CONCLUSIONS 200

PRIMITIVE SOUND RECORDERS . . . 202

ANCIENT AND MODERN PHYSIOGNOMY . . 220

THE FACE OF THE FUTURE 240

LOOKING BACKWARD 245

LITERATURE CITED 247

INDEX 261

ILLUSTRATIONS

PAGE

OUR FACE FROM FISH TO MAN . . *Frontispiece*

    1. Devonian shark, *Cladoselache;* 2. Upper Devonian
air-breathing, lobe-finned fish, *Eusthenopteron;* 3. Lower
Carboniferous amphibian, *Eogyrinus;* 4. Permo-Carboniferous reptile, *Seymouria;* 5. Triassic mammal-like
reptile, *Ictidopsis;* 6. Cretaceous mammal, *Eodelphis;*
7. Lemuroid primate, *Propithecus;* 8. Recent Old World
monkey; 9. Chimpanzee; 10. Tasmanian; 11. Roman
athlete.

FIGURE

1.—THE FIRST MOUTHS 5

    A. Slipper animalcule (*Paramœcium*) with gash-
like mouth.

    B. Jellyfish (*Tessera*), a two-layered sac with
primitive mouth.

    (Both after Parker and Haswell.)

2.—TWO EARLY STAGES IN THE EVOLUTION OF A
    HEAD . . . . . . *facing* 6

    A. Flatworm (*Planaria*), showing head-and-tail
differentiation, including the beginnings of a brain and
of eyes.

    B. Sand-flea (*Orchestia*), showing the interrelations
of eye, brain, mouth, leg-jaws and nerve cord.

    (Both after Parker and Haswell.)

3.—THE RISE OF THE VERTEBRATES IN GEOLOGIC
    TIMES 9

4.—SOME OF OUR EARLIEST KNOWN KINSFOLK:
    UPPER SILURIAN AND DEVONIAN OSTRACO-
    DERMS 11

    A. *Pterolepis.* (After Kiaer.)
    B. *Tremataspis.* (After Rohon.)

xiii

ILLUSTRATIONS

FIGURE   PAGE

    C.   *Tremataspis.* (After Patten.)

    D.   *Pteraspis.* (After Powrie and Lankester.)

    E.   *Cephalaspis.* (Composite, mainly after Patten.)

5.—THE FACE OF THE MOST PRIMITIVE LIVING
SHARK, *Chlamydoselachus anguineus* . *facing* 12
(After Garman.)

6.—INSTRUMENTS OF PRECISION IN THE HEAD OF A
SHARK, *Chlamydoselachus anguineus* . . 13
(After Allis.)
Lateral line canals black, bordered with white;
nerves white; muscles streaked; cartilage stippled.

7.—CARTILAGINOUS SKELETON OF HEAD OF SHARK 17
Comprising braincase, primary upper and lower jaws
and branchial arches.

8.—JAW MUSCLES OF SHARK (*Chlamydoselachus*) . 18
Showing the essential similarity of the jaw muscles
to the constrictors of the branchial arches. (Composite drawing based on the data of Allis and Garman.)

9.—CROSS-SECTION OF THE SKULL OF A FOSSIL GAN-
OID FISH, SHOWING THE BONE CELLS (*Osteo-
lepis* FROM THE DEVONIAN OF RUSSIA) . *facing* 20
(After Pander.)

10.—THE WEDGE-SHAPED BRAINCASE OF A FISH,
ACTING AS A THRUST-BLOCK OR FULCRUM
FOR THE BACKBONE 22
The surface bones of the left cheek region have been
removed to show the base of the skull and the elements
dependent from it on the right side. (Modified from
a drawing of the skull of the Striped Bass by F. A.
Lucas.)

11.—THE FACIAL ARMOR AND JAWS OF A DEVONIAN
LOBE-FINNED GANOID FISH (*Osteolepis*) *facing* 22
(After Pander.)
The skull seen from above.

ILLUSTRATIONS

FIGURE   PAGE

12.—FIRST CLAIMANT TO THE LINE OF ANCESTRY
     OF THE HIGHER VERTEBRATES. DEVONIAN
     "LOBE-FIN" (*Eusthenopteron*)   .   .   *facing* 23
        (Reconstruction by Bryant.)

13.—SECOND CLAIMANT TO THE LINE OF ANCESTRY OF
     THE HIGHER VERTEBRATES. DEVONIAN DIP-
     NOAN (*Dipterus*)   .   .   .   .   *facing* 24
        (Restoration by Pander.)

14.—EMBRYOS OF MODERN LOBE-FINNED FISH (A)
     AND AMPHIBIAN (B)   26
        A. Embryo of *Polypterus bichir*. (After Budgett.)
        B. Embryo of *Amblystoma punctatum*. (After S. F.
        Clarke.)

15.—ONE OF THE MOST PRIMITIVE KNOWN AMPHIB-
     IANS (*Eogyrinus*) FROM THE LOWER CARBON-
     IFEROUS OF ENGLAND   28
        Restoration of skeleton. (Based on data of D. M. S.
        Watson.)

16.—SKULL OF ONE OF THE OLDEST KNOWN AMPHIB-
     IANS (*Loxomma allmani*)   .   .   .   *facing* 28
        (After Embleton and Atthey.)
        A. Upper surface.
        B. Under side.

17.—SKULLS OF LOBE-FINNED FISH AND EARLY
     AMPHIBIAN, SHOWING LOSS OF OPERCULAR
     SERIES IN THE LATTER   30
        A. Lobe-finned fish, essentially *Rhizodopsis*. (From
        data by Traquair and Watson.)
        B. Primitive amphibian, *Palæogyrinus*.   (After
        Watson.)
        In the primitive amphibians the space formerly
        covered by the opercular region was covered by the
        tympanum or drum membrane.

ILLUSTRATIONS

FIGURE   PAGE

18.—CROSS-SECTION OF LABYRINTHODONT TEETH
following 30

    A. Lobe-finned Devonian fish (*Polyplocodus*). (After Pander.)

    B. Primitive amphibian of Carboniferous age (*Loxomma allmani*). (After Embleton and Atthey.)

19.—TWO CRITICAL STAGES IN THE EARLY EVOLUTION OF THE SKULL 33

    A. Generalized reptile (*Seymouria*), retaining the full complement of amphibian skull elements. The temporal region, covering the upper jaw muscles, is still covered with a shell of bone as in primitive amphibians and fishes. The otic notch (where the tympanum, or drum membrane, was attached) is retained. (After data of Broili, Watson, Williston.)

    B. Primitive theromorph reptile (*Mycterosaurus*) with reduced number of skull elements and perforated temporal roof. The otic notch has disappeared. (After Williston.)

20.—SKULLS OF EARLIER AND LATER MAMMAL-LIKE REPTILES FROM SOUTH AFRICA . . 35

    A. *Scymnognathus*, a primitive, more reptile-like member of the therapsid series.

    B. *Ictidopsis*, a more advanced mammal-like member of the same series. Specimens in the American Museum of Natural History, with data from Broom, Watson, Haughton.

21.—PROGRESSIVE UPGROWTH OF THE DENTARY BONE OF THE LOWER JAW TO FORM A NEW JOINT WITH THE SKULL 37

    A. Primitive mammal-like reptile (*Scymnognathus*).
    B. Advanced mammal-like reptile (*Ictidopsis*).
    C. Primitive mammal (*Thylacinus*).

22.—ORIGIN OF THE INTERARTICULAR DISC, OR MENISCUS, LYING BETWEEN THE LOWER JAW AND ITS SOCKET IN THE SKULL . . 38

    (After Gaupp.)

xvi

ILLUSTRATIONS

FIGURE   PAGE

23.—ORIGIN OF THE FACIAL MUSCLES OF MAN .   42

A. Primitive reptile (*Labidosaurus*) with continuous bony mask covering skull. (After Williston.) The mask was covered with thick skin without muscles, as in the alligator.

B. Modern reptile (*Sphenodon*) with an open or fenestrated skull covered with thick, non-muscular skin. The seventh nerve (heavy black line) is seen beneath the sphincter colli muscle, a broad band around the throat. (From Fürbringer, modified from Ruge.)

C. Primitive mammal (*Echidna*) in which the sphincter colli system has grown forward over the face. (After Ruge.)

D. Gorilla. E. Man. (Both after Ruge.)

24.—DIAGRAM SHOWING THE CHIEF BRANCHES OF THE FACIAL NERVE   44

A. Gorilla. (After Ruge.)
B. Man. (After Weisse.)

25.—SUCCESSIVE DOMINANCE OF THE AMPHIBIANS, REPTILES, MAMMALS AND BIRDS, MAN . 46

26.—THE COMMON OPOSSUM, A "LIVING FOSSIL" FROM THE AGE OF DINOSAURS .   . *facing* 46

27.—SKULL PARTS OF EXTINCT OPOSSUM (*Eodelphis*) FROM THE UPPER CRETACEOUS OF MONTANA 48
Superposed on outlines of skull of recent opossum.

28.—SKULLS OF (A) ADVANCED MAMMAL-LIKE REPTILE (*Ictidopsis*) FROM THE TRIASSIC OF SOUTH AMERICA AND OF (B) A MODERN OPOSSUM   49

29.—LONG-SNOUTED RELATIVES OF OURS FROM THE CRETACEOUS OF MONGOLIA   .   .   . 50

A. Skull of *Deltatheridium pretrituberculare*. Natural size.

ILLUSTRATIONS

FIGURE   PAGE

    B. Restoration of same.

    C. Skull of *Zalambdalestes lechei*. Natural size.

    D. Restoration of same.

    (All after Gregory and Simpson.)

30.—THE PEN-TAILED TREE-SHREW OF BORNEO *facing* 52

    A "living fossil" representing a little-modified survivor of the Cretaceous ancestors of the Primates. (Based on photographs and data given by Le Gros Clark.)

31.—THE SPECTRAL TARSIER OF BORNEO   . *facing* 53

    A highly specialized modern survivor of a diversified group of primates that lived in the Lower Eocene epoch over fifty million years ago. (Drawn from specimen preserved in formalin, with aid of data from photograph of a living *Tarsius* by H. C. Raven.)

32.—SKELETON OF A PRIMITIVE FOSSIL PRIMATE (*Notharctus osborni*), FROM THE EOCENE OF WYOMING .   .   .   .   . *facing* 54

33.—SKULL OF A PRIMITIVE PRIMATE OF THE EOCENE EPOCH (*Notharctus osborni*) .   . 55

    Natural size. (After Gregory.)

34.—ASCENDING GRADES OF FACES IN THE LOWER PRIMATES .   .   .   .   . *facing* 56

    A. Lemur (*Lemur variegatus*) with fox-like muzzle and laterally-placed eyes. (After Elliot.)

    B. South American Monkey (*Cebus capucinus*) with shortened muzzle and widely separated nostrils. (After Elliot.)

    C. Old World Monkey (*Lasiopyga pygerythrus*) with nostrils approximated and forwardly-directed eyes. (After Elliot.)

35.—TOP VIEW OF THE SKULL IN REPRESENTATIVES OF SIX FAMILIES OF PRIMATES, SHOWING THE MORE FORWARD DIRECTION OF THE ORBITS IN THE HIGHER FORMS 58

FIGURE   PAGE

    A. Fossil lemuroid (*Notharctus*). Eocene epoch.
    B. African lemur (*Arctocebus*).
    C. *Tarsius spectrum*, Borneo.
    D. Marmoset (*Midas*).
    E. Gibbon (*Hylobates*).
    F. Chimpanzee (*Anthropopithecus*).

36.—SIDE VIEW OF SKULLS OF PRIMATES, SHOWING PROGRESSIVE SHORTENING OF THE MUZZLE, DOWNWARD BENDING OF THE SUBORBITAL FACE AND FORWARD GROWTH OF THE CHIN   59

    A. Eocene lemuroid (*Notharctus*).
    B. Old World Monkey (*Lasiopyga kolbi*). (After Elliot.)
    C. Female chimpanzee. (After Elliot.)
    D. Man.

37.—EPITOME OF THE FOSSIL HISTORY OF HUMAN AND PREHUMAN PRIMATES. 1927   .   .   61

Showing the range in geologic time of the different groups, their dental formulæ, the side view of the tooth-bearing part of the lower jaw, the lower dental arch seen from above, and the back part of the lower jaw.

    A. Tree-shrews, represented by jaw of *Leipsanolestes siegfriedti*. (After Simpson. Back part of jaw from modern tree-shrew *Ptilocercus*).

    B. Primitive lemuroid, represented by jaw of *Pelycodus trigonodus*. (After Matthew.)

    C. Proto-anthropoid, represented by jaw of *Parapithecus fraasi*. (After stereoscopic photograph by J. H. McGregor.)

    D. Proto-anthropoid, represented by jaw of *Propliopithecus hæckeli*. (After stereoscopic photograph by J. H. McGregor.)

    E. Man-like anthropoid, represented by jaw of *Sivapithecus himalayensis*. (After Pilgrim.)

    F. Dawn-man, represented by jaw of *Eoanthropus dawsoni*. (After A. S. Woodward.)

ILLUSTRATIONS

FIGURE   PAGE

    G. Primitive man, represented by jaw of *Homo heidelbergensis.* (After Schoetensack.)

    H. Modern man, represented by jaw of *Homo sapiens.* (After Gregory.)

38.—EPITOME OF THE FOSSIL HISTORY OF HUMAN AND PREHUMAN PRIMATES (*continued*) . . 62

    A. Primitive tree-shrew, represented by a left lower molar of *Leipsanolestes.*

    B. Primitive tree-shrew, represented by left upper molar of *Indrodon.*

    C. Primitive lemuroid, represented by left lower molar of *Pelycodus.* (After Matthew.)

    D. Primitive lemuroid, represented by left upper molar of *Pelycodus.* (After Matthew.)

    E. Proto-anthropoid, represented by left lower molar of *Parapithecus.* (From stereoscopic photograph by J. H. McGregor.)

    F. Proto-anthropoid, represented by left lower molar of *Propliopithecus.* (From stereoscopic photograph by J. H. McGregor.)

    G. Proto-anthropoid. Attempted restoration of upper molar to fit known lower molar.

    H. Anthropoid, represented by left lower molar of *Dryopithecus rhenanus.* (From stereoscopic photograph by J. H. McGregor.)

    I. Anthropoid, represented by left upper molar of *Dryopithecus rhenanus.* (From stereoscopic photograph by J. H. McGregor.)

    J. Dawn-man, represented by left lower molar of *Eoanthropus dawsoni.* (From stereoscopic photograph by J. H. McGregor.)

    K. Neanderthal man (*Homo neanderthalensis*), represented by left lower molar of "Le Moustier." (From stereoscopic photograph by J. H. McGregor.)

    L. Neanderthal man, represented by left upper molar of "Le Moustier." (From stereoscopic photograph by J. H. McGregor.)

ILLUSTRATIONS

FIGURE   PAGE

M. Modern man (*Homo sapiens*), represented by
left lower molar.

N. Modern man (*Homo sapiens*), represented by
left upper molar.

39.—ONE OF OUR NEAREST LIVING RELATIVES.
FEMALE CHIMPANZEE AND YOUNG   . *facing* 64

(After Yerkes, from a photograph taken for Mme.
Rosalia Abreu.)   The baby chimpanzee was born in
Mme. Abreu's private collection of living primates,
at Quinta Palatine, Havana, Cuba.

(From "Almost Human."   Courtesy of the author
and The Century Co.)

40.—MALE AND FEMALE CHIMPANZEES . . *facing* 65

(After J. A. Allen, from photographs by Herbert Lang.)

41.—LEFT LOWER CHEEK TEETH OF FOSSIL ANTHRO-
POID (*Dryopithecus*, B) FROM INDIA AND
FOSSIL PRIMITIVE MAN (*Eoanthropus*, A) FROM
PILTDOWN, ENGLAND .   .   .   . *facing* 66

The lower molars of the Piltdown jaw, although
much ground down by wear, show the pure "*Dryopithecus* pattern" characteristic of recent and fossil
apes.

(A, from photograph by J. H. McGregor; B, after
Gregory and Hellman.)

42.—FOSSIL ANTHROPOID AND HUMAN SKULLS   .   68

A. *Australopithecus.*   A young extinct anthropoid,
Bechuanaland, South Africa.   (After Dart.)

B. *Eoanthropus*, England.   (After A. S. Woodward
and J. H. McGregor.)

C. *Pithecanthropus erectus*, Java.   (After Dubois.)

D. Neanderthal (La Chapelle-aux-Saints), Europe.
(After Boule.)

E. Talgai, Australia.   (After Stewart A. Smith.)

F. Rhodesian, South Africa.   (After A. S. Woodward.)

xxi

ILLUSTRATIONS

FIGURE   PAGE

G. Cro-Magnon. (After Verneau.)

In the female and young skulls the brow ridges are less projecting or entirely lacking.

43.—ANTHROPOID AND HUMAN SKULLS. TOP VIEW   69

    A. Chimpanzee. (After Boule.)
    B. *Pithecanthropus.* (After Dubois.)
    C. Neanderthal (La Chapelle-aux-Saints). (After Boule.)
    D. Cro-Magnon. (After Boule.)

44.—ANTHROPOID AND HUMAN SKULLS. FRONT VIEW   70

    (After Boule.)
    A. Chimpanzee.
    B. Neanderthal (La Chapelle-aux-Saints).
    C. Modern European.

45.—COMPARATIVE VIEWS OF SECTIONED LOWER JAWS   71

    A. *Dryopithecus.* (After Gregory and Hellman.)
    B. Chimpanzee.
    C. Piltdown. (After A. S. Woodward.)
    D. Heidelberg. (After Schoetensack.)
    E. Ehringsdorf. (After Virchow.)
    F. Neanderthal (Le Moustier). (After Weinert.)
    G. Cro-Magnon. (After Verneau.)

46.—THE "ALMOST HUMAN" SKULL OF *Australopithecus*, A YOUNG FOSSIL ANTHROPOID . *facing* 72

    (After Dart.)

47.—RESTORATION OF THE HEAD OF THE YOUNG *Australopithecus* . . . . *facing* 73

    (After a drawing by Forrestier made under the direction of Professor G. Elliot Smith.)

48.—EVOLUTION OF THE HUMAN SKULL: TEN STRUCTURAL STAGES   78

    I. Lobe-finned fish, Devonian age (essentially *Rhizodopsis*). (After Traquair, Watson, Bryant.)

ILLUSTRATIONS

FIGURE   PAGE

II. Primitive amphibian (*Palæogyrinus*), Lower Carboniferous. (After Watson.)

III. Primitive cotylosaurian reptile (*Seymouria*), Permo-Carboniferous. (After Broili, Williston, Watson.)

IV. Primitive theromorph reptile (*Mycterosaurus*), Permo-Carboniferous. (After Williston.)

V. Gorgonopsian reptile (*Scymnognathus*), Permian. (After Broom.)

VI. Primitive cynodont reptile (*Ictidopsis*), Triassic. (After Broom, Haughton.)

VII. Primitive marsupial (*Eodelphis*), Upper Cretaceous. (After Matthew.)

VIII. Primitive primate (*Notharctus*), Eocene. (After Gregory.)

IX. Anthropoid (female chimpanzee), Recent.

X. Man, Recent.

49.—EVOLUTION OF THE HUMAN SKULL-ROOF . 79

Same series as in Fig. 48, except that in No. VII the recent opossum instead of its fossil ancestor is used.

Abbreviations: *na*, nasal; *fr*, frontal, *pa*, parietal; *it*, intertemporal; *st*, supratemporal; *tab*, tabular; *dso*, dermosupraoccipital.

50.—EVOLUTION OF THE HUMAN JAWBONES . . 80

Same series as in Fig. 49.

Abbreviations: *pmx*, premaxilla; *mx*, maxilla; *dn*, dentary.

51.—EVOLUTION OF THE CIRCUMORBITAL BONES . 81

Same series as in Fig. 49.

Abbreviations: *prf*, prefrontal; *la*, lacrymal; *ju*, jugal (malar); *po*, postorbital.

52.—EVOLUTION OF THE BONES BEHIND THE JAWS (TEMPOROMANDIBULAR SERIES) . . . 82

Same series as in Fig. 49.

Abbreviations: *sq*, squamosal (squamous portion of

ILLUSTRATIONS

FIGURE   PAGE

temporal); *quj*, quadratojugal; *sur*, surangular; *an*,
angular; *pospl*, postsplenial; *spl*, splenial.

Figures 48–52 give excellent examples of "Williston's
law" of the progressive elimination of skull elements
in passing from fish to man.

53.—EVOLUTION OF THE UNDER SIDE OF THE SKULL   85

I. Lobe-finned fish (*Eusthenopteron*), Devonian.
(After Bryant, Watson.)

II. Primitive amphibian (*Baphetes*), Carboniferous.
(After Watson.)

III. Primitive cotylosaurian reptile (*Seymouria*),
Permo-Carboniferous. (After Watson.)

IV. Advanced cotylosaurian reptile (*Captorhinus*),
Permo-Carboniferous. (Original.)

V. Gorgonopsian reptile (*Scymnognathus*), Permian. (After Watson.)

VI. Advanced mammal-like reptile (*Cynognathus*),
Triassic. (Mainly after Watson.)

VII. Marsupial mammal (*Thylacinus*), Recent.
(Original.)

VIII. Eocene lemuroid primate (*Adapis*). (After
Stehlin.)

IX. Anthropoid (female chimpanzee). (Original.)

X. Man (Australian aboriginal). (Original.)

Abbreviations: *pmx*, premaxilla; *mx*, maxilla; *ju*,
jugal; *quj*, quadratojugal; *qu*, quadrate; *nar*, internal
naris; *pv*, prevomer; *pl*, palatine; *ectpt*, ectopterygoid;
epipt, epipterygoid; *pt*, pterygoid; *pas*, parasphenoid (=
vomer, *v*); *bs*, basisphenoid; *bo*, basioccipital; *exo*, exocci-
pital; *ops*, opisthotic; *mst*, mastoid portion of periotic;
bul, auditory bulla; *sq*, squamosal; *alsp*, alisphenoid.

54.—ANATOMY OF THE LANCELET (*Amphioxus*), THE
MOST PRIMITIVE LIVING CHORDATE (PRE-
VERTEBRATE) ANIMAL   92

(After Delage and Hérouard.)
A. Entire animal, seen as a semi-transparent object.
B. Longitudinal section.

ILLUSTRATIONS

FIGURE   PAGE

55.—LARVÆ OF ECHINODERMS (A, B) AND OF THE
    "ACORN WORM" (*Balanoglossus*) .   .   .   93

    A. *Auricularia*, larva of a sea-cucumber.
    B. *Bipinnaria*, larva of a starfish.
    C. *Tornaria*, larva of *Balanoglossus*.
    (A, B, C, after Delage and Hérouard.)

56.—INNER AND OUTER MOUTH POUCHES IN EMBRYO
    VERTEBRATES   94

    A. Larval lamprey, longitudinal section of head.
(After Minot.) Showing the nasal pit, hypophysis
and mouth cavity arising as infolds from the ectoderm
or outer cell-layer.
    B. Embryo rabbit, longitudinal section of head.
(After Mihalcovics.)

57.—ATTEMPTED RESTORATIONS OF THE MOUTH AND
    GILL REGION OF TWO CEPHALASPID OSTRACO-
    DERMS BY STENSIÖ   95

    A. Horizontal section through the ventral part of
the head of *Kiæraspis*, showing the assumed position
of the gill-sacks.
    The ducts (*k. ebr.*) leading from the gill-sacks are
preserved in the original fossils, also the ridges (*i b s*)
between the ducts, so that by comparison with the
anatomy of recent lampreys there is no substantial
doubt that the gill-sacks were placed as in the restoration.
    B. Underside of the head shield of *Cephalaspis*,
showing the probable position of the gill openings
(*ebr. c ebr. c*) and mouth (*m*).

58.—SWIFT-MOVING OSTRACODERM (*Pterolepis nitidus*)
    FROM THE SILURIAN OF NORWAY   .   .   96

    (After Kiaer.)

59.—A MODERN DESCENDANT OF THE OSTRACODERMS   97

    A. Adult lamprey. (After Jordan and Evermann.)
    B. Longitudinal section of larval lamprey, enlarged
(After Goodrich.)

ILLUSTRATIONS

FIGURE   PAGE

60.—DEVELOPMENT OF TEETH IN LAMPREY AND SHARK **99**

(After Goodrich.)

Sections of developing tooth germs:

A. Lamprey.

B. Shark. First stage, showing tooth papilla beneath basal layer of epithelium.

C. Shark. Second stage, showing secretion of the enamel layer.

D. Shark. Advanced stage, showing lips of shagreen denticles breaking through the epithelium.

61.—EVOLUTION OF THE JAW MUSCLES FROM FISH TO MAN **103**

I. Shark (*Chlamydoselache*). (Data from Allis.)

II. Lobe-finned ganoid (*Polypterus*). (After L. A. Adams.)

III. Primitive amphibian (*Eryops*). Restoration. (After L. A. Adams.)

IV. Primitive mammal-like reptile (*Scymnognathus*). Restoration. (Skull mainly from Broom.)

V. Advanced mammal-like reptile (*Cynognathus*). Restoration. (After L. A. Adams.)

VI. Primitive marsupial (Opossum). (After L. A. Adams.)

VII. Primitive Eocene primate (*Notharctus*). Restoration.

VIII. Chimpanzee.

IX. Modern man.

62.—METHODS OF ATTACHMENT OF THE PRIMARY UPPER JAW TO THE UNDER SIDE OF THE SKULL   **105**

A. Hyostylic attachment (by means of the hyomandibular cartilage), characteristic of shark. (After Gegenbaur.)

B. Autostylic attachment (by means of an epipterygoid process from the primary upper jaw). Car-

ILLUSTRATIONS

FIGURE   PAGE

tilaginous braincase and primary upper jaw of fœtal salamander. (After Gaupp.)

C. Skull of primitive fossil reptile (*Diadectes*) from the Permo-Carboniferous of Texas.

In C the bony mask covering the temporal region is cut through and a part of it removed to show the primary upper jaw (comprising the palatine, pterygoid, epipterygoid and quadrate bones) and their relations to the braincase.

63.—UNDER SIDE OF THE SKULL OF (A) DEVONIAN FOSSIL FISH (LOBE-FINNED), AIR-BREATHING CROSSOPT (*Eusthenopteron*) AND (B) PRIMITIVE FOSSIL AMPHIBIAN (*Baphetes*). (A AFTER BRYANT AND WATSON; B AFTER WATSON) . 108

The secondary upper jaws (premaxillæ, maxillæ) are on the margins; the primary upper jaws (palatoquadrates) are largely covered by tooth-bearing plates of the primary palate.

64.—RIGHT HALF OF THE LOWER JAW OF LOBE-FINNED FOSSIL FISH (A, C), AND PRIMITIVE FOSSIL AMPHIBIAN (B, D), AND RECENT TURTLE EMBRYO (E) 111

A. *Megalichthys*, outer side. (After Watson.)
B. *Trimerorhachis*, outer side. (After Williston.)
C. *Megalichthys*, inner side. (After Watson.)
D. *Trimerorhachis*, inner side. (After Williston.)
E. Recent turtle embryo, inner side. (After Parker.)

Abbreviations of names of bones: *ang*, angular; *art*, articular; *cor*, coronoids (I, II); *dn*, dentary; *preart*, prearticular; *pospl*, postsplenial; *spl*, splenial; *surang*, surangular bone.

In the embryo turtle Meckel's cartilage is very plainly seen on the inner side of the jaw, extending the full length of the jaw. The rear end forms the articular bone of the adult.

These jaws are made mostly of the dermal sheathing bones that in the embryo surround the primary carti-

FIGURE   PAGE

laginous jaw.   The only part of the primary jaw present
in the adult is the articular bone.

65.—EARLY EMBRYONIC STAGES IN THE DEVELOP-
MENT OF THE NOSE IN MAN   .   .   .   120
(After Keith.)

66.—COMPARATIVE ANATOMY OF THE HUMAN PALATE   121
A.   Recent shark, showing groove from nose to
front of mouth.   (After Keith.)
B.   Lizard, in which internal opening (choana)
from the nose opens in the forepart of the mouth cavity.
(After Plate, *Allgem. Zool.*, Gustav Fischer.)
C.   Lion pup with cleft palate, recalling in form the
palate of reptiles; showing internal opening of the nose
(indicated by the arrow-point) in the forepart of the
mouth cavity.   In this abnormal specimen the secondary palate has failed to grow over to the mid-line.
(After Keith.)
D.   Human embryo of the end of the sixth week,
showing the secondary palatal plates beginning to grow
in toward the mid-line and the "primitive choanæ"
(arrow-point) still exposed in the forepart of the roof
of the pharnyx.   (After Keith.)

67.—LONGITUDINAL SECTION OF HEAD IN YOUNG
GORILLA (A) AND IN MAN (B), SHOWING
RELATION OF TONGUE TO SURROUNDING PARTS   124
(After Klaatsch.)

68.—LONGITUDINAL SECTION OF LOWER JAW OF
MONKEY (A) AND MAN (B), SHOWING ATTACH-
MENT OF THE TONGUE MUSCLE TO THE BACK
OF THE JAW   125
(After Robinson.)
In B the subdivision of the tongue muscle into strands
is over-emphasized in order to show how the upper
surface of the tongue could be thrown into different
contours by the contraction of different strands of the
genioglossus muscle.

ILLUSTRATIONS

FIGURE   PAGE

C. Diagram of the genioglossus muscle in pronouncing the sound "oo." (After Robinson.)

D. Diagram of the genioglossus muscle in pronouncing the letter "T." (After Robinson.)

69.—HUMAN EMBRYO OF THE THIRD WEEK . . 127
(From Eidmann, after His.)
Oblique front view of the head, showing mouth, primary upper and lower jaw buds, gill arches and gill slits.
(From *Entw. d. Zähne.* . . , Hermann Meusser, Berlin.)

70.—OLD CHIMPANZEE, SHOWING EXTRAORDINARY PROTRUSION OF THE LIPS IN ANTHROPOIDS
facing 132
(From J. A. Allen, from a photograph by Herbert Lang.)

71.—THREE STAGES IN THE DEVELOPMENT OF HUMAN TEETH 135
A. Future tooth-bearing skin still on the surface of the mouth cavity. From a human embryo eleven millimeters long.
B. Beginnings of the tooth-pouch. From a human embryo sixteen millimeters long.
(A, B, from Eidmann, after Ahrens. *Entw. d. Zähne...*, Hermann Meusser, Berlin.)
C. Beginnings of the pulp cavity. From a human embryo thirty-two and one-half millimeters long. (After Corning, *Lehrb. d. Entw. des Menschen*, J. F. Bergmann.)

72.—CENTRAL INCISORS OF GORILLA AND MAN. ENLARGED 137
A. Upper left incisor of young gorilla, palatal side, showing small mammillæ on incisal edge, basal swelling, raised marginal rims and low lingual ridges.
B. Upper left incisor of fossil Neanderthal (Le Moustier), showing mammillate incisal edge, basal swelling and ridges. (After Weinert.)

xxix

ILLUSTRATIONS

FIGURE   PAGE

C. Upper left incisor of fossil Neanderthal (Ehrings-dorf), showing basal swelling and ridges. (After Virchow.)

D. Upper left incisor of old Egyptian, showing mammillate incisal edge, marginal rims and lingual ridges. (After Hrdlička.)

E. Lower right incisor of young gorilla, showing mammillate incisal edge and faint lingual ridges.

F. Lower right incisor of Neanderthal (Le Moustier.) (After Virchow.)

G. Lower right incisor (labial surface) of white boy, showing mammillate incisal edge and labial ridges. (From Hrdlička, after Zuckerkandl.)

73.—THE THREE TYPES OF CENTRAL UPPER INCISORS   139

(After J. Leon Williams.) Lower row, first type; middle row, second type; upper row, third type.

74.—PALATAL ARCHES OF ANTHROPOIDS AND MEN .   140

A. Gibbon, female. (From Selenka, after Röse.)

B. Gorilla, male. (From Selenka, after Röse.)

C. Chimpanzee, female. (From Selenka, after Röse.)

D. Orang, female. (After Hrdlička.)

E. Neanderthal man (Le Moustier). (From Weinert, after Dieck.)

F. Modern white man, composite. (From Selenka, after Röse.)

75.—LOWER FRONT PREMOLARS OF FOSSIL ANTHRO-POIDS AND MAN   144

A. Fossil anthropoid, *Dryopithecus fontani*. (After Gregory and Hellman.)

B. Fossil anthropoid, *Dryopithecus cautleyi*. (After Gregory and Hellman.)

C. Fossil anthropoid, *Sivapithecus himalayensis*. (After Pilgrim.)

D. Fossil Neanderthaloid (Ehringsdorf). (After Hans Virchow.)

E. *Homo sapiens*. (After Selenka, from Röse.)

ILLUSTRATIONS

FIGURE   PAGE

76.—MILK TEETH OF MAN AND GORILLA   .   .   146

    A. White child. (From Selenka, after Röse.)

    B. Gorilla child. (From Selenka, after Röse.)

77.—TEN STRUCTURAL STAGES IN THE EVOLUTION OF THE HUMAN DENTITION FROM ASCENDING GEOLOGICAL HORIZONS   147

    I. Substage *a*. Permo-Carboniferous. *Mycterosaurus*, primitive theromorph reptile. (After Williston.) Substage *b*. Permian. *Scylacosaurus*, primitive mammal-like reptile. (After Broom.) Substage *c*. Triassic. *Cynognathus*, advanced mammal-like reptile. (After Seeley.)

    II. Triassic. *Diademodon*, advanced mammal-like reptile. (Mainly after Seeley. Occlusion diagram by author.)

    III. Jurassic. Pantotherian (primitive proplacental). (Kindness of Dr. G. G. Simpson. Occlusion diagram by Simpson.)

    IV. Cretaceous. Pre-Trituberculate, *Deltatheridium*. (From the original specimen. Occlusion diagram by author.)

    V. Lower Eocene. Primitive placental, *Didelphodus*. (From the original specimen. Occlusion diagram by author.)

78.—TEN STRUCTURAL STAGES IN THE EVOLUTION OF THE HUMAN DENTITION (*continued*)   .   148

    VI. Middle Eocene. Primitive primate, *Pronycticebus*. (After Grandidier. Occlusion diagram by author.)

    VII. Upper Eocene. Advanced tarsioid primate, *Microchœrus*. (After Stehlin. Occlusion diagram by author.)

    VIII. Miocene. Primitive anthropoid primate, *Dryopithecus*. (Upper molars mainly after Pilgrim; lower molars from type of *Dryopithecus cautleyi*. Occlusion diagram by author and Milo Hellman.)

ILLUSTRATIONS

FIGURE   PAGE

IX. Pleistocene. Primitive man, Mousterian. (From stereoscopic photographs by J. H. McGregor and from the published photographs by Weinert and by Virchow (m$_3$). Occlusion diagram by author.

X. Recent. Modern man, white. (From the original specimen. Occlusion diagram by author.)

79.—THE *Dryopithecus* PATTERN IN THE LOWER MOLAR TEETH OF RECENT AND FOSSIL ANTHROPOIDS   150

(After Gregory and Hellman.)

A. Fossil anthropoid (*Dryopithecus fontani*). The first lower molar shows the fovea anterior, the five main cusps and the fovea posterior.

B. Fossil anthropoid (*Dryopithecus cautleyi*). The third lower molar (at the left) shows a perfect *Dryopithecus* pattern.

C. Fossil anthropoid (*Dryopithecus frickæ*). (Compare Fig. 80 C.)

D. Recent orang-utan. The *Dryopithecus* pattern is somewhat obscured by the secondary wrinkles of the enamel.

E. Recent chimpanzee. The *Dryopithecus* pattern in this particular specimen is slightly obscured by the secondary wrinkles of the enamel. Cusp 6, a bud from the hinder rim of the tooth is present in the second lower molar. (Compare Fig. 80D.)

F. Recent gorilla. The teeth are elongated in a fore-and-aft direction and the cusps are high and nipple-like.

80.—PROGRESSIVE REDUCTION AND LOSS OF THE *Dryopithecus* PATTERN IN THE LOWER MOLARS OF FOSSIL AND RECENT MEN.   .   .   .   151

(After Gregory and Hellman.)

A. Fossil Heidelberg man. Worn lower molar crowns, showing clear traces of the *Dryopithecus* pattern.

FIGURE   PAGE

B. Fossil Ehringsdorf man. Both the first and the
second lower molar clearly show the fovea anterior.
(Compare Fig. 79A.) The second lower molar shows
an early stage in the formation of the cruciform or
plus pattern.

C. Fossil Neanderthal man (Le Moustier), showing
modified *Dryopithecus* pattern. Cusp 6, occasionally
found in the anthropoids, is present.

D. Recent Australian aboriginal. In the first
molar the *Dryopithecus* pattern is very evident; the
base of cusp 3 is in contact with the base of cusp 2;
cusp 6 is unusually large. In the second lower molar
the *Dryopithecus* pattern is changing into the plus
pattern.

E. Modern Hindu, showing *Dryopithecus* pattern
in the first lower molar, and plus pattern in the second.

F. Modern White, with modified *Dryopithecus* pattern in the first lower molar, a complete plus pattern
in the four-cusped second molar, and a reduced third
lower molar.

81.—DISSECTION OF HEAD OF SHARK, SEEN FROM
     ABOVE, TO SHOW RELATIONS OF OLFACTORY
     CAPSULES TO BRAIN, EYES AND INTERNAL
     EARS   155
     (Modified from Marshall and Hurst.)

82.—JACOBSON'S ORGAN IN THE HUMAN FŒTUS   .   159
     A. Location of Jacobson's organ. The sound is
     inserted into the opening of the organ. (After Corning.)
     B. Frontal section of fœtal human nose, showing
     vestige of Jacobson's organ. (After Corning.)
     (A, B, from *Lehrb. d. Entw. des Menschen*, J. F.
     Bergmann.)

83.—LONGITUDINAL SECTION OF THE SKULL IN MAN
     AND CHIMPANZEE   160
     A. Adult female chimpanzee.
     B. Man. (After Cunningham.)

ILLUSTRATIONS

FIGURE   PAGE

84.—BROAD, FORWARDLY-DIRECTED NOSE OF HUMAN FŒTUS (A), (AFTER KOLLMANN) AND GORILLA FŒTUS (B), (FROM SCHULTZ, AFTER DENIKER)   161

85.—CONNECTIONS OF THE FRONTAL, ETHMOID AND SPHENOID SINUSES WITH THE NASAL MEATI   163

(After Keith.)

86.—DEVELOPMENT OF THE FACE IN MAN   .   .   165

(From Eidmann, *Entw. d. Zähne*. . . , Hermann Meusser, Berlin).

A. Embryo of about 9 millimeters length. (From Eidmann, after His.)

B. Embryo of about 10.5 millimeters length. (From Eidmann, after His.)

C. Embryo of about 11.3 millimeters length. (From Eidmann, after Rabl.)

D. Embryo of about 15 millimeters length. (From Eidmann, after Retzius.)

E. Embryo of about 18 millimeters length. (From Eidmann, after Retzius.)

87.—DEVELOPMENT OF THE FACE IN MAN (*continued*)   166

A. Late fœtal stage: embryo of 52 millimeters length. (From Eidmann, after Retzius, *Entw. d. Zähne*. . . , Hermann Meusser, Berlin.)

B. Diagram of adult face, showing derivation of different areas from the primary embryonic parts. (Modified from Keith.)

88.—NASAL PROFILES AND RELATED PARTS IN MAN   168

(After Schultz.)

A. Negro child.

B. Negro adult.

C. White child.

D. White adult.

Median or septal cartilage, black.

ILLUSTRATIONS

FIGURE   PAGE

      Shows the correlation of the extent of the septal cartilage, the position of the front teeth and the form of the nose.

89.—EXTREMES OF NOSE FORM IN MAN   . *facing* 170

      A. Excessively wide short nose in African pygmy. (From Martin, after Czekanowski.)

      B. Excessively narrow high nose in a white man (Tyrolese). (From Martin, after Czekanowski.)

      C. Excessively high nose bridge and long nose in an Armenian. (After von Luschan.)

      D. Excessively low nose bridge in South African Bushman. (From Martin, after Schultz.)

      (A, B, D, from *Lehrb. d. Anthropol.*, Gustav Fischer.)

90.—EXTREMES IN FACE FORM AND COLOR . *facing* 172

      A. Hottentot woman. (From Martin, after Poech, *Lehrb. d. Anthropol.*, Gustav Fischer.)

      B. Nordic Swede. (From Lundborg and Runnström, "The Swedish Nation," H. W. Tullberg.)

91.—THE BEGINNINGS OF EYES 175

      A. Section of an ocellus, or eye spot, at the base of a tentacle of a jellyfish (*Catablema*). (From Plate, after Linko.)

      B. Section of a "goblet eye" of a jellyfish (*Sarsia*). (From Plate, after Linko.)

      (A, B, from *Allgem. Zool.*, Gustav Fischer.)

92.—EYE CAPSULES OF FLATWORM   .   .   . 177

      A. Location of eyes in flatworm (*Planaria*). (After Parker and Haswell.)

      B. Section of "goblet eye" of flatworm (*Planaria*). (From Plate, after Hesse, *Allgem. Zool.*, Gustav Fischer.)

93.—HOW THE EYE CAPSULES OF A FLATWORM SERVE AS DIRECTIONAL ORGANS 178

      (From Plate, after Hesse, *Allgem. Zool.*, Gustav Fischer.)

ILLUSTRATIONS

FIGURE   PAGE

The arrows show the varying directions of the light. In each case only a particular part of each retina is stimulated, the rest being in shadow.

94.—EYE OF SQUID (HORIZONTAL MEDIAN SECTION)   179

(From Plate, after Hensen, *Allgem. Zool.*, Gustav Fischer.)

95.—DEVELOPMENT OF THE EYE IN CEPHALOPOD MOLLUSCS   181

(After Plate, *Allgem. Zool.*, Gustav Fischer.)

A. Early embryonic stage, showing the spherical retina (represented in the Pearly Nautilus).

B. Snaring off of the eyeball and beginning of the iris-folds and of a primary cornea.

C. Development of the lens on either side of the primary cornea, or transparent septum.

D. Development of a secondary or outer cornea.

96.—LIGHT CELLS OF *Amphioxus*   183

A. Forepart of a young *Amphioxus*, enlarged, showing light cells (*Becheraugen*). (From Plate, after Joseph, *Allgem. Zool.*, Gustav Fischer.)

B. Cross-section of the spinal cord of *Amphioxus*, showing the light cells, which are essentially like the goblet eyes (*Becheraugen*) of invertebrates.

(From Plate, after Hesse, *Allgem. Zool.*, Gustav Fischer.)

97.—EVOLUTION OF THE VERTEBRATE EYE AS CONCEIVED BY STUDNICKA   185

(From Plate, after Studnicka, *Allgem. Zool.*, Gustav Fischer.)

In still earlier stages it is supposed the vertebrate eyes arose, as in invertebrates, through a down-pocketing of the light cells (Fig. 91) on the surface of the embryonic nerve furrow, or medullary fold. When the fold closed over, as it does in the developing vertebrate embryo, the future eye spots found themselves

ILLUSTRATIONS

FIGUREPAGE

in the inner lining of the nerve tube or brain, with the "rods" turned away from the light.

A. Stage in which the dorsal pair of "eyes" (pineal and parapineal) are beginning to grow outward, as well as the "paired" eyes.

B. Stage in which the eye stalks are forming.

C. Stage in which the lens and retina are beginning.

D–I. Subsequent stages in the formation of the optic cup.

98.—THE RIGHT EYEBALL AND ITS SIX MUSCLES . 190
(From Plate, after Merkel and Kallins, *Allgem. Zool.*, Gustav Fischer.)

99.—THE RIGHT EYE OF A SHARK IN HORIZONTAL SECTION 192
(From Plate, after Franz, *Allgem. Zool.*, Gustav Fischer.)

100.—DIAGRAM OF HORIZONTAL SECTION OF THE RIGHT HUMAN EYE 193
(Simplified from Plate, after Luciani, *Allgem. Zool.*, Gustav Fischer.)

101.—TEAR-DRAINING CANALS OF THE EYE . . 194
(After Keith.)

102.—FRONT VIEW OF INFANT AND YOUNG SKULLS OF ANTHROPOIDS (A, B, C) AND OF MAN (D) 197
A. Chimpanzee. (After Selenka.)
B. Gorilla. (After Selenka.)
C. Orang. (After Selenka.)
D. Human child. (After Martin, *Lehrb d. Anthropol.*, Gustav Fischer.)

103.—THE HUMAN ORGAN OF HEARING AND BALANCE 203
(A and C, after Cunningham.)
A. Transverse section.

FIGURE   PAGE

    B.   Diagram section of the cochlea, showing the
ascending and descending spiral duct and the cochlear
duct containing the organ of Corti or true organ of
hearing.

    C.   Greatly enlarged view of the cochlear duct,
showing the organ of Corti with its damper, hair cells
and hearing nerves.

104.—SERIES SHOWING THE MEMBRANOUS LABYRINTH
    OR INNER EAR FROM FISH TO MAN   .   .   205

    (After Retzius.)   Right side; outer view.

    A.   Shark (*Acanthias*).

    B.   Ganoid fish (*Lepidosteus*).

    C.   Primitive reptile (*Hatteria*).

    D.   Alligator.

    E.   Primitive mammal (Rabbit).

    F.   Man.

105.—DEVELOPMENT OF THE LABYRINTH OR INNER
    EAR OF MAN   206

    (After Streeter.)

106.—TRANSVERSE SECTION OF THE HEAD IN A
    FROG, SHOWING THE RELATIONS OF THE
    MIDDLE EAR (THERE IS NO OUTER EAR)
    TO THE INNER EAR AND OF THE LATTER TO
    THE BRAIN   208

    (After T. J. Parker and W. N. Parker.)

107.—EMBRYO STURGEON, SHOWING GILL CLEFTS   209

    (After W. K. Parker.)

108.—HUMAN (A) AND MACAQUE (B) EMBRYOS,
    SHOWING ORIGIN OF THE EXTERNAL EAR
    FROM SIX TUBERCLES   211

    A.   From Leche, after Selenka.

    B.   From Leche, after His, Keibel.

    (A, B, from *Der Mensch*, Gustav Fischer.)

ILLUSTRATIONS

FIGURE   PAGE

109.—Ears of Fœtal Macaque (A) and of a Six
Months' Human Fœtus (B) . . . 212

(From Plate, after Schwalbe, *Allgem. Zool.*, Gustav
Fischer.)

110.—External Ears of Anthropoids and Men   213

(After Keith.)

   A. Chimpanzee.
   B. "Small chimpanzee type" (human).
   C. "Chimpanzee type" (human).
   D. Orang.
   E. "Orang type" (human).
   F. Gorilla.
   G. Gibbon.
   H. Lemuroid (*Nycticebus*).

111.—The Middle Ear of Man, Showing the
Auditory Ossicles 216

(After Cunningham.)

A. View of the left tympanum (drum membrane)
from the inner side. The ossicles are cut away except
the handle of the malleus, which is inserted into the
drum membrane.

B. The same, showing the three ossicles in place.

112.—Relations of the Parts of the Middle Ear
in an Extinct Mammal-like Reptile . 217

A. Side view of back part of lower jaw of *Permocynodon*, a cynodont reptile from the Permian of Russia. (Mainly after Sushkin.)

The broken line indicates the position of the pouch
from the tubo-tympanal cavity as inferred by Watson
and Sushkin.

B. Rear view of the skull of *Permocynodon*, showing the perforate stapes in position. (After Sushkin.)

The broken lines (added by the present author)
indicate his interpretation of the position of the middle-
ear chamber and of the tympanic membrane. The
existence of an extra columella, as in primitive rep-

ILLUSTRATIONS

FIGURE   PAGE

tiles, is inferred from the presence of a facet on the
lower outer end of the quadrate.

113.—ORIGIN OF AUDITORY OSSICLES   .   .   .   218

    A. Back part of the lower jaw of *Cynognathus*,
inner side. (Based chiefly on a cast of the type of
Cynognathus craternotus, combined with observations
and figures of Seeley and Watson.)

    B. Fœtal mammal, *Perameles*. (Slightly modified
from R. W. Palmer.)

114.—RELATIONS OF OSSICLES TO LOWER JAW ON
    FŒTAL ARMADILLO (*Tatusia hybrida*) .   .   221

    (Composed from two figures by W. K. Parker.)

115.—THE REPTILIAN STAGE IN THE DEVELOPMENT
    OF THE AUDITORY OSSICLES   .   .   .   221

    A. Lower jaw and attached auditory ossicles in
a fœtal hedgehog (*Erinaceus*). (After W. K. Parker.)

    B. Lower jaw and attached auditory ossicles in a
human fœtus of 43 millimeters length. (After
Macklin.)

116.—YOUNG CHIMPANZEE, SHOWING FACIAL EXPRES-
    SION   .   .   .   .   .   . *facing* 222

    (From a photograph by Herbert Lang.)

117.—STOCKARD'S LINEAR AND LATERAL GROWTH
    TYPES   232

    (After Stockard.)
    A. Infant.
    B. "Linear" adult.
    C. "Lateral" adult.

118.—SIDE VIEW OF HUMAN FIGURE, TO INDICATE
    THE ANTERIOR TIP AND THE GENERAL DIREC-
    TION OF THE LATERAL LINE   .   .   .   234

    (After Stockard.)

OUR FACE FROM FISH TO MAN

OUR FACE FROM FISH TO MAN

PART I

PORTRAIT GALLERY OF OUR ANCIENT RELATIVES AND ANCESTORS

THE VALUE OF A FACE

For a billion years or more the ceaseless game of life has been concerned with the capture and utilization of energy for the benefit of the individual and with the rhythmic storage and release of energy for the reproduction of the race.

In all ages and in all branches of the animal kingdom a face of some sort has been indispensable to all but sessile animals, just because a face is concerned primarily with:

The detection of desirable sources of energy;

The direction of the locomotor machinery toward its goal;

The capture and preliminary preparation of the energy-giving food.

3

Among the highest animals the face acts also as a lure for the capture of a mate.

In nearly all the lower vertebrate animals, however, the most constant and dominating element of the face is the gateway formed by the mouth and arching jaws to the "primitive gut" or digestive tract.

Around this architectural centerpiece the higher facial designs gradually developed.

THE BEGINNINGS OF OUR FACE

Doubtless it is a far cry from the lowly Slipper Animalcule, whose face consists only of a gash in the side of its moccasin-like body, to the human face divine, but among the thousands of known living and fossil forms Nature has left us a number of significant vestiges on the long pathway of creation. Among the more primitive of the many-celled animals the jellyfishes consist essentially of a two-layered parachute-like sac, the inner layer serving as a primitive gut, the outer layer chiefly as an envelope. The mouth of the sac is greatly puckered and the folds are produced into tentacles, often endowed with nettle-like, stinging threads. A diffuse nerve net extends everywhere

4

between the inner and the outer layer and is concentrated into a ring around the mouth. This mouth is far from being homologous with our own. It represents at most the "primitive streak" of the early embryos of vertebrate animals. Never-

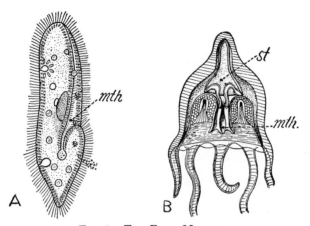

FIG. 1. THE FIRST MOUTHS.

Slipper animalcule (A) with gash-like mouth; Jellyfish (B), a two-layered sac with primitive mouth. (Both after Parker and Haswell.) For details, see p. xiii.

theless it was the starting-point for further developments.

The direct line of ascent toward the vertebrates is not yet definitely known and we can only surmise what the next few steps may have been. The flatworms appear to represent highly developed descendants of the jellyfish group, which had abandoned the drifting habits of their remote ancestors and taken to living on the bottom in shallow water. The simple pulsations of a bell-shaped body, which were sufficient for jellyfishes, were modified into writhings or contractions in definite directions. Anyhow, radial symmetry gave way to bilateral symmetry, the animals began to progress in a fore-and-aft direction and the sharp differentiation of heads and tails was in full play.

The early evolution of a primitive head is also well illustrated in certain flatworms (Fig. 2A), in which the slender nerve threads are drawn together to form the first rudiments of a brain and a very simple type of eyes is attained. In the annelid worms the head is further advanced, since the mouth is now surrounded by various accessory organs for the testing of the food, by horny jaws moved by muscles for the capture of the food, by elaborate eyes and by an extensive fusion of nerve fibers into an incipient brain. The trilobites and higher crustaceans (Fig. 2B) carry the story onward, showing us how some of the jointed projections from the sides of the body, which had originally been developed as primitive legs, very early began to serve the mouth by drawing, kick-

6

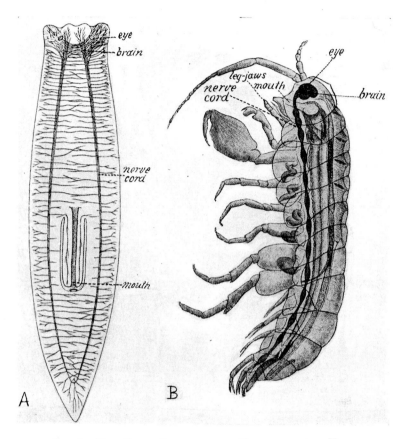

FIG. 2. TWO EARLY STAGES IN THE EVOLUTION OF A HEAD
(AFTER PARKER AND HASWELL).

Flatworm (A), showing a head-and-tail differentiation, including the beginnings of a brain and of eyes; Sand-flea (B), showing the interrelations of eye, brain, mouth, leg-jaws and nerve cord.

For details see p. xiii.

ing or pushing the food within its reach, these mouth-legs finally culminating in the various and highly refined burglar tools so well wielded by the swarming hosts of insects.

According to Professor Patten of Dartmouth, the vertebrates were derived from the arachnid stem—an ancient branch of the jointed animals (arthropods), that is represented today by *Limulus*, the "king-crab" (which is not a crab at all), and by the arachnids (scorpions and spiders). But if these disagreeable creatures are our remote relatives, then the highly developed head which they had acquired after so many millions of years of struggle all had to be largely made over when the vertebrate stage of organization was reached. They had to sacrifice their elaborate leg-jaw apparatus, their very mouths were stopped and a new mouth and jaws were formed, their eyes were turned upside down and inside out and a new set of swimming organs had to be developed.

According to the more orthodox view, the vertebrates from their earliest stages stood in wide contrast to the crustaceans, arachnids and insects. For while both groups comprise segmental animals,

7

moving in a fore-and-aft direction and building up a complex head through the fusion of simple segments, yet the arthropods developed their jaws out of jointed locomotor appendages while the vertebrates utilized for this purpose the cartilaginous bars of the first two gill pouches. According to Patten's view the fossil ostracoderms (Fig. 4) were more or less intermediate between these two great groups; but the objections to this view are formidable.

No matter from what group of invertebrates the vertebrates may have sprung, their origin took place many hundreds of millions of years after the first synthesis of living matter from less complex substances. When the first fishes took form the seas already swarmed with thousands of species of marine invertebrates,—protozoans, sponges, corals, trilobites, crustaceans, brachiopods, arthropods, molluscs, etc., and so far as the marine invertebrates were concerned, all the major problems of feeding, locomotion, sexual and asexual reproduction had been solved æons ago. And when the vertebrates started on their long career they too had already solved all the same fundamental problems by rigorously sacrificing much of their old

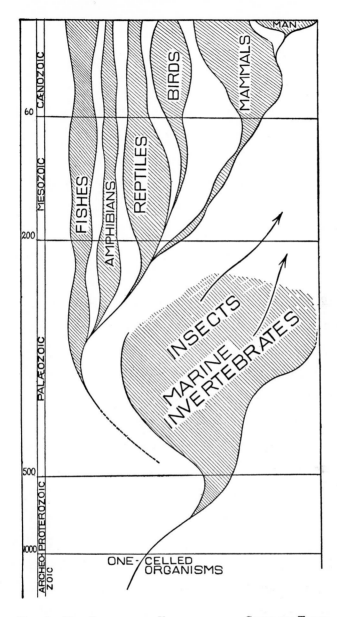

FIG. 3. THE RISE OF THE VERTEBRATES IN GEOLOGIC TIMES.
Figures at left give estimated time in millions of years.

9

equipment and by profoundly changing what was left of their original heritage. The earliest known vertebrates (or more properly, chordates) are indubitably far nearer to us in geologic time and in the ground-plan of their whole organization than they were to the first living creatures; even their faces reveal them, as we shall presently see, as early kinsfolk of ours; the real beginnings of our facial type are either hidden in still unexplored rocks of pre-Silurian ages or wiped out forever by the destructive forces of erosion. From the viewpoint of earth history as a whole, even the earliest vertebrates of Silurian times (Fig. 4) rank among the younger children of life, yet from the viewpoint of mankind their antiquity is at first inconceivably vast, since according to all recent geological inquiry, it must be reckoned in hundreds of millions of years.

The recent monographic researches of Kiær and especially of Stensiö upon the amazingly well preserved ostracoderms of the Silurian and Devonian ages of Norway and of Spitzbergen have definitely shown that these curious forms are more or less directly ancestral to the hagfishes and lampreys of the present day, which comparative

10

anatomists have long regarded as standing far
below the grade of the sharks in the scale of
vertebrate life. In some of these fossils the infil-

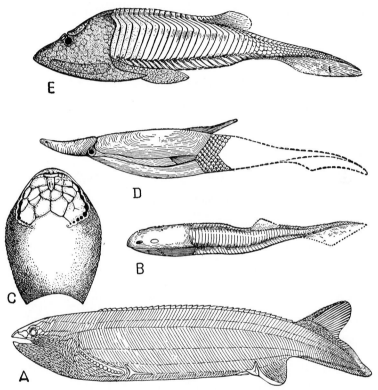

FIG. 4. SOME OF OUR EARLIEST KNOWN KINSFOLK.
UPPER SILURIAN AND DEVONIAN OSTRACODERMS.

For details, see pp. xiii, xiv.

trated mud has made a natural cast of even the
principal nerves and blood vessels of the head, so
that Stensiö has been able to show that they com-

11

pare very closely in the ground-plan of the anatomy of their heads with the larval stages of the lampreys.

In all these lowly creatures as well as in ourselves the head is essentially the complex of sense organs, brain and brain covering, mouth and throat, by means of which the creature is directed to its food and enabled to engulf it.

THE SHARK'S FACE AND OURS

The ancestors of the higher vertebrates did not settle down and become specialized bottom-living fishes but long maintained themselves in the fierce competition of free-swimming, predaceous types. Whatever the first steps leading toward the vertebrate head may have been, the shark shows us our own facial anatomy stripped of all elaborations and reduced to simplest terms. Like Shylock, the shark might well plead that he has eyes, nose and a mouth, affections, passions; accordingly we find that in zoölogical classes all over the world the humble dogfish affords an invaluable epitome and ground-plan of human anatomy.

Men have been insulted by the implications of this fact and still more by the statement that man

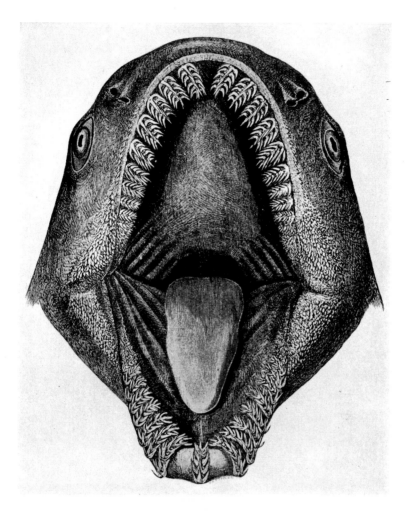

Fig. 5.   The Face of the Most Primitive Living Shark (after Garman).
For details see p. xiv.

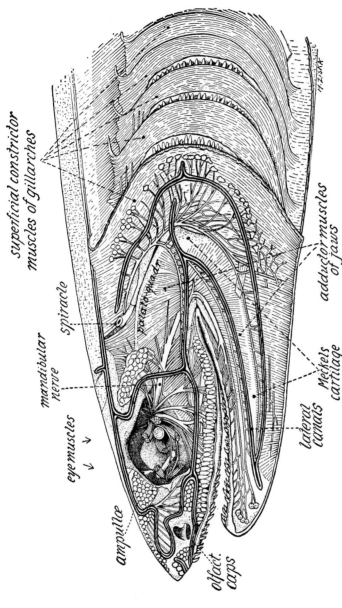

superficial constrictor
muscles of gillarches

adductor muscles
of jaws

mandibular
nerve

spiracle

Mechels
cartilage

eye muscles

lateral
canals

ampullæ

olfact.
caps

FIG. 6. INSTRUMENTS OF PRECISION IN THE HEAD OF A SHARK. (AFTER ALLIS.)
Lateral line canals black, bordered with white; nerves white; muscles streaked; cartilage stippled. For details, see p. xiv.

13

is far nearer in architectural plan to the shark than the latter is to whatever invertebrates we may choose to name as the starting-point of the whole vertebrate tree of life; but such are the secure judgments of comparative anatomy.

Much that might appear mysterious and inscrutable in the anatomy of the human face may reasonably be explained as a heritage from far-off shark-like ancestors, which human embryos also recall. Let us therefore look a little more closely into the construction and functioning of the face of this human prototype.

Always remembering that the face is merely the food-detecting and food-trapping mask in front of the brain, we find in the shark's apparently simple face a truly marvelous assemblage of instruments of precision (Fig. 6). First among these food-detecting devices rank the smelling organs, rosette-like membranes exposed in the olfactory capsules under the nostrils, capable of detecting chemically the very minute quantities of blood or other animal matter dissolved in sea water. These smelling capsules lead by prominent nerve tracts to the large forebrain, in which the smelling centers are the dominant elements (Fig. 81).

14

OUR ANCIENT RELATIVES

In the brain these olfactory messages stimulate the motor nerves controlling the eye muscles and other nerves controlling the locomotor muscles, in such a way that the shark turns and moves toward the source of the odor.

The eyes of a shark are fundamentally similar to those of a man but their marvelous intricacy forbids an attempt to discuss them in this brief space. Each eye is moved by six sets of eye muscles (Fig. 6), which turn the pupil toward the goal of movement.

As the food is reached and the stimulation of smell, sight and other senses reaches its climax, there is a convulsive expansion of the jaws, the food is torn by the jagged teeth, the jaws snap shut with the vicious force of a bear-trap, and the intense pleasure of swallowing the precious life-giving morsel is experienced.

Thoroughly equipped research laboratories could profitably occupy the time for decades to come with a study of what really happens when a shark detects its food and rushes forward to engulf it, for this apparently simple but in reality vastly complex sequence holds many secrets of vital importance to human beings.

However, the fact that even the true nature of nerve currents is as yet very imperfectly known does not prevent us from realizing the value of even a homely face to all animals that navigate the waters or move upon the land or in the air.

Not the least important of the shark's detecting and navigating instruments are the very numerous "ampullæ" that are so thickly scattered all over the surface of the head. Each of these pits is connected with a nerve tendril and thousands of these nerves run together into larger tracts, which finally run into the brain itself. Possibly these ampullæ detect vibrations of low frequency in the water and in some way coöperate with the olfactory nerves in giving stimuli proportional to the nearness of the source.

Then there are the taste organs scattered over the mouth cavity, all wired most carefully and elaborately and connected with the appropriate brain centers.

The so-called "internal ears" embedded in the cartilage on either side of the hindbrain, consist chiefly of the ingenious semi-circular canals (see pages 202–6, Fig. 104), arranged like our own in three planes and capable of analyzing any movement of the body into three directional components.

These instruments of precision communicate their findings to the brain and form essential partners to the instruments carried by the face.

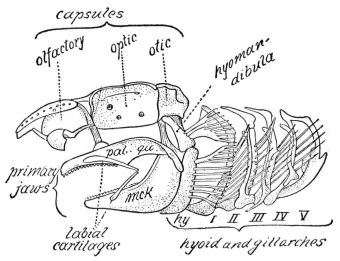

Fig. 7. Cartilaginous Skeleton of Head of Shark, Comprising Braincase, Primary Upper and Lower Jaws and Branchial Arches.

The scaffolding or skeleton of the face (Fig. 7) consists of three principal parts: first, the cartilaginous capsules (olfactory, optic, otic) that support the paired organs of smelling, sight and balancing; second, the cartilaginous trough and box that enclose the brain; third, the cartilaginous upper and lower jaw-bars (palatoquadrate, Meck-

17

el's cartilage), with certain connecting bars (hyo-mandibular, ceratohyal) that tie the jaws on to the braincase.

These jaw cartilages resemble the bars of cartilage (I–V) that form the supporting frame-work for the gills.

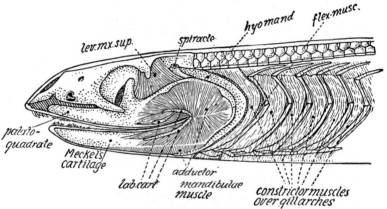

FIG. 8. JAW MUSCLES OF SHARK, SHOWING THE ESSENTIAL SIMILARITY
OF THE JAW MUSCLES TO THE CONSTRICTORS OF
THE BRANCHIAL ARCHES.
For details, see p. xiv.

Even the jaw muscles appear to be modified gill-arch muscles. The principal jaw muscles (Fig. 8) are simply bands or sheets of muscle wrapped around the angular bend where the upper and lower jaw segments articulate with each other. The lower jaw is pulled downward chiefly by a backward pull of the horizontal muscles.

18

OUR ANCIENT RELATIVES

All these muscles, like those of the locomotor apparatus, are composed of striped muscle fibers and each little fiber is a sort of engine, deriving its fuel from the chemical glycogen in the blood and its explosive impulse from a tiny nerve fiber.

Over the whole of this great complex is stretched a tough but flexible envelope, the skin, which is studded with minute teeth, or shagreen.

Around the jaw-bars the shagreen gives rise to large teeth.

Thus in barest outline we have the elements of the face and its connections with the braincase in the shark. If we are fond of mysticism we will say that in the cramped brain-box lives the shark himself, who receives the multitudinous messages from his detecting instruments and shapes his actions accordingly. In this anthropocentric philosophy a shark's face is highly expressive of the shark's piratical and cruel character. If we wish to be thoroughly behavioristic, on the other hand, we will regard the shark's conduct as the automatic resultant of the various stimuli received by his sensorium, which were transmitted to the complex apparatus in the central nervous system, the office of which in turn is to play off one stimulus against the other and to shape the motor responses into profitable combinations. In this case the shark's face is innocent of cruelty or piracy and is merely an assemblage of coördinated instruments of precision packed into the forepart of a vessel of appropriate streamline form.

At this place we do not have to discuss what brought about this marvelous aggregation of coördinated apparatus. All we need emphasize is that in the face of a shark a man may behold, as in a glass darkly, his own image.

Nevertheless a man should not flatter himself that he is a direct descendant of some powerful robber-baron such as the tiger-shark. Always in earlier times we have been only the little stealers of small fry and even when we attained the mammalian grade we were still specializing in capturing small living things.

THE MASK-FACE OF OUR GILLED ANCESTORS

A skull finds but little favor with the man in the street and possibly it would not interest him much to be told that every one of his twenty-eight skull bones has been inherited in an unbroken

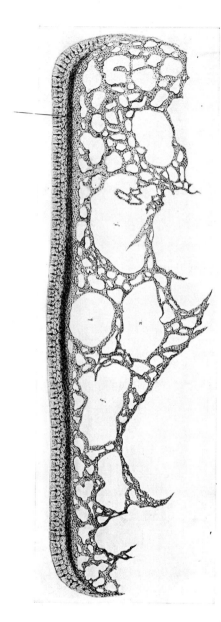

FIG. 9. CROSS-SECTION OF THE SKULL OF A FOSSIL GANOID FISH, SHOWING THE BONE CELLS (AFTER PANDER).

For details see p. xiv

succession from the air-breathing fishes of pre-Devonian times.

However, we wish to go even back of that and are curious to know why animals ever acquired a skull at all. The "basic patent" for the strengthening of all skeletal parts is the bone-cell, which invades both the skin covering the head, where it forms "derm bones," and the underlying cartilage or braincase; everywhere it deposits phosphate of lime and other salts, thereby greatly stiffening the skin and strengthening the brain-box.

The skull of all vertebrates above the sharks is a complex bony structure consisting of an outer shell, or dermocranium, originally derived from the many-layered skin, and an inner skull, or endocranium, derived from the cartilaginous brain-trough and its associated three pairs of capsules for the nose, eyes and inner ears.

The same kind of cells surround the elastic notochord or primitive axial rod, and deposit the bony tissue along certain tracts between the tough membranes that separate the muscle segments. In this way rods called ribs are produced as well as the bony arches above the notochord. All this results in a strong framework, which supports the powerful body muscles that drive the body through the water.

The braincase is the thrust-block (Fig. 10) that receives the forward push from the backbone and

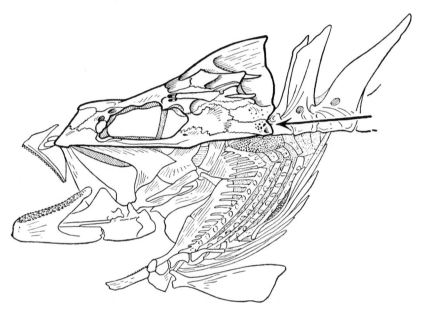

FIG. 10. THE WEDGE-SHAPED BRAINCASE OF A FISH, ACTING AS A THRUST-BLOCK OR FULCRUM FOR THE BACKBONE.

For details, see p. xiv.

the reaction from the water. The roofing bones over the braincase and the keel bone (parasphenoid) on the under side of the braincase together form a long wedge which is thrust forward into the water. To the sides of the skull are attached first,

FIG. 11. THE FACIAL ARMOR AND JAWS OF A DEVONIAN LOBE-FINNED
GANOID FISH (AFTER PANDER).

The skull seen from above.   For details see p. xiv.

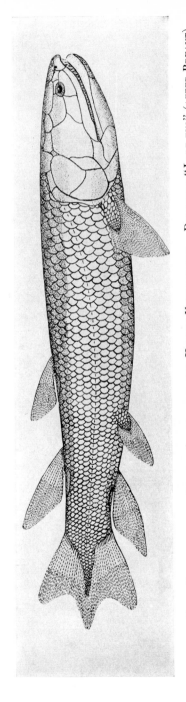

FIG. 12. FIRST CLAIMANT TO THE LINE OF ANCESTRY OF THE HIGHER VERTEBRATES. DEVONIAN "LOBE-FIN" (AFTER BRYANT).

For details see p. xv.

the complex jaws, consisting of the primary or originally cartilaginous upper and lower jaws plus their bony dermal covering, and second, the sliding bony covers of the gill chamber.

In the modern sharks the skeleton is stiffened by calcium carbonate rather than by phosphate of lime, the skin is stiffened chiefly by the shagreen or little teeth on its surface and the skeleton as a whole remains in a low stage of evolution.

On the other hand, in the ancient lobe-finned ganoid fishes, which stand much nearer to the direct line of human ascent than do the sharks, phosphate of lime is deposited by true bone-cells and the skull comprises a bony mask and a bony braincase as described above.

The whole surface of the mask (Fig. 11) is covered by a thin enamel-like layer, smooth and shining, called ganoine.

The jaws of the ancient ganoids, well covered both on the inner and outer sides by an armor of bony dermal plates, carried large sharp teeth with deeply infolded or labyrinthine bases (Fig. 18A).

There is every reason to regard these mail-clad robbers as lying not far off the main line of ascent. The alligator-gar of the lower Mississippi system, although belonging to another order of ganoid fishes, bears a striking general resemblance to its Devonian relatives.

Among these ancient ganoid fishes there are two groups that have claims for the honor of standing nearest to the main line of ascent. The first lot were fierce, predatory, pike-like forms, which had stout fan-shaped paddles, two pairs, corresponding to the fore and hind limbs of land-living vertebrates. To judge from the fact that they had internal nares or nostrils as well as external ones, these ancient lobe-finned ganoids already possessed a lung in addition to gills and were therefore able to breathe atmospheric air directly when the streams and swamps in which they lived temporarily became dry. Today this group of lobe-finned or crossopterygian ganoids is represented, if at all, only by two living genera of fishes: the bichir (*Polypterus*) of the Nile and its elongate relative *Calamoichthys*. In its mode of embryonic development *Polypterus* shows resemblances both to the lung-fishes and to the Amphibia.

The rival claimants for the honor of standing in the human line of ascent were the true lung-fishes, or Dipnoi. The several survivors of this group at

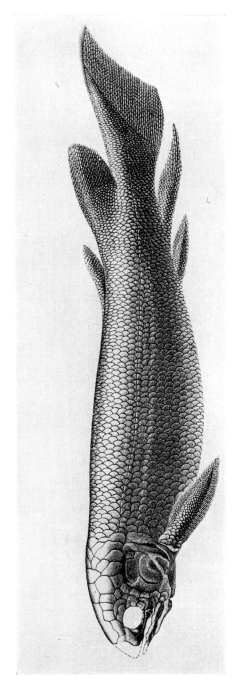

FIG. 13. SECOND CLAIMANT TO THE LINE OF ANCESTRY OF THE HIGHER VERTEBRATES. DEVONIAN DIPNOAN (AFTER PANDER).

For details see p. xv.

the present time, including the famous lung-fish (*Neoceratodus*) of Australia, all have very well-developed and functional lungs in addition to gills. Moreover, the embryonic development of the modern lung-fish, it has been shown, closely parallels that of certain existing salamanders.

Nevertheless, all the fossil and recent fishes of this dipnoan group had definitely and hopelessly removed themselves from the main line of ascent, since they had already either reduced or lost the marginal bones of the upper jaw and had developed peculiar and specialized fan-shaped cutting plates on the roof of the mouth and on the inner side of the lower jaw.

The earliest of the land-living or four-footed vertebrates, on the contrary, retained the marginal jaw bones and never developed the fan-shaped cutting plates on the roof of the mouth.

To make a long story short, the real ancestors of the higher vertebrates were probably neither true dipnoans, nor any of the Devonian lobe-finned ganoids, but were the still undiscovered common ancestors of these rather closely related groups living somewhere, perhaps in Lower Devonian or Upper Silurian times.

The evidence of embryology and comparative anatomy points unmistakably to the derivation of the land-living vertebrates from air-breathing fishes, with stout paired fore and hind paddles and a complex skull of the general type described above. The lobe-finned fishes as a whole appear to be

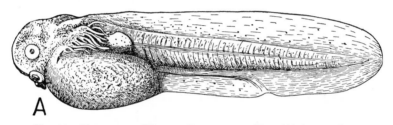

Fig. 14.　Embryos of Modern Lobe-finned Fish (A) (after Budgett) and Amphibian (B) (after S. F. Clarke).

For details, see p. xv.

near to the direct line of ascent, although each of the known members of the group is probably too late in time and too specialized in certain details of skull structure to be the **actual** ancestor of the land-living vertebrates.

In view of the mobility and fleshiness of the human and other mammalian faces it may be deemed surprising that one should seek to derive the higher vertebrates from fishes whose whole head and face were covered with a porcelain-like armor; but in the following pages we shall follow this amazing transformation step by step.

OUR ANCESTORS COME OUT OF THE WATER

Plant life is believed to have originated in the sea in early Archeozoic times. As far back as Devonian time it had succeeded after long ages of struggle in adapting itself to terrestrial life and there were great forests of low types of trees preceding the still greater swamps of the Coal age. No remains of amphibians have hitherto been found associated with Devonian plants, and the transformation of air-breathing fishes into lowly amphibians took place during the millions of years in which the fossil record of vertebrate life is still defective. But at the time of the formation of the older coal beds of Great Britain there were still surviving some very low types of amphibians which retained more of the fish-like characters in the skeleton than did any later forms known.

These highly interesting remains were imperfectly described by earlier authors but they have been successfully restudied by Professor D. M. S. Watson of University College, London, in the light of his extensive knowledge of later fossil amphibians. Under his keen scrutiny these oldest known land vertebrates have yielded many facts of far-reaching significance. He has shown that in certain of these forms the shoulder-girdle was

FIG. 15. ONE OF THE MOST PRIMITIVE KNOWN AMPHIBIANS FROM THE LOWER CARBONIFEROUS OF ENGLAND (RESTORATION AFTER WATSON'S DATA).

For details, see p. xv.

still attached to the skull by a bony plate, as it is in typical fishes, and that the bony plates of the shoulder-girdle were still readily identifiable with those of fishes, whereas in later types these plates became highly modified.

The bony mask covering the face and braincase of these oldest tetrapods [1] is of the greatest interest in the present connection, for in it we find the starting-point for everyone of the twenty-eight

[1] A name often applied to the oldest four-footed land-living forms, both amphibians and reptiles.

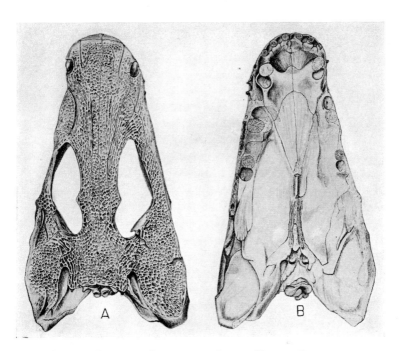

FIG. 16. SKULL OF ONE OF THE OLDEST KNOWN AMPHIBIANS
(*Loxomma allmani*).

After Embleton and Atthey.
A. Upper surface.   B. Under side.

bones of the human skull, together with many other bony elements which were reduced and gradually eliminated in the long procession of forms from fish to man.

Before looking forward to man, let us look backward and see how the skulls of these earliest explorers of the land compared with those of their collateral ancestors, the air-breathing, lobe-finned ganoids.

The greatest change is seen in the region of the gill chamber, just behind the upper jaws. In the fish this was covered by a beautifully jointed series of bony plates, as perfectly articulated as any suit of armor ever made by man. In the oldest amphibians, however, these bony plates behind the jaws have disappeared completely, leaving an exposed area called the otic notch just behind the upper jaw. This is the region of the middle ear or sound-transmitting apparatus in modern amphibians and apparently these ancient amphibians had already acquired this new instrument of precision. In the lower jaw the bony plates covering the under surface of the throat had also disappeared. In the region above the nostrils the mosaic of small bones found in the lobe-finned

29

fishes had been replaced by two large bones hence-
forth traceable directly to the nasal bones of man.
The several bony plates on the face surrounding
the eye had also been changed in proportions.

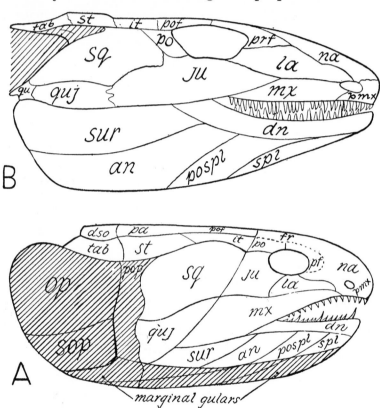

FIG. 17. SKULLS OF LOBE-FINNED FISH (A) AND EARLY AMPHIBIAN
(B), SHOWING LOSS OF OPERCULAR SERIES IN THE LATTER
(A, AFTER TRAQUAIR AND WATSON, B, AFTER WATSON).

In the primitive amphibians the space formerly covered by the
opercular region was covered by the tympanum or drum membrane.
For details, see p. xv.

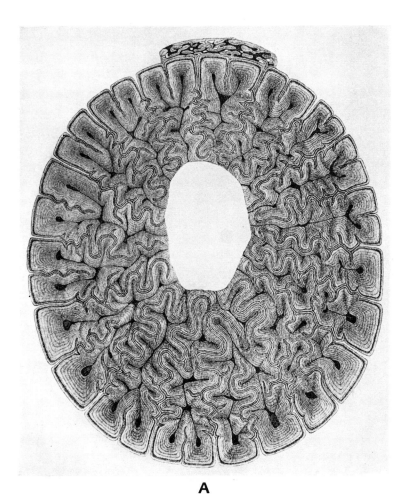

A

FIG. 18A. CROSS-SECTION OF LABYRINTHODONT TEETH. LOBE-FINNED
DEVONIAN FISH (AFTER PANDER).

For details see p. xvi.

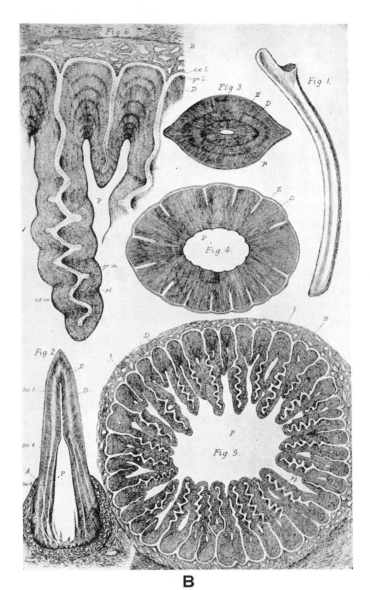

B

Fig. 18B. Primitive Amphibian of Permian Age (after
Embleton and Atthey).

On the other hand, many of the bony plates of the skull roof were taken over with little change by these oldest amphibians and the same is true of the derm bones of the lower jaw. On the under side of the skull (Fig. 53) the parasphenoid or keel bone had grown backward so as to cover the base of the braincase.

The teeth of the oldest amphibians were closely similar to those of the lobe-finned ganoids, both in general appearance and in microscopic structure. The porcelain-like outer layer of the skin bones covering the head of the lobe-finned fish had disappeared, leaving a rough surface. Thus the face of the oldest known amphibian, still consisting chiefly of a bony mask, was not as different from that of a lobe-finned fish as one might have expected.

Truly Nature's ways are not as man's ways. After producing a beautiful mask-face of great perfection and serviceableness, Nature started in to reduce and simplify it and eventually to cover up this mask with tender, sensitive flesh. From now on, the story of the human skull is the story of simplification and sacrifice of numbers, together with the refinement and constant differentiation of the elements that remained.

31

OUR FACE FROM FISH TO MAN

WHAT WE OWE TO THE EARLY REPTILES

The recent frogs, newts and salamanders, as every high school student knows, go through a fish-like or tadpole stage of development in the water and resort to this ancestral medium at the breeding season. The presence of fossilized gilled young of amphibians in the Coal ages shows that this water-breeding habit dates back very early in geological time and is in harmony with the origin of amphibians from swamp-living fishes. A great and revolutionary advance occurred when some daring amphibians succeeded in raising their eggs entirely on dry land, for thus arose the reptilian grade of organization and with it came the possibility of all higher forms of life, including man.

With regard to the bony face, the most primitive known reptile, *Seymouria*, has much in common with the older amphibians. It still retains the otic notch characteristic of the older forms and on its skull roof it preserves the full complement of small bony plates inherited from the amphibians and lobe-finned fishes. Also its outer upper jaw bones (maxillæ) still retain their primitive slenderness.

In the same age which yielded *Seymouria* (the

Permian of Texas) lived another, decidedly higher reptile, which had already acquired a significant resemblance to some of the lower mammal-like

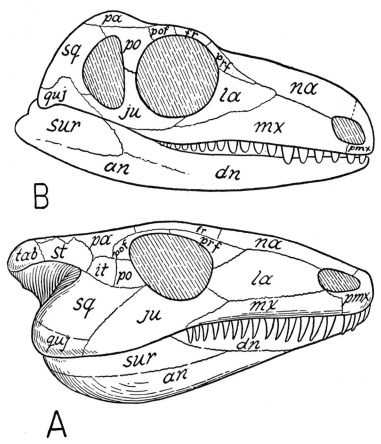

FIG. 19. TWO CRITICAL STAGES IN THE EARLY
EVOLUTION OF THE SKULL.

A. Generalized reptile, retaining the full complement of amphibian skull elements. (After data of Broili, Watson, Williston.)

B. Primitive theromorph reptile, with reduced number of skull elements (after Williston).   For details, see p. xvi.

33

reptiles of South Africa. This interesting form (*Mycterosaurus*) was carnivorous, like other progressive reptiles, but had not become too far specialized in this direction.

The most remarkable feature of its skull is a circular hole on the side of the skull behind the eye. This perforation in the bony mask of the temporal region was the first foreshadowing of the "temporal fossa" of the human skull.

As to the origin of this opening, studies on recent and fossil skulls of many kinds of reptiles indicate that the perforation arose through the progressive thinning of the bone, due to the absorbent action of the membranes surrounding the jaw muscle, which was attached to its inner surface. Meanwhile, in resistance to the stresses induced by the same muscle, the borders of the muscle area became strengthened into bony bars or ridges.

The bony tract below the temporal opening distinctly prophesied the mammalian zygomatic arch, the cheek bone of man.

Another progressive character of *Mycterosaurus* is the vertical growth of the upper jaw bone (maxilla), which up to that time had remained a shallow bar in front of the eyes. In the lower

34

jaw the principal tooth-bearing bone, or dentary,
one on each side of the head, was relatively larger

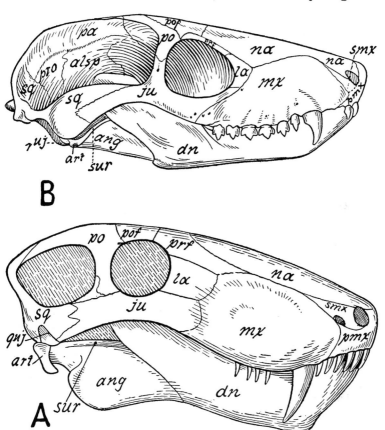

FIG. 20.   SKULLS OF EARLIER AND LATER MAMMAL-LIKE
REPTILES FROM SOUTH AFRICA.

(Data from Broom, Watson, Houghton.)
For details, see p. xvi.

as compared with the other bony plates of the jaw
lying behind it, than it had been in earlier stages.

OUR FACE FROM FISH TO MAN

The next stage in the long ascent is found among the extinct mammal-like reptiles of the Karroo system of rocks in South Africa. Among these the lowest (Fig. 20A) are nearly as reptilian as lizards, while the highest (Fig. 20B) almost reach the mammalian grade of organization. The bony mask skull advances in various details toward the mammalian type especially in the modelling of the lower jaw, in the further development of a temporal fossa, or muscle opening, and of a cheek arch essentially of mammalian type.

THE ONE-PIECE JAW REPLACES THE COMPLEX TYPE

In later members of the series leading toward the mammals the dentary bone increased in size until it so far dominated over the elements behind it that finally they were crowded out entirely and the lower jaw of the adult thus came to consist solely of the two dentary bones (one on each side) connected at the front end, or symphysis. This result was fraught with momentous consequences for the further evolution of the bony face toward the human and other mammalian types.

Meanwhile the dentary bone (Fig. 21) by reason of its enlargement came eventually to press against

36

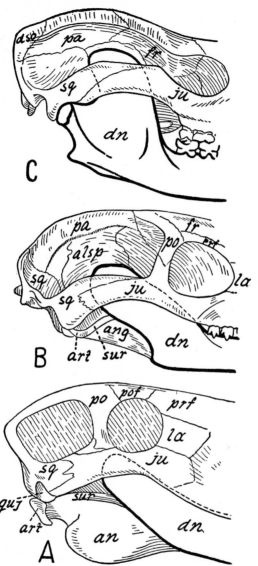

FIG. 21. PROGRESSIVE UPGROWTH OF THE DENTARY BONE OF THE LOWER JAW TO FORM A NEW JOINT WITH THE SKULL.

A. Primitive mammal-like reptile; B. Advanced mammal-like reptile; C. Primitive mammal.

For details, see p. xvi.

the very jaw muscles in which its upper end was embedded. In other cases when a muscle mass becomes subjected repeatedly to new pressures or friction across its line of action the surrounding

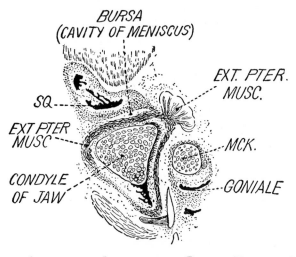

FIG. 22. ORIGIN OF THE INTERARTICULAR DISC, OR MENISCUS, LYING BETWEEN THE LOWER JAW AND ITS SOCKET IN THE SKULL. (AFTER GAUPP.)

membranes give rise to a cushion or sac of connective tissue filled with a clear liquid, which serves to prevent the opposing surfaces from grinding against each other. In an early embryo (Fig. 22) of a primitive mammal (*Perameles*) Professor E. Gaupp, the eminent comparative anatomist of Fribourg, found that a part of one

38

of the jaw muscles (the external pterygoid) during the course of its development passed between the lower jaw and its socket in the skull and there gave rise to the bursa or cushion (meniscus); this disc in all typical mammals prevents the lower jaw bone from grinding into its socket in the temporal (squamosal) bone.

In the immediate ancestors of the mammals the pressure of the dentary bone of the lower jaw transmitted through the meniscus or interarticular disc somehow resulted in the formation of a corresponding socket in the squamosal (temporal) bone of the skull.

Thus a new or mammalian joint was formed between the dentary bone of the lower jaw and the skull, while the old or reptilian joint, lying between the quadrate bone of the upper jaw and the articular bone of the lower jaw, was now greatly reduced in size, continued in the service of the middle ear and gave up its jaw-supporting function.

These great changes made possible all the new lines of evolution of the teeth that the mammals developed, which had never been possible for the reptiles; with these improved dental equipments the mammals soon overran the world, driving out the reptiles and finally producing the primates, which eventually gave rise to man.

Thus the human face owes the fundamental plan of its upper and lower jaws to the mammal-like reptiles and earliest mammals in which these improvements were first worked out.

OUR MASK-FACE BECOMES MOBILE

The origin of the mammals is one of the most dramatic incidents in the whole story of human transformation from fish to man. The central problems set for the mammal-like reptiles were to speed up all their vital processes and to maintain them at a relatively high level; also to resist the extreme changes of temperature of the harsh, highly variable climates then prevalent, when periods of glaciation alternated with tropical heat. Means had to be found to insulate the body in slowly conducting substances so as to defy the cold; on the other hand, to enable the body to cool itself safely when over-heated. Reptiles have this power to a limited degree but it is greatly enhanced in the mammals. For this purpose many "basic patents" had to be worked out in the heat-conserving organs, in the circulation of body

40

fluids, in the breathing organs. The locomotor machinery was vastly improved, the brain and nervous system had to keep pace with the general advance and a new and much less wasteful method of reproduction had to be perfected.

Among the heat-regulating devices arising in the mammals, we note the following: (a) the diaphragm, a complex structure arising from the conjunction of various muscle layers of the neck and abdomen; it acts as a bellows to draw fresh air into the lungs and thus to increase the consumption of oxygen; the liberation of heat is a by-product; the glands in the skin multiplied and gave rise to (b) sebaceous glands, pouring out a wax-like substance that tends to keep the skin soft and pliable; (c) sudoriparous or sweat glands, lowering the body temperature by evaporation of the exuded moisture.

Chief among the heat-retaining structures was (d) the hair, which seems to have arisen from small tactile outgrowths of the skin. These at first grew out between the scales and later supplanted them. We do not know exactly when this substitution took place, as the skin of soft-skinned animals is very rarely, if ever, fossilized, but the later mammal-like reptiles of the Triassic age were already so far advanced toward the mammalian grade that it would not be surprising if the initial stages in

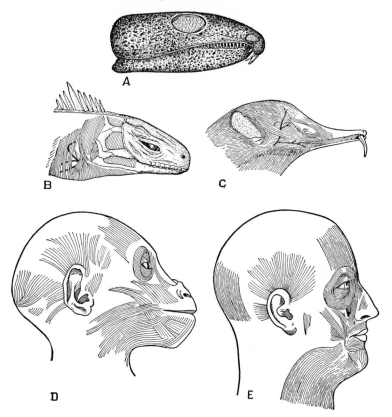

FIG. 23.   ORIGIN OF THE FACIAL MUSCLES OF MAN.

A. Primitive reptile with continuous bony mask covering skull.   The mask was covered with thick skin without muscles, as in the alligator. (After Williston.)   B. Modern reptile with an open or fenestrated skull covered with thick, non-muscular skin.   (From Fürbringer, modified from Ruge.)   C. Primitive mammal in which the sphincter colli system has grown forward over the face.   D. Gorilla.   E. Man.   (C, D and E after Ruge.)   For details, see p. xvii.

the formation of hair had already begun in them. At any rate, there is evidence that the bony mask of the earlier reptiles was already beginning to become leathery on its outer layer.

Even in the most primitive of living mammals the hard bony mask of the face has already begun to sink beneath the surface and a more or less pliable skin has been developed. But the most remarkable fact is that as the bony mask sank beneath the surface the "facial muscles," so characteristic of mammals alone among vertebrates, came into being. Where did they come from? In the reptiles the neck and throat are covered by a thin wide band of muscle called the primitive sphincter colli, which is activated by a branch of the seventh cranial nerve. In mammals this muscle, besides giving rise to the platysma muscle, has grown forward between the bony mask and the skin, along the sides and top of the face. As it grew forward over the cheek it sent out various subdivisions which either surrounded the eyes, or covered the forehead and cheeks, or surrounded the lips, or connected the lips with the cheeks, or were attached to the ears. Whenever the muscle mass sent forth a new branch it also sent into this branch a twig from the main facial division of the seventh nerve (Fig. 24). Thus what are called the mimetic or facial muscles of mammals arose by the forward migration and subdivision of a muscle formerly covering the neck. For this doc-

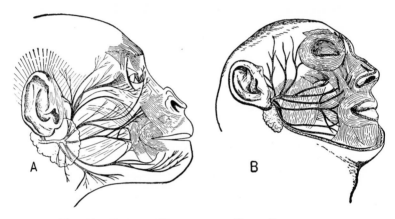

FIG. 24. DIAGRAM SHOWING THE CHIEF BRANCHES OF
THE FACIAL NERVE.

A. Gorilla. (After Ruge.) B. Man. (After Weisse.)

trine the anatomists Ruge and Huber have brought forward the most detailed and convincing evidence. Thus while mammals were exposed to cruel lacerations of the tender facial muscles, these same muscles became of great use in moving the lips, in closing the eyes, in moving the external ears and finally, in the apes and man, as a means of expressing emotion.

OUR ANCIENT RELATIVES

For many millions of years during the Age of
Reptiles the ancestral mammals enjoyed all the
advantages of a higher level of vital activity, a
higher body temperature, a better locomotor
system, larger brains and more economical repro-
ductive methods, which had made them far superior in grade to the group from which they sprang.
Nevertheless, in all parts of the world where fossils
have been found these advantages did not enable
the mammals to supplant immediately their swarming relatives the reptiles. On the contrary, the
reptilian class, which very early broke up into
many orders, including the turtles, lizards, snakes,
crocodilians, dinosaurs, birds, flying reptiles and
many others, for millions of years dominated the
earth, while both the mammals and the birds
remained small and inconspicuous. For all the
millions of years during which the dinosaurs ruled
the land, the fossil record of life as it is preserved
in Europe and North America so far reveals
extremely few mammalian remains, and these only
from very thin layers in widely separated parts
of the world.

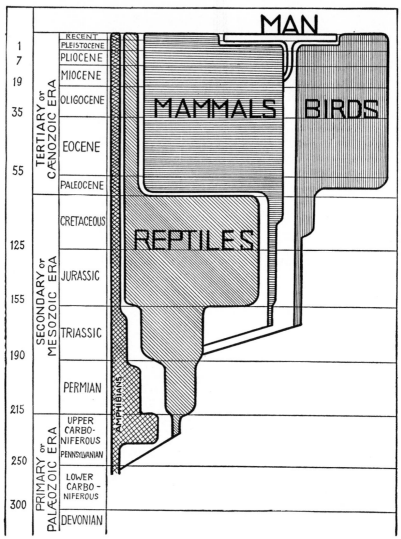

FIG. 25. SUCCESSIVE DOMINANCE OF THE AMPHIBIANS, REPTILES, MAMMALS AND BIRDS, MAN.

Numerals at left stand for millions of years since beginning of period, according to rate of "radium emanation" from uranium minerals, based on Barrell's estimates.

46

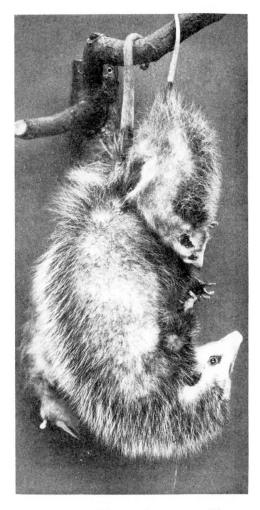

FIG. 26. THE COMMON OPOSSUM, A "LIVING FOSSIL" FROM THE AGE OF DINOSAURS.

OUR ANCIENT RELATIVES

The known mammalian remains from these great formations consist mostly of very fragmentary jaws, with a few teeth in them, of tiny mammals. Most of these mammals were no bigger than mice, but in the closing stages of the Age of Reptiles a few of them became as large as beavers. Some of the mammals of the Age of Reptiles in Europe and North America are believed by certain authorities to be related to that most archaic of mammals, the egg-laying Platypus of Australia. Others seem to have been remotely related to the existing marsupials or pouched mammals, which today live chiefly in Australia.

The most primitive marsupial of today, however, is the common opossum of North America, which is one of our oldest "living fossils." It is, in fact, the little-changed descendant of a group of mammals that lived in the latter part of the Age of Reptiles. One of these ancestral opossums, represented by a fossil jaw and parts of the skull (Fig. 27), was found by Barnum Brown embedded beneath a large dinosaur skull in Upper Cretaceous rocks of Montana. This form, named *Eodelphis* (dawn-opossum) by Dr. W. D. Matthew, has the known jaw and skull parts so nearly like those of its modern relative that we can actually fit the contours of the fossil opossum skull fragments into the skull of a recent opossum with very little adjustment of the latter; so that we may safely study the lowly 'possum as a representative and

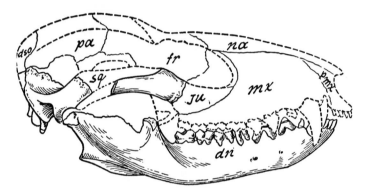

FIG. 27. SKULL PARTS OF EXTINCT OPOSSUM, SUPERPOSED ON OUTLINES OF SKULL OF RECENT OPOSSUM.
For details, see p. xvii.

descendant of the pouched mammals of the latter part of the Age of Reptiles.

Even the modern opossum skull is at first sight strangely similar to that of one of the mammal-like reptiles of the far-off Triassic. It will easily be seen from Fig. 28 that the opossum, like any primitive mammal, has inherited the entire ground-plan of its skull from its progressive reptilian ancestor. Considering the great advance in gen-

48

eral grade of organization described above, it is
surprising that in the side view of the skull the

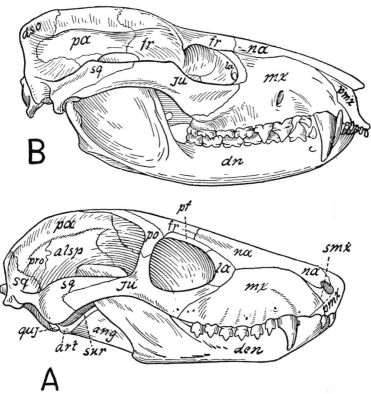

FIG. 28. SKULLS OF (A) ADVANCED MAMMAL-LIKE REPTILE AND
(B) MODERN OPOSSUM.

For details, see p. xvii.

higher structural level of the opossum is indicated
chiefly by the few conspicuous features figured
below (Figs. 48–52). The jaw muscles of the
opossum now cover the parietal and part of the

frontal bones, whereas in the earliest stages they lay beneath these bones.

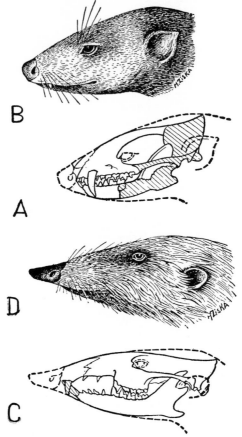

FIG. 29. LONG-SNOUTED RELATIVES OF OURS FROM THE CRETACEOUS OF MONGOLIA. (RESTORATIONS.)

For details, see pp. xvii., xviii.

It has been explained above how this shift in relations began, by the overlapping of the edges of these bones by the jaw muscles, which finally crept over and completely submerged the bone. Thus by the time we reach the primitive mammal stage of evolution almost the entire bony mask, which had originated as the bony skin on the surface, is now found covered by the facial and jaw muscles.

The relatives of the opossum and other primitive pouched mammals until several years ago were the only mammals of Cretaceous times of which anything definite was known as to their skull structure. In 1924 and 1925, however, Roy C. Andrews and his colleagues of the American Museum of Natural History discovered in the Cretaceous formation of Mongolia half a dozen imperfectly preserved skulls which appear to represent the forerunners of the higher or placental mammals (see also Fig. 77 iv below). These little skulls, which have been described by the present writer with the collaboration of Dr. G. G. Simpson, bring strong evidence for the conclusions of Huxley, Henry Fairfield Osborn, Max Weber, W. D. Matthew and others that the remote ancestors of the placental or higher mammals of the Age of Mammals were small insectivorous

51

animals with sharp cusps and blades on their tritubercular or triangular upper molar teeth. In these little Cretaceous placentals the skull and teeth were in many ways like those of certain existing insectivorous mammals, such as the tenrec of Madagascar.

All the evidence available from several sources indicates that the remote ancestors of the line leading to all the higher mammals, including man, were small long-snouted mammals, of insectivorous habits and not unlike some of the smaller opossums and insectivores in the general appearance of the head.

BETTER FACES COME IN WITH LIFE IN THE TREE-TOPS

Immediately upon the close of the Age of Reptiles the mammals appear in certain regions in North America and Europe in great numbers and variety. Palæontologists think it probable that they came from Asia, possibly by way of the Behring Straits land-bridge. In the Basal Eocene or Paleocene rocks of New Mexico and a few other places have been found thousands of fragments of fossilized jaws and teeth and several incomplete skeletons of mammals, ranging in size from mice

Fig. 30.   The Pen-tailed Tree-shrew of Borneo.

A "living fossil" representing a little-modified survivor of the Cretaceous ancestors of the Primates.   (Based on photographs and data given by Le Gros Clark.)

FIG. 31. THE SPECTRAL TARSIER OF BORNEO.

A highly specialized modern survivor of a diversified group of Primates that lived in the Lower Eocene epoch over fifty million years ago. (Data from specimen and photograph by H. C. Raven.)

to large badgers. These belong mostly to wholly extinct families of placental mammals, usually with very small brains and teeth variously adapted for eating insects, flesh or vegetation.

In the Basal Eocene formation of Montana have been found teeth and bits of jaws of mammals that apparently were somewhat nearer to the line of human ascent. One lot of teeth and jaws appear to be related remotely to the existing tree-shrews of the Indo-Malayan region. These little animals in many ways approach the lowest of the Primates, especially in the construction of the skull and teeth.

The second lot of teeth from the Basal Eocene of Montana are judged by Dr. Gidley of the U. S. National Museum to be related distantly to the existing tarsier of Borneo and the Philippine Islands. These very curiously specialized noc-turnal primates (Fig. 31) have enormous eyes, large but simple brains, very short noses and very long hind legs, upon which they hop about among the trees. In brief, the tarsier family appears to be one of those numerous groups that after attain-ing a high level of general organization at a rela-tively early period, start off on an extremely specialized side line and thus remove themselves from the direct line of ascent to higher forms.

Much more conservative and central in structural type are the fossil primates of the extinct family Notharctidæ from the Eocene of Wyoming and New Mexico. The fossil skeletons of these animals (Fig. 32) have grasping hands and feet of the tree-living type preserved in the modern lemurs of Madagascar. The same is true of the feet of the extinct lemuroid primates of the family Adapidæ from the Eocene of Europe.

Comparative anatomical and palæontological evidence unite to support the view that all the primates first went through an arboreal stage, some of them afterward coming down to the ground and carrying with them many of the structural "patents" acquired during their long schooling in the trees.

The hind foot of all known fossil and recent primates below man is of the tree-grasping type with a divergent great toe and there is no substantial doubt, after the exhaustive critical discussions of this subject by Gregory (1916, 1921, 1927), Miller (1920), Keith (1923), Schultz (1924), Morton (1924, 1927) and others, that the whole order was from its first appearance primarily tree-living

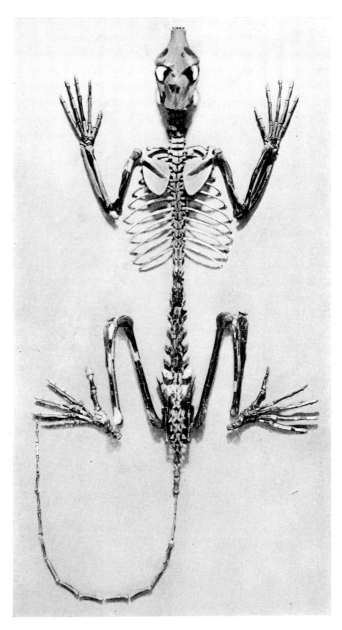

FIG. 32. SKELETON OF A PRIMITIVE FOSSIL PRIMATE FROM
THE EOCENE OF WYOMING (AFTER GREGORY).

For details see p. xviii.

in habit and that the foot of man has been derived from a grasping type with a divergent great toe.

Tree-living, possibly combined with nocturnal habits, favored the evolution of keen sight, and in the oldest known skulls of primates, from the

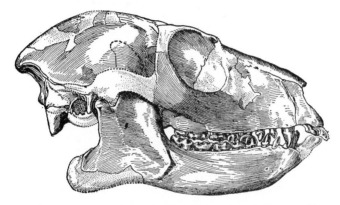

FIG. 33.   SKULL OF A PRIMITIVE PRIMATE OF THE EOCENE EPOCH (AFTER GREGORY).

For details, see p. xviii.

Eocene perhaps fifty million years ago, we find the eye orbits already larger and better defined than those of contemporary terrestrial mammals.

The skull of one of the best known members of this group is drawn in Fig. 33, from fossil specimens in the American Museum of Natural History. In this form the chief advance beyond the primitive mammalian type (Fig. 27) is seen in the increase in the size of the eyes and the beginning of the shifting of the eyes toward the front of the **head.** The muzzle, or olfactory chamber, is not yet reduced.

The still surviving primates afford a remarkably well graded series of faces, from the fox-like face of *Lemur* (Fig. 34A) to the quaint old-man-like faces of some of the Old World monkeys (Fig. 34C). In the lower forms (*Lemur*, etc.) a rhinarium, or moist patch, is present at the tip of the long snout, the opposite lips are separated by a notch in the mid-line and lack the mobility seen in the higher forms. In the latter, with the shortening of the muzzle, the rhinarium gives place to a true nose, the mucous-secreting skin being limited to the inner side of the nostrils and the nose eventually growing out between the nostrils. Meanwhile the opposite upper lips have become more broadly joined at the mid-line and finally the lips become highly protrusile through the constricting action of the strong orbicularis oris muscle.

In the New World, or platyrrhine, monkeys (Fig. 34B), which appear to represent an independent offshoot from some primitive tarsioid stock, the nostrils are widely separated, opening outwardly on each side of the broad median part of

56

FIG. 34. ASCENDING GRADES OF FACES IN THE LOWER
PRIMATES (AFTER ELLIOT).

A. Lemur; B. South American monkey; C. Old World monkey.

For details see p. xviii.

the nose. In the Old World, or catarrhine series (including the monkeys, apes and man), the nostrils are drawn downward and inward toward the mid-line, so that they tend to make a V, with the tip pointing downward. The subsequent history of the nose and lips will be considered below (pages 129, 153).

The external ears of the lower primates also show many gradations from a more ordinary mammalian type (see below, pages 211–213) to the man-like ears of the chimpanzee and gorilla.

The habit of living either in trees or in a forested region, in so far as it afforded opportunities for securing insects, buds, tender shoots and fruits, made possible the various lines of evolution of the teeth which we observe in studying the fossil and recent primates. In the earliest forms the dentition as a whole retains clearer traces of an earlier insectivorous stage, with triangular sharp-cusped upper molar teeth. In the anthropoid the habit of eating tender shoots and buds is reflected in the molar teeth, which now have broad crowns with low-ridged cusps. The human dentition, while secondarily adapted for a more varied diet, still bears many indubitable traces of its derivation

57

from a primitive anthropoid stage like that of the fossil apes *Dryopithecus* and *Sivapithecus*.

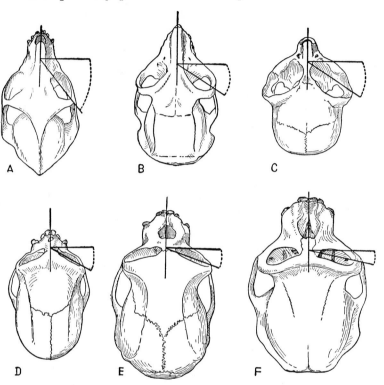

FIG. 35. TOP VIEW OF THE SKULL IN REPRESENTATIVES OF SIX FAMILIES OF PRIMATES, SHOWING THE MORE FORWARD DIRECTION OF THE ORBITS IN THE HIGHER FORMS.

A. Fossil lemuroid; B. African lemur; C. Tarsier; D. Marmoset; E. Gibbon; F. Chimpanzee.
For details, see pp. xviii, xix.

In some of the existing lemurs of Madagascar that retain the fox-like muzzle with its large smelling chamber, the eyes are less enlarged and look

58

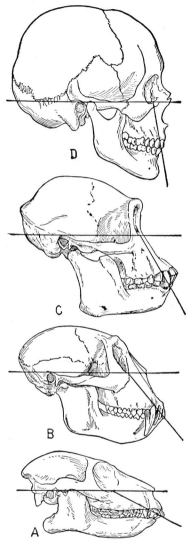

Fig. 36. Side View of Skulls of Primates, Showing Progressive
Shortening of the Muzzle, Downward Bending of the
Face Below the Eyes and Forward Growth of the Chin.

A. Eocene lemuroid; B. Old World monkey; C. Female chimpanzee,
D. Man. (B and C after Elliot.) For details, see p. xix.

59

partly outward as well as forward. But in all the more advanced lemuroids the eyes are larger, with more or less protruding orbits which tend to shift forward, finally restricting greatly the interorbital space and nasal chamber. This process culminates in the nocturnal galagos and in *Tarsius* (Fig. 31), in which the eyes are enormous and the eyes themselves are directed forward, although the orbits are directed obliquely outward.

In none of the lower primates, however, are the bony orbits directed fully forward and in none of them are the upper jaws prolonged downward beneath the eyes, as they are in the monkeys, apes and man.

The families of man, apes, monkeys, tarsioids, lemurs and tree-shrews are exceedingly rare as fossils except in a few localities and geologic horizons and the known remains usually consist chiefly of broken jaws with a few teeth. Nevertheless these fossils are of high value when studied together with the manifold families, genera and species of primates still living. In a series of publications beginning in 1910 I have shown how fully these recent and fossil forms, from tree-shrews to man, reveal the structural stages in the

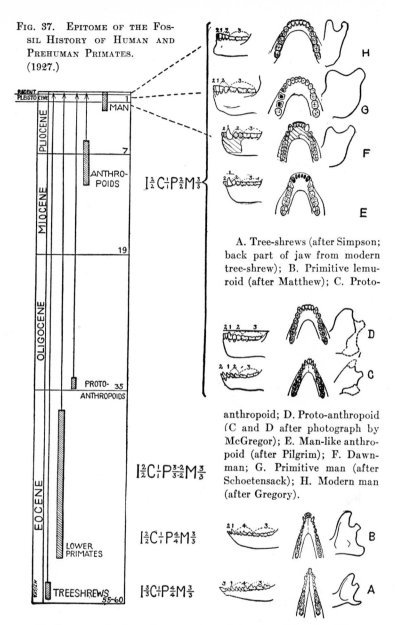

FIG. 37. EPITOME OF THE FOSSIL HISTORY OF HUMAN AND PREHUMAN PRIMATES. (1927.)

H

G

F

$I\frac{2}{2}C\frac{1}{1}P\frac{2}{2}M\frac{3}{3}$

E

A. Tree-shrews (after Simpson; back part of jaw from modern tree-shrew); B. Primitive lemuroid (after Matthew); C. Proto-

D

C

anthropoid; D. Proto-anthropoid (C and D after photograph by McGregor); E. Man-like anthropoid (after Pilgrim); F. Dawnman; G. Primitive man (after Schoetensack); H. Modern man (after Gregory).

$I\frac{2}{2}C\frac{1}{1}P\frac{3-2}{3-2}M\frac{3}{3}$

$I\frac{2}{2}C\frac{1}{1}P\frac{4}{4}M\frac{3}{3}$

B

$I\frac{3}{3}C\frac{1}{1}P\frac{4}{4}M\frac{3}{3}$

A

The figures on the right give the estimated duration of time in millions of years since the beginning of each epoch. For details, see pp. xix, xx.

61

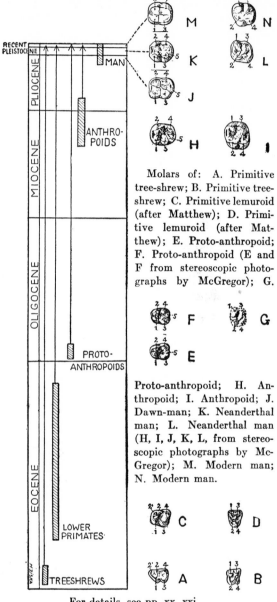

Molars of: A. Primitive tree-shrew; B. Primitive tree-shrew; C. Primitive lemuroid (after Matthew); D. Primitive lemuroid (after Matthew); E. Proto-anthropoid; F. Proto-anthropoid (E and F from stereoscopic photographs by McGregor); G.

Proto-anthropoid; H. Anthropoid; I. Anthropoid; J. Dawn-man; K. Neanderthal man; L. Neanderthal man (H, I, J, K, L, from stereoscopic photographs by McGregor); M. Modern man; N. Modern man.

For details, see pp. xx, xxi.

evolution of the teeth, jaws, braincase, middle and inner ear, vertebral column, pelvis, hands and feet.

Meanwhile Elliot Smith, Tilney, Hunter, Le Gros Clark and others have shown how the existing tree-shrews, lemurs, monkeys, apes and man present a progressive series in the evolution of the brain as a whole and of the various nuclei and centers controlling bodily functions and behavior.

Sir Arthur Keith and others have also traced step by step the structural adjustments in the diaphragm, abdomen and pelvic floor, as the originally horizontal body assumes a sitting position or moves erect as in the gibbon and man.

It is remarkable how completely the results of the students of the nervous system and of the anatomy of the viscera accord with studies on the evolution of the teeth, skull, limbs, etc., and on the classification and fossil history of the families and genera of Primates.

Taken together, these results afford cumulative evidence for the conclusions that man still bears in his whole organization an indelible stamp of the tree-living habits of his remote primate ancestors and that these tree-living adaptations were overlaid by a later but very extended series of adaptations for bipedal running on the ground.

THE ALMOST HUMAN FACE APPEARS

Doubtless many factors conditioned the progressive enlargement and differentiation of the brain, which is so marked a characteristic of the whole Primate order, but perhaps the leading factor was the correlated use of eyes and hands and at first, feet, not only in locomotion but in the seizure and manipulation of food. And no doubt the habit of sitting upright also tended to free the hands for the examination of nearby objects, while the habit of climbing in an erect posture, as in the gibbon, finally gave rise to the almost human face of the anthropoid apes, as will presently be shown.

We do not yet know the exact time and place in which certain advanced primates began to take on specifically human characters, although there is much evidence at hand indicating that the time was not much earlier than the Lower Miocene, and the place somewhere within the known area

FIG. 39.   ONE OF OUR NEAREST LIVING RELATIVES.   FEMALE
CHIMPANZEE AND YOUNG.

(From "Almost Human," by R. M. Yerkes.   Courtesy of the author
and The Century Company).

For details see p. xxi.

FIG. 40.   MALE AND FEMALE CHIMPANZEES.

(After J. A. Allen, from photographs by Herbert Lang.)

of the anthropoid stock at that time, which ranged from India to Spain. But Darwin's conclusion that mankind represents a peculiar and specialized offshoot from the anthropomorphous subgroup of Old World primates, after three-quarters of a century of anatomical and palæontological research, is backed by a mountain of evidence.

The female chimpanzee in the side view of the skull stands nearer in resemblance to man than it does to the primitive Eocene primate *Notharctus.* The chimpanzee in fact has acquired all the "basic patents" in skull architecture which were prerequisite for the final development of the human skull.

The most eminent students of the brains of animals and men conclude that partly as a result of the necessity for keen sight in actively climbing animals, the eyes in primates (Fig. 35) moved around from the sides of the face, where they are in the lower vertebrates, and were brought to the front, where in the anthropoid apes they finally acquired biconjugate movements and stereoscopic vision. In the anthropoid apes, moreover, the sense of smell no longer dominates the brain system as it did in lower vertebrates, but its reign is usurped by the sense of sight. Concomitantly, the brain of the chimpanzee has increased greatly so that the braincase is distinctly subhuman in appearance. The erect position assumed by apes that climb so much by means of their arms as do the anthropoids has conditioned the bending downward of the face upon the braincase (Fig. 36).

Everyone recognizes in the chimpanzee (Fig. 40) a gross caricature of the human face, in which the mouth and lips are absurdly large and the nose flat with little or no bridge. But from the anthropoid viewpoint the human face may well appear equally grotesque, with its weak little mouth, exposed lips and unpleasantly protruding nose. Possibly the common ancestor of man and apes would be shocked by each of his descendants. But allowing for much divergent evolution in the end forms, what makes men and anthropoids so much more like each other in fundamental features of the face than either is to the oldest forerunners of the entire order, long antedating their nearer common ancestor? First, let us set down in parallel columns a few of these resemblances and differences.

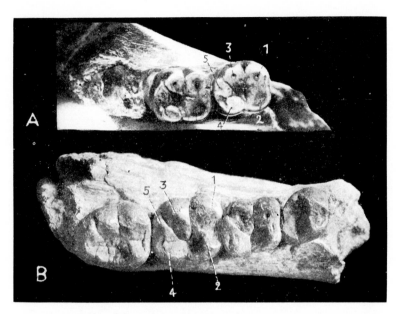

Fig. 41. Left Lower Cheek Teeth of Fossil Anthropoid (B) from India and Fossil Primitive Man (A) from Piltdown, England.

(A, from photograph by J. H. McGregor; B, after Gregory and Hellman).

The lower molars of the Piltdown jaw, although much ground down by wear, show the pure *"Dryopithecus* pattern" characteristic of recent and fossil apes.

For details see p. xxi.

	EARLIER PRIMATES (Cf. Figs. 33, 34A, 35A, 36A)	ANTHROPOIDS AND PRIMITIVE MAN (Cf. Figs. 35E, F, 42, 43, 44)
Muzzle and snout	Long, pointed, extended chiefly forward	Short, wide, extended chiefly downward
Mouth	Narrow, elongate	Wide, short
Tongue	Narrow	Broad
Lips	Not protrusile	Strongly protrusile
Number of premolars, upper	Four	Two
Number of premolars, lower	Four	Two
Form of first and second upper molars	Triangular, three main cusps	Quadrangular, four main cusps
Cusps of lower molars	Sharp	Low, blunt
Lower jaw	Long, slender	Short, deep
Opposite halves of lower jaw	Separate	Fused in front
Eyes	Look outward and forward	Look forward, binocular, biconjugate
Bony partition behind eye orbits	Barely begun	Complete
Premaxilla and maxilla	Separate	Fused in adult
Occipital condyles	On rear of brain base	More on under side of brain base

This comparison could be greatly extended by the inclusion of technical anatomical details, but is sufficient to indicate the main features of the bony face in which man and the anthropoids have advanced beyond the primitive primates. In the earliest primates the characters mentioned above are already adapted to a diet of insects and vege-

67

tation and to a horizontal position of the vertebral column; the anthropoids, on the other hand, are chiefly frugivorous and their vertebral column is more or less erect.

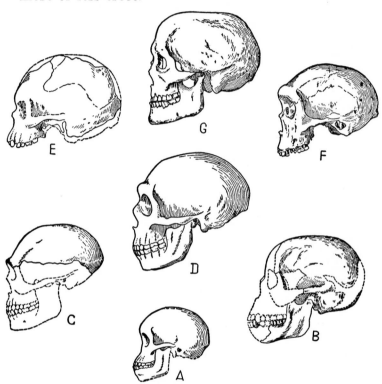

FIG. 42.   FOSSIL ANTHROPOID AND HUMAN SKULLS.

A. *Australopithecus,* a young extinct anthropoid (after Dart); B. *Eoanthropus* (after A. S. Woodward and J. H. McGregor); C. *Pithecanthropus erectus* (after Dubois); D. Neanderthal (after Boule); E. Talgai (after S. A. Smith); F. Rhodesian (after A. S. Woodward); G. Cro-Magnon (after Verneau).

In the female and young skulls the brow ridges are less projecting or entirely lacking.   For details, see pp. xxi, xxii.

OUR ANCIENT RELATIVES

The close anatomical relationship of man to the anthropoids, together with the fundamental iden-

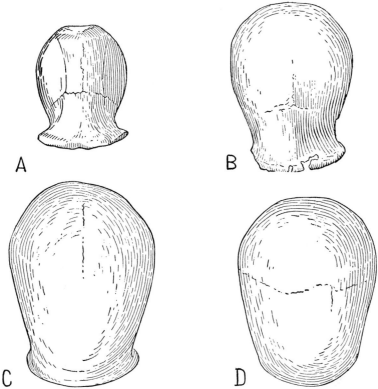

FIG. 43. ANTHROPOID AND HUMAN SKULLS. TOP VIEW.
A. Chimpanzee (after Boule); B. *Pithecanthropus* (after Dubois);
C. Neanderthal (after Boule); D. Cro-Magnon (after Boule).

tity in the molar patterns (Fig. 41) of the most ancient fossil men to those of still older anthropoids, indicates that man has been derived from frugivorous pro-anthropoids and that after man

69

left or had been driven forth from the ancient forests, his omnivorous-carnivorous habits were developed during the age-long and bitter struggle for life on the plains. Thus the gentle pro-anthropoids, quiet feeders on the abundant fruits of the forest, introduced a long period of peaceful development in the strenuous upward struggle.

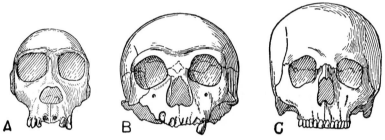

FIG. 44. ANTHROPOID AND HUMAN SKULLS (AFTER BOULE).
A. Chimpanzee; B. Neanderthal; C. Modern European.

This peace was rudely broken when from some zoological Garden of Eden, that is, from the center of post-anthropoid evolution, the ancestral horde of savage pro-hominids were turned out on the plains to devastate the world.

AT LAST THE "PERFECT" FACE

As yet there is an immense hiatus in the palæontological history of man, covering at least several million years in the Pliocene epoch. All known

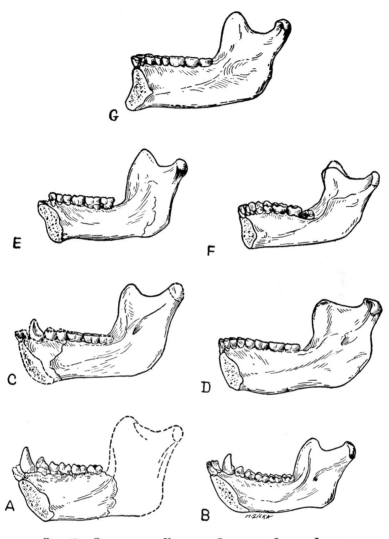

FIG. 45. COMPARATIVE VIEWS OF SECTIONED LOWER JAWS.

A. *Dryopithecus* (after Gregory and Hellman); B. Chimpanzee;
C. Piltdown (after A. S. Woodward); D. Heidelberg (after Schoeten-
sack); E. Ehringsdorf (after Virchow); F. Neanderthal (after Weinert);
G. Cro-Magnon (after Verneau).

71

early human fossils are unquestionably human in one way or another—even including the famous *Pithecanthropus*, which zealous anti-evolutionists stoutly refuse to admit to the human family. But it is also noteworthy that each of these earliest human relics is ape-like in a different way. The Piltdown lower jaw (Fig. 41) and teeth are extraordinarily ape-like; the *Pithecanthropus* skull (Fig. 42C) is ape-like both in its projecting brow ridges and in certain features of the occiput, while the braincast, according to all expert analysis, is far inferior in certain respects to that of *Homo sapiens;* the Heidelberg jaw (Fig. 45D) has a receding chin and the Mousterian skull has many primitive ape-like details in the teeth (Fig. 45F) that are usually lost in *Homo sapiens.* The Rhodesian skull (Fig. 42F) shows remarkably gorilla-like details of the bony lower border of the nose, indicating a very low form of nasal cartilages and nostrils; the Talgai (Australia) skull is a proto-Australoid type with extreme prognathism (Fig. 42E). The *Australopithecus* skull (Fig. 42A) is that of a young anthropoid with an exceptionally well developed brain (Dart, Sollas, Broom). While it may be nearer to the chimpanzee than to man, its brain, skull

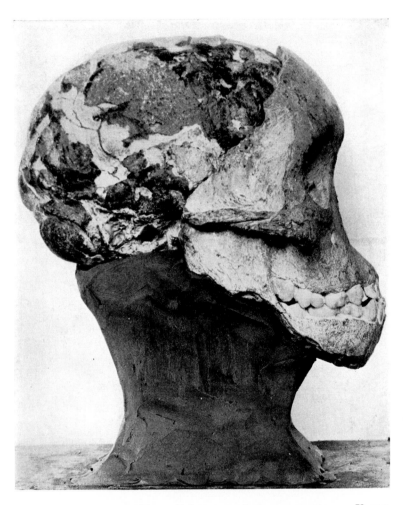

FIG. 46. THE "ALMOST HUMAN" SKULL OF AUSTRALOPITHECUS, A YOUNG
FOSSIL ANTHROPOID (AFTER DART).

FIG. 47.   RESTORATION OF THE HEAD OF THE YOUNG
AUSTRALOPITHECUS.

(After a drawing by Forrestier made under the direction
of Elliot Smith.)

and teeth tend to bridge the gap between the highest apes and the lowest men.

Such were the last fleeting souvenirs of the prehuman stage, surviving millions of years after the first separation of the human and great ape families. They represent various degrees of approximation toward the modernized type of face, from the almost ape-like lower jaw of Piltdown to the highbred old man of Cro-Magnon (Fig. 42G). Thus the scant evidence suggests that even in Lower Pleistocene times there were already several different types of mankind, some (such as Piltdown) more progressive or less ape-like in the shape of the forehead, while more conservative in the form of the dentition and jaw, others (*Pithecanthropus*) with a lower form of forehead and not improbably a more progressive form of jaw. Whether these represent individual, racial or specific difference is not fully demonstrated; in any case they suggest that within the family of mankind there was a remarkably wide range of variability in facial characters, as there still is.

The profound agreement between mankind and the anthropoid group in anatomical characteristics and in physiological reactions and to a certain

extent in basic mental traits (Yerkes, Koehler) all
sufficiently establish the fact that at one time the
human and anthropoid groups converged backward to a common source. It is also the plain
teaching of comparative anatomy that the modernized white human face with its small mouth, weak
jaws, reduced dentition, projecting chin, delicate
projecting nose and pale skin, has changed far
more from the primitive man-anthropoid starting-
point than has the face of a young chimpanzee,
with huge mouth, strong teeth, receding chin and
flat nose. Professor Osborn holds that the separation of man and apes from the primitive anthropoid stock began as far back as the Lower Oligocene epoch, possibly some thirty-five million years
ago, while the present writer is inclined to date
this event from the next higher epoch, namely
the Lower Miocene, possibly nineteen million
years ago.[1]

Whichever date, if either, may eventually prove
to be the true one, the fact remains that in its
present form the modernized human face is *sui*

[1] These figures are according to the tentative estimates of the geological epochs worked out by Barrell by the "radium emanation"
method, based on the rate of disintegration of radioactive ores from
different geological horizons.

generis, just as the face of any other species of mammal is unique in its specific attributes. But there are thousands of good scientific reasons for accepting as a fact the evolution of man from lower mammals, there is a convincing chain of known forms in the long series from fish to man; and even in civilized man the human face is most obviously related rather closely to that of the anthropoids; therefore only the most confirmed mystic by preference will insist that the evolution of the human face is a "mystery." It is true that every event of the kind abounds in mystery, since no matter how fully we can describe by what stages it happens, we uncover infinitely ramifying problems whenever we attempt to isolate the causal factors.

Undoubtedly when primitive man left the forests and came out on the plains to live by hunting there was a change in food, a change from a frugivorous to at least a partly carnivorous diet, there was a change of locomotion from erect tree-climbing (brachiation) to bipedal running on the plains; speech arose and the brain grew so large that it grew faster than the face; the period of individual growth and development was greatly extended; all

75

the system of the ductless glands which has so profound an effect upon growth and development was affected in innumerable ways and differently in different individuals and races. Thus we begin to sense the complexity of the factors influencing the emergence of the typical human face from a primitive anthropoid type.

Whatever the causes may have been, the evidence indicates that, starting with a face not dissimilar to that of an immature female chimpanzee (Fig. 40B), the forehead rapidly became larger, the incisor teeth became less inclined, more vertical and smaller in size, the canine teeth diminished in size and in such a way that the tip of the lower one finally passed behind the front edge of the upper canine; the premolars and molars also decreased in fore and aft diameter. In addition to the reduction and backward displacement of the teeth there was a positive outgrowth of the bony chin, which possibly on account of the early development of the tongue could not retreat further backward. The later stages of this process may be reconstructed by comparing the faces of different races, from the projecting muzzles, very large mouth, broad flat nose and retreating chin of some of the Tasmanians (Fig. 10, Frontispiece) to the narrow, forwardly-projecting, pointed nose and pointed chin of the Alpine, European type (Fig. 11 Frontispiece).

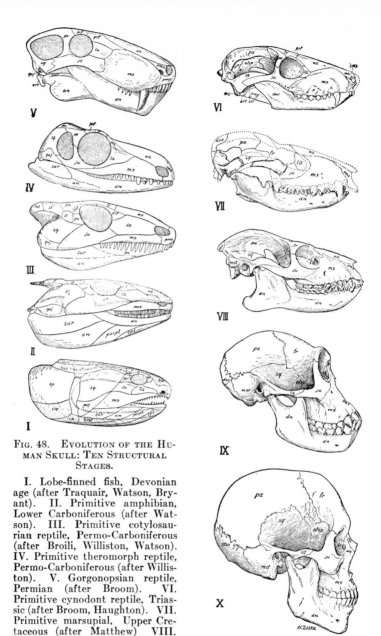

FIG. 48. EVOLUTION OF THE HU-
MAN SKULL: TEN STRUCTURAL
STAGES.

I. Lobe-finned fish, Devonian
age (after Traquair, Watson, Bryant). II. Primitive amphibian,
Lower Carboniferous (after Watson). III. Primitive cotylosaurian reptile, Permo-Carboniferous
(after Broili, Williston, Watson).
IV. Primitive theromorph reptile,
Permo-Carboniferous (after Williston). V. Gorgonopsian reptile,
Permian (after Broom). VI.
Primitive cynodont reptile, Triassic (after Broom, Haughton). VII.
Primitive marsupial, Upper Cretaceous (after Matthew) VIII.
Primitive primate, Eocene (after Gregory). IX. Anthropoid (female
chimpanzee), Recent. X. Man, Recent.

For details, see pp. xxii, xxiii.

78

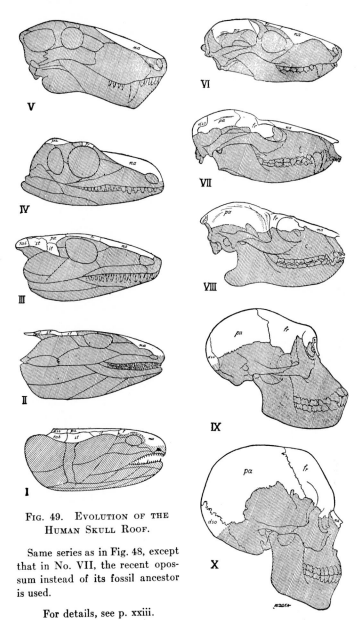

FIG. 49.   EVOLUTION OF THE
     HUMAN SKULL ROOF.

Same series as in Fig. 48, except
that in No. VII, the recent opossum instead of its fossil ancestor
is used.

For details, see p. xxiii.

79

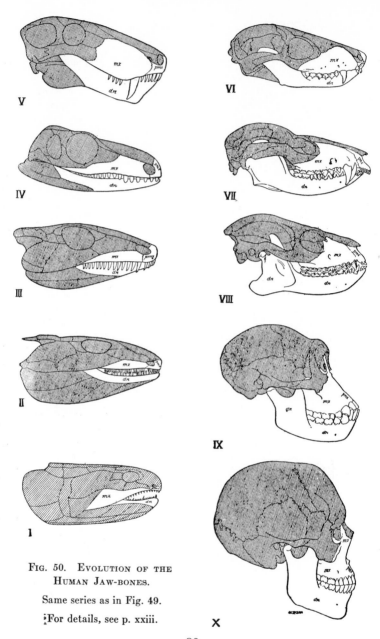

V

VI

IV

VII

III

VIII

II

IX

I

FIG. 50. EVOLUTION OF THE
HUMAN JAW-BONES.

Same series as in Fig. 49.

For details, see p. xxiii.

X

80

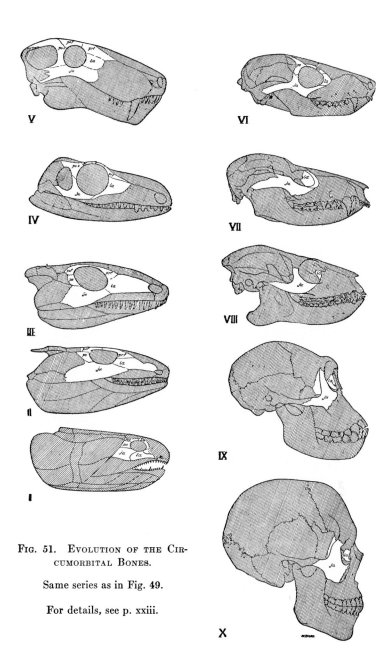

FIG. 51. EVOLUTION OF THE CIR-
CUMORBITAL BONES.

Same series as in Fig. 49.

For details, see p. xxiii.

81

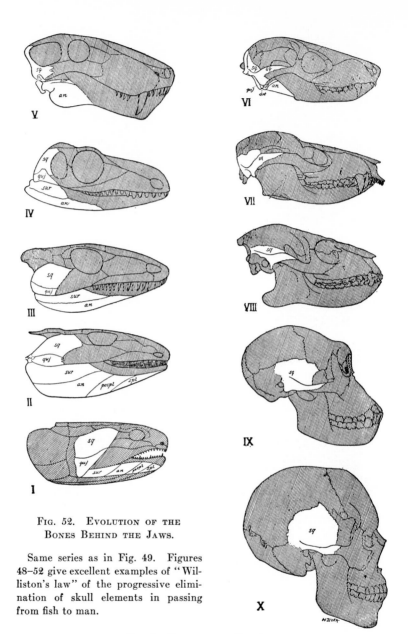

FIG. 52. EVOLUTION OF THE
BONES BEHIND THE JAWS.

Same series as in Fig. 49. Figures
48–52 give excellent examples of "Williston's law" of the progressive elimination of skull elements in passing
from fish to man.

For details, see pp. xxiii, xxiv.

PART II

CONCISE HISTORY OF OUR BEST FEATURES

The Bony Framework of the God-Like Mask

To review at this point the history of the bony framework of the face, we note that the human skull as a whole is a complex consisting of a chondrocranium, or inner skull, which is preformed in cartilage, and an outer shell of dermal bones, formed in membrane. The chondrocranium comprises the base of the skull, the sphenoid bone and the olfactory and otic capsules. The outer, or dermocranium, comprises: (a) the roofing bones (nasals, frontals, parietals, and the membranous part of the supraoccipital); (b) the orbital elements (lacrymal, jugal, or malar); (c) the squamous part of the temporal bone; (e) the maxillary elements (upper and lower jaw bones); (f) the palatal bone and the internal pterygoid plate of the sphenoid; (g) the vomer.

The illustrations submitted herewith (**Figs.**

83

48–53) set forth a few of the facts which have convinced modern anatomists that man, like other mammals, was not created at one stroke, but that he reached his present condition by gradual stages of modification, which, thanks to the unremitting labors of many palæontologists and anatomists, now appear to be fairly well understood. None of these stages is hypothetical; they are either known fossil forms or are the surviving and little-modified descendants of known fossil forms.

From the imperfect nature of the fossil record we can never expect to recover the infinite number of links in the direct line of ancestry of man or of any other mammal. The record affords us only successive structural stages that are more or less nearly related to the main line of ascent from fish to man.

The story told in these illustrations has not been invented by the writer. It has slowly revealed itself as the palæontologists and anatomists of a century past have gradually unearthed it. During the past fifteen years great progress has been made all along the line of stages I to X, either in the discovery of hitherto unknown or little-known forms, or in the determination of the sutural

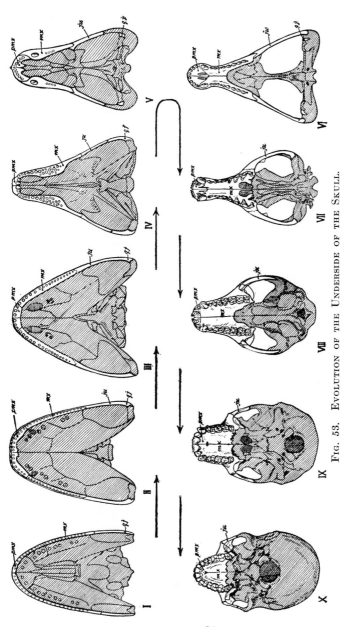

FIG. 53. EVOLUTION OF THE UNDERSIDE OF THE SKULL.

I. Lobe-finned fish, Devonian (after Bryant, Watson). II. Primitive amphibian, Carboniferous (after Watson). III. Primitive cotylosaurian reptile, Permo-Carboniferous (after Watson). IV. Advanced cotylosaurian reptile, Permo-Carboniferous (original). V. Gorgonopsian reptile, Permian (after Watson). VI. Advanced mammal-like reptile, Triassic (mainly after Watson). VII. Marsupial mammal, Recent (original). VIII. Eocene lemuroid primate (after Stehlin). IX. Anthropoid (female chimpanzee) (original). X. Man (Australian aboriginal). For details, see p. xxiv.

85

limits of the individual bones, or in the vital problems of determining the systematic relationships of each of the forms figured and of the groups that they represent. Recent palæontologists who have contributed especially to these subjects include D. M. S. Watson (in connection with Stages I, II, III, V, VI), Bryant (in connection with Stage I), Williston (in connection with Stages III, IV), Broili (in connection with Stage III), Broom (in connection with Stages V, VI), Haughton (in connection with Stage VI), Matthew (in connection with Stage VII), Gregory (in connection with Stages VIII, IX). The drawings, like most of the others in this book, were skilfully executed by Mrs. Helen Ziska, working under the constant advice and supervision of the author. For whatever errors the figures may still bear, after many appeals to the original data, the writer alone therefore must be held responsible.

To recapitulate, the outstanding changes in the lateral view of the skull from fish to man appear to have been as follows:

Of the bones on the roof of the skull (Fig. 49), namely the nasals, frontals, parietals, interparietals (or dermo-supraoccipitals) and tabulars, only the last disappear entirely in the mammals. As the brain enlarges these roofing bones are lifted into greater prominence, the frontals, parietals, inter-parietals and occipitals becoming the dominant elements in the great vault of the human skull.

The superior maxillary bone (Fig. 50) begins as a slender, vertically shallow element, but by the time of the early mammal-like reptiles (Fig. 50 V) it has extended dorsally and gained contact with the nasals. In the mammals (Fig. 50 VII–X) its dominance is still more pronounced; one fork reaches the frontals while another fork finally separates the lacrymal from the jugal and the whole bone becomes shortened antero-horizontally and deepened vertically. In the anthropoids and man the premaxillæ early unite with the maxillæ.

The inferior maxillary (dentary) at first is confined to the anterior half of the mandible. In the higher mammal-like reptiles it becomes dom-inant, the post-dentary elements retreating before it. In the earliest mammals the ascending ramus of the dentary effects a new contact with the squamosal, the temporo-mandibular articulation, which is transmitted without further essential modification to man.

OUR FACE FROM FISH TO MAN

Of the bones around the eye (Fig. 51), originally
five in number, three (the prefrontal, postfrontal,
postorbital) are eliminated by the time of the
earliest mammals, so that man inherits only two
of the original five, namely the lacrymal and the
jugal or malar.

The temporo-mandibular series (Fig. 52), originally including eight bones (the intertemporal,
supratemporal, squamosal, quadrato-jugal, surangular, angular postsplenial, splenial), suffers
gradual reduction, until in the earliest mammals,
as in man, only the squamosal remains, at least in
the lateral view of the skull. In the mammals the
squamosal has fused with the enlarged periotic
mass and in the anthropoids and man the tympanic is added, the whole complex forming the
temporal bone.

At every successive stage of evolution advances
in skull structure were dependent upon improvements in the brain itself, upon shiftings and
enlargements of the parts containing the sense
organs, upon modifications of the jaws and teeth,
accompanying or accompanied by changes of
habits. The skull in turn is closely integrated
with both the active and the passive elements of

the locomotor apparatus, a topic which will be developed elsewhere.

To each of the stages described above man owes certain "basic patents," or adaptive improvements which have been of critical importance in his survival. Thus to certain far-off Devonian air-breathing fishes man owes the general ground-plan of the vertebrate skull, the combination of primary "gill-arch" jaws with sheathing or outer jaws, and each and every one of the twenty-eight normal skull bones which he still retains.

Next, he is indebted to the first amphibians for partially solving the innumerable problems caused by emergence from the water. These old pioneers cast off the whole series of bones that covered the branchial chamber and made for themselves an ear-drum out of the skin around the notch where the opercular was formerly located. The early reptiles safeguarded most of the inheritance from their semi-aquatic ancestors, dropping only the inter- and supratemporals. To the first of the mammal-like series man owes the beginnings of his temporal fossa and zygomatic arch, and the dominance of the superior maxilla. From the higher mammal-like reptiles he has inherited the further development of the temporal fossa and especially the dominance of the inferior maxillary or dentary bone of the lower jaw. To these progressive pro-mammals man can render thanks for the differentiation of his dentition into incisors, canines, premolars and molars, and apparently he can also thank them for the reduction of the numerous successional teeth to two sets, corresponding to the milk teeth and the permanent set.

The earliest mammals invented one of the most useful features of man's skull by eliminating from the masticatory apparatus all the elements lying behind the dentary and by establishing the temporo-mandibular joint. They also cast off the reptilian prefrontal, postfrontal and postorbital bones and cleared the way for the final simplification of the bony scaffolding of the face.

To the earliest primates, well schooled in arboreal life, man owes the first steps in the glorification of the eyes, which become increasingly dominant. These still lowly but thrifty forebears made good the loss of the reptilian postorbital bar by elaborating a new one from conjoining processes from the frontal and jugal (or malar) bones.

But still greater was our debt to the arboreal

pro-anthropoids, those intelligent beings who elected to develop sight at the expense of smell. These skilled acrobats, moving in a vertical position, met and solved a new series of problems connected with the turning downward of the skull upon the upright column. They also made the first notable attempts to shorten and deepen the face and even took a long step toward enlarging the brain and brain chamber.

Starting with these and many like advantages gained during a long training in arboreal life, it was the task of our relatively nearer precursors (beginning possibly in Miocene times, or earlier) to re-adapt all these arboreal adaptations for a life on the ground and to take the final steps upward that have brought humanity to its present levels of intelligence.

Wholly ignorant of the facts, the ancient Jewish priests indulged themselves in the fancy that man was made in the image of God; but modern science shows that the god-like mask which is the human face is made out of the same elements as in the gorilla; and that in both ape and man the bony framework of the face is composed of strictly homologous elements, inherited from a long line of lower vertebrates.

OUR FACE FROM FISH TO MAN

FISH-TRAPS AND FACES

THE FIRST MOUTHS

From air-breathing fish to man the *general* course of evolution seems clear enough, at least in its broad outlines. But when we inquire whence

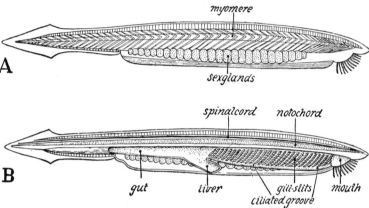

FIG. 54. ANATOMY OF THE LANCELET, THE MOST PRIMITIVE LIVING CHORDATE ANIMAL (AFTER DELAGE AND HÉROUARD).

A. Entire animal, seen as a semi-transparent object; B. Longitudinal section.   For details, see p. xxiv.

came the fish, the evidence while extensive is somewhat ambiguous and there is room for sharp differences of opinion. On the one hand, there is Professor Patten, who derives the whole vertebrate series from very ancient jointed animals remotely allied to the modern scorpions and *Limulus;* on the other hand, there are the more orthodox

92

zoologists, who infer that the greatly simplified form *Amphioxus* (Fig. 54), together with all the vertebrates, represent offshoots of some still undiscovered stock that also gave rise to the acornworms (*Balanoglossus*), the starfishes and certain other peculiar groups. According to this view,

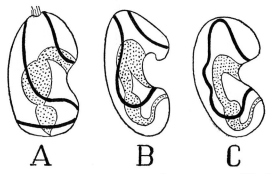

A   B   C

FIG. 55. LARVÆ OF ECHINODERMS: SEA-CUCUMBER (A), STARFISH (B) AND OF THE "ACORN-WORM" (AFTER DELAGE AND HÉROUARD).

For details, see p. xxv.

the common ancestors of all these diversified groups were exceedingly simplified, free-swimming, marine organisms, consisting chiefly of a digestive tube bent at a right angle and enclosed in a thin balloon-like tissue, more or less folded into plaits and provided with strips of cilia, by the lashing of which the floating bag moved slowly through the water. Such forms (Fig. 55) are found living today as the larvæ or young stages of starfishes, sea-cucumbers, and also of the acorn-worm *Balan-oglossus*. The mouth of these forms is the original mouth of the primitive gut or digestive tract.

There is evidence from embryology that the mouth of the vertebrates is a compound structure

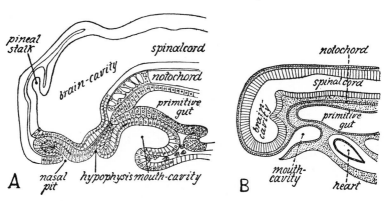

FIG. 56. INNER AND OUTER MOUTH POUCHES IN EMBRYO VERTE-BRATES: LARVAL LAMPREY (A) (AFTER MINOT); EMBRYO RABBIT (B) (AFTER MIHALCOVICS).

For details, see p. xxv.

formed from the union of a down-pocketing of the outer layer or ectoderm, meeting a pouch growing out from the primitive gut. These inner and outer mouth pouches in the early embryos of lampreys, sharks and higher vertebrates, are similar to the inner and outer pouches that give rise to the gill openings, with which indeed they are supposed to be homologous. Moreover Stensiö has recently shown that in the cephalaspid ostracoderms (Fig. 57) the mouth cavity was in series with the cavities of the gill openings and was probably homologous with them.

The predecessors of the vertebrates probably fed upon small organisms and organic matter,

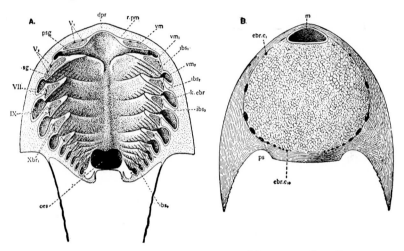

FIG. 57. ATTEMPTED RESTORATIONS OF THE MOUTH AND GILL REGION OF TWO CEPHALASPID OSTRACODERMS BY STENSIÖ.

For details, see p. xxv.

which were scooped into the mouth cavity and may have been passed along to the stomach by the lashing of cilia located in a groove, as in the living *Amphioxus* (Fig. 54).

This method of ingestion by means of cilia may also have been practised by some of the ostracoderms, the earliest known forerunners of the vertebrates (Figs. 4, 57). Such food habits would seem reasonable both for those ostracoderms, like *Pteraspis* (Fig. 4D), which had narrow mouths placed below a long rostrum and therefore adapted for feeding in the mud, and for those like *Tremataspis* (Fig. 4B, C) in which the fore part of the body was flattened into a broad rounded shovel and the mouth was a wide slit-like opening at the

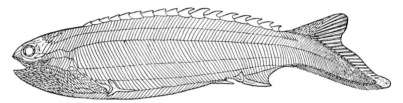

FIG. 58.   SWIFT-MOVING OSTRACODERM FROM THE SILURIAN
OF NORWAY (AFTER KIAER).

For details, see p. xxv.

front border of the head. In *Cephalaspis* (Fig. 57B) also the mouth appears to have been in series with the gill-arches.

But there were still other ostracoderms of the order Anaspida (Fig. 4A), in which the body-form seems adapted for swift movement through the water and in which the mouth, while not too large to be powerful, was strengthened by a bony strip with a knob on its front end. Such ostracoderms may have already embarked on the career of

96

piracy which seems to have characterized the more remote ancestors of man for countless ages. But up to this point in their evolution true teeth had not been attained by the early predecessors of the vertebrates.

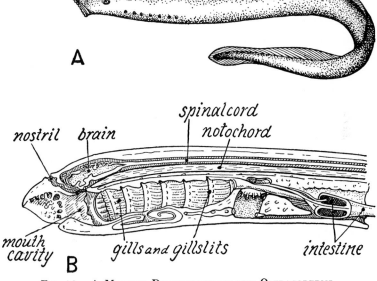

FIG. 59.   A MODERN DESCENDANT OF THE OSTRACODERMS.

A. Adult lamprey (after Jordan and Evermann); B. Longitudinal section of larval lamprey, enlarged (after Goodrich).

THE BEGINNINGS OF TEETH

The ostracoderms as a whole may be transitional between the method of "ciliary ingestion" and the devouring of living flesh by the existing cyclostomes (lampreys, hags), which Stensiö has

97

shown to be the highly specialized, eel-like, and in some respects degenerate derivatives of the ostracoderms of Silurian times. Even today (Fig. 59) in the early larval lamprey (*Ammocoetes* stage) the pharynx is provided with a prominent "ciliated groove," which (like that of *Amphioxus*) appears to be reminiscent of the earlier days of feeding on microscopic organisms; the adult lamprey, on the other hand, is a cruel pirate, rasping off chunks of flesh from the sides of helpless fishes and occasionally eating its way, it is said, into their interiors, finally reducing them to floating shells.

The lampreys and their allies are enabled to carry on their nefarious business by means of thorny teeth, set in concentric rows about the mouth and flanking a protrusile rasp, which is likewise covered with horny teeth and can be drawn back and forth like the rasp of a whelk.

The teeth of the lampreys (Fig. 60A) are of extraordinary interest, since they have always been regarded as representing a very early stage in the evolution of the teeth of vertebrates. Each tooth consists of a thick, horny, epithelial thorn with a pulp cavity within, which is ready to grow another thorn as soon as the outer one is broken

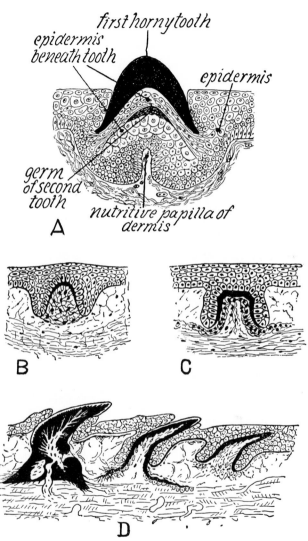

FIG. 60. DEVELOPMENT OF TEETH IN LAMPREY (A) AND SHARK (B, C, D). (AFTER GOODRICH.)

For details, see p. xxvi.

off or shed. Nevertheless the teeth of the higher vertebrates probably arose not from horny epithelial teeth like those of the modern lampreys, but from enamel-covered shagreen denticles such as covered the whole body of *Lanarkia*, one of the Scotch Silurian ostracoderms. In the sharks (Fig. 60B, C, D) each little shagreen denticle on the surface of the skin consists of a little cone in which a porcelain-like layer of "enamel" is laid down between the epithelial covering and the pulp cavity. These shagreen denticles, together with the stratified bony deposits in the deepest layers of skin, gave rise not only to the teeth of higher vertebrates but also to the enamel-covered bony plates that cover the braincase, the bony tooth-bearing plates that cover the primary cartilaginous jaws and the bony tooth-bearing plates on the roof of the mouth, both in the air-breathing, lobe-finned fishes and in their successors, the earliest amphibians.

These enamel-covered plates were also homologous with the bony ganoid scales on the surface of the body.

Thus we are again reminded of the remarkable potentialities of the many-layered skin in the

100

ancestors of the vertebrates, since it gave rise in different groups to horny thorns, to shagreen denticles, to true stratified bony scales, to enamel-covered skull plates, as well as to many different kinds of sense organs.

Nor can it be too often pointed out that the whole organization of primitive vertebrates was adapted for the pursuit and capture of living prey, that sharp teeth were made from the shagreen of the skin, first for holding and then for cutting living prey, that in every geological age until we reach the primitive anthropoid stock of relatively recent times, the herbivorous forms, derived from the more primitive carnivores, acquired various types of specialized teeth which could never have given rise to the higher carnivorous types. Any hypothesis that would derive the earlier carnivorous vertebrates from herbivorous predecessors would be definitely contradicted by all the available evidence afforded by a comparative study of the brain, sense organs, the locomotor apparatus and the digestive system.

After a century of intensive research we can only speculate, almost idly, as to what may have been the mode of origin of the mouth, jaws and teeth below the ostracoderm grade of evolution. But when we reach the grade of evolution represented by the shark, we find that *the shark stands unquestionably nearer to man in the construction of its jaws and teeth than it does to any known group of invertebrates; while between shark and man many intermediate conditions of the mouth are definitely known.*

THE PRIMARY JAWS

The gill pouches of fishes and of the embryos of higher vertebrates, including man, are supported by cartilaginous bars (Figs. 7, 8), the so-called "visceral arches," and the mouth pouches of sharks and embryo vertebrates are likewise supported by cartilaginous bars, the oral cartilages, which have every appearance of belonging in series with the gill arches. The primary upper jaw cartilages, one on either side, are called the palatoquadrate cartilages, while the primary lower jaw cartilages are called Meckel's cartilages, or the mandible. The "labial cartilages" in front of the jaws (Figs. 7, 8) are possible remnants of at least one "premandibular" arch.

In the predecessors of the sharks, we may infer,

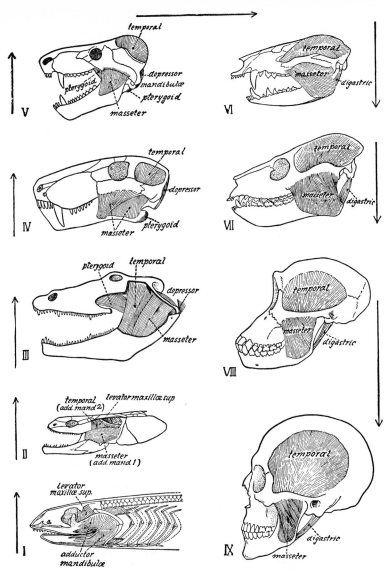

FIG. 61. EVOLUTION OF THE JAW MUSCLES FROM FISH TO MAN.

I. Shark (data from Allis). II. Lobe-finned ganoid (after L. A. Adams). III. Primitive amphibian (after L. A. Adams). Restoration. IV. Primitive mammal-like reptile (skull mainly from Broom). Restoration. V. Advanced mammal-like reptile (after L. A. Adams). Restoration. VI. Primitive marsupial (after L. A. Adams). VII. Primitive primate. VIII. Chimpanzee. IX. Modern man.
For details, see p. xxvi.

103

none of these "visceral arches" (labial cartilages, jaws or gill arches) were connected with the brain-case except by connective tissue and as the living prey was presumably small there was no need of special bracing for these arches. But as the race grew larger the size of the prey likewise increased and convulsive swallowing efforts were made by the fish to force the prey past the region of the gill pouches down into the stomach. At the same time the contractile muscles around the whole branchial series grew stronger, those attached to the future jaw arches increased faster than their fellows and so did the future jaws themselves. In this way the jaw muscles of the shark and of higher vertebrates (Fig. 61) were apparently derived by enlargement from muscles corresponding to the constrictor muscles of the gill arches.

For a long time the primary upper jaw was suspended from the skull mainly through its attachment to the second or hyoid arch (Fig. 62A) but in the amphibians and higher vertebrates the primary upper jaw itself becomes attached to the skull (Fig. 62, B, C). When large tooth-bearing bony plates came to sheath and cover over the primary upper and lower jaws they gradually

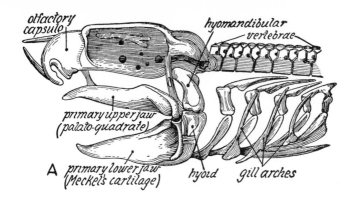

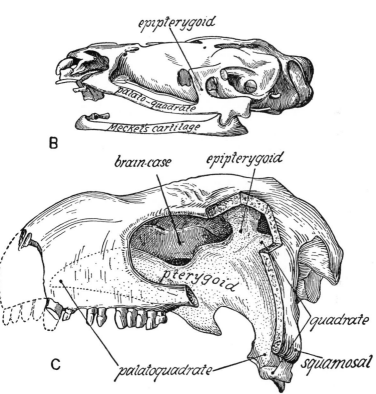

Fig. 62. Methods of Attachment of the Primary Upper Jaw to the Under Side of the Skull.

In C the bony mask covering the temporal region is cut through and a part of it removed to show the primary upper jaw and its relations to the braincase. For details, see pp. xxvi, xxvii.

105

supplanted them, at least in the tooth-bearing regions. In mammals (including man) clear traces of the primary upper jaw may be found in early embryonic stages of development (see Keith, *Human Embryology and Morphology*, 1921, pages 138, 148, 172).

THE RISE OF THE SECONDARY JAWS AND THEIR TEETH

Up to the present time we have been dealing with the origin and early evolution of the *primary* upper and lower jaws, but in the higher vertebrates, including man, these primary jaws are completely overshadowed and masked by the *secondary* jaws. In the sharks the secondary jaws are represented merely by the skin that is wrapped around the primary jaws, or palatoquadrate and Meckel's cartilage, both on the outside and on the inside of the mouth. In the sharks this skin has no bony base but in the higher fishes and early amphibians the primary upper and lower jaws are covered with many-layered bony plates originally provided with a porcelain-like surface of "ganoine" and usually bearing numerous teeth. In the early lobe-finned, air-breathing fishes (Figs. 11, 12)

106

these plates are of exactly the same nature as the roof-bones of the skull and the scales on the body. Thus arises the hard "facial mask" so often referred to in the preceding pages.

As used in this book the term "secondary jaws" is limited to the tooth-bearing plates covering the external borders of the primary upper and lower jaws. There are three of these elements on each side of the head throughout the series (Fig. 50) from fish to man and their amazing constancy is an item of evidence of the unity of plan and origin of all the higher vertebrates. The first of these secondary jaw elements is the *premaxilla*, one on each side of the mid-line, at the front end of the jaw; this is followed by the *maxilla*, one on each side behind the premaxillæ. When we compare the under side of the skull (Fig. 63, I, II) of one of the fossil lobe-finned (crossopt) ganoids of the Devonian with that of one of the early amphibians of the Coal Measures, we can hardly doubt that the premaxilla and maxilla of the former are each completely homologous with the corresponding element in the latter. And from the earliest amphibian to man they can be traced in convincing detail (Figs. 50, 53).

The third of the secondary jaw elements is the *dentary* bone, one on each side of the lower jaw. In the lobe-finned or crossopt fishes this bone,

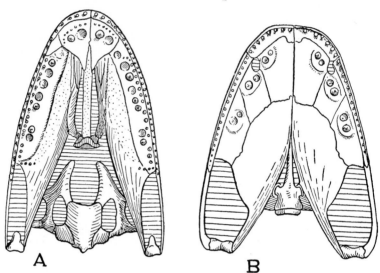

FIG. 63. UNDER SIDE OF THE SKULL OF DEVONIAN FOSSIL FISH (A) AND PRIMITIVE FOSSIL AMPHIBIAN (B). (A AFTER BRYANT AND WATSON; B AFTER WATSON).

The secondary upper jaws are on the margins; the primary upper jaws are largely covered by tooth-bearing plates of the primary palate. For details, see p. xxvii.

while bearing a stout series of teeth, had not yet assumed the primacy it acquired in later types. We have already (pages 36–39) traced its progress in the mammal-like reptiles and have seen it encroach on the other membrane bones of the lower jaw until it finally secured a contact with the squamosal bone covering the side of the temporal part of the skull, by which time it had succeeded in crowding its fellows quite off the map.

Meanwhile, how did the crossopts and early amphibians acquire the strong teeth with which they carried on their predatory lives? In the most primitive sharks (Fig. 5) the shagreen-bearing skin is rolled around over the upper and lower jaw cartilages and as the old teeth are broken off the new teeth are gradually pushed up into place on the edge of the jaws in a continuous succession. In the typical sharks the tooth-bearing roll of skin lies in a depression in the calcified cartilaginous primary upper and lower jaws, but the teeth are not separately connected with the jaws and when in use are tied in place only by the strong dental ligament attached to their bases.

In the crossopts (lobe-finned fishes) of the Devonian period the primary upper jaw (palato-quadrate), now completely saturated with bone cells, is covered with bony dermal tracts bearing teeth, some very large and compressed, some small and conical. In front there is also a pair of tooth-bearing dermal plates, the prevomers, on either side of the mid-line. Likewise the secondary upper jaws, the premaxilla and maxilla, bear compressed conical teeth. The dentary plate of the lower jaw (Fig. 64) covering the outer side of the primary lower jaw or Meckel's cartilage, bears a row of conical teeth which fit between the marginal teeth of the secondary upper jaw and the larger teeth on the dermal plates covering the primary upper jaw. Thus we have the teeth of the secondary upper jaw over-hanging or biting outside of those of the dentary or lower jaw, an arrangement that persists throughout the subsequent series upward to the primitive mammals, traces of it even being preserved in man. The coronoid bones, covering the inner side of the primary lower jaw, in the lobe-finned fish bear large teeth which doubtless sheared into the struggling prey and pressed it against the large teeth on the roof of the mouth. Thus neither the Meckel's cartilage, or primary lower jaw, nor the palato-quadrate, or primary upper jaw, now have any direct relations with the teeth, which are supported entirely on their own bony plates, as they are in all higher vertebrates, including man. The primary lower jaw from this point onward takes a subordinate part, except that its nearer (proximal)

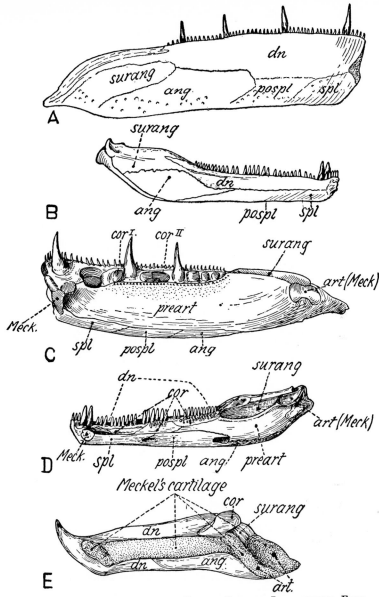

Fig. 64. Right Half of the Lower Jaw of Lobe-finned Fish (A, C) and Primitive Fossil Amphibian (B, D), and Recent Turtle Embryo (E). (A, C, after Watson; B, D, after Williston; E, after Parker.)

For details, see pp. xxvii, xxviii.

end, after becoming ossified (after which it is called the *articular* bone) serves for the main articulation of the lower jaw with the primary upper jaw; this arrangement persists from the crossopt fishes up to the most advanced mammal-like reptiles, which are the immediate predecessors of the mammals.

Each tooth of the above described fossil crossopt fishes consists essentially of an enlarged cone with an open pulp cavity, the sides of the cone being very deeply infolded toward the base, so that in cross-section the primary and secondary folds give rise to the characteristic labyrinthodont pattern (Fig. 18). The surface of the tooth is deeply covered with enamel-like ganoine, which is folded into the primary and secondary folds, and the interior consists of dense, stratified bone or dentine. The derm bone which bears the tooth is strongly attached to it and is folded into its sides along with the primary and secondary folds.

This labyrinthodont mode of attachment of the teeth to the jaw bones is a far more primitive and important method than any of those commonly cited in textbooks on comparative dental anatomy, which usually describe only the either degenerate or highly specialized modes of attachment found in modern amphibians and reptiles, since it was the starting-point of the conditions found in the higher vertebrates, including man.

To sum up then, the lobe-finned fishes exhibit a great advance upon the sharks toward the amphibians and higher vertebrates in the following respects: (1) the primary upper and lower jaws are now covered with tooth-bearing bony plates, only the back part of the primary upper jaw (forming the quadrate bone) and of the primary lower jaw (forming the articular bone) being exposed and forming the articulation between the upper and lower jaws; (2) the secondary upper and lower jaw (premaxilla, maxilla, dentary) for the first time appear as ossified tooth-bearing plates, which may be compared directly with those of amphibians and higher vertebrates; (3) each tooth represents an enlarged denticle with the base infolded into the labyrinthodont pattern. It is fastened to the bone by the infolding of the latter into the labyrinthodont folds; (4) thus the upper and lower jaws as a whole are of complex construction, including a large number of distinct bony plates, some of which disappear as we pass

113

to the higher vertebrates, but three of which (premaxilla, maxilla, dentary) persist even in man (Fig. 50).

All these highly predatory adaptations were transmitted by heredity to the oldest known amphibians of the Coal Measures, which are at the very least rather close relatives if not actual descendants of the osteolepid crossopts. The chief advance in these oldest amphibians is the elimination (Fig. 17) of the whole series of plates connected with the opercular tract and consisting of the plates named operculum, suboperculum, interoperculum, preoperculum, and a series of small lateral gulars or branchiostegals. All these were sacrificed when the amphibians eliminated the internal gills in the adult stage.

The loss of these plates not only constitutes a fine example of Williston's law of the progressive reduction in the number of bony elements, as we pass from fish to man, but also serves to bring out the fact that *evolution proceeds fully as much by the loss of superfluous parts as by the further differentiation of those that remain* (Figs. 50, 52).

Many of the amphibians adopted the easy method of lying in wait in the water for their prey, perhaps even with their mouths open, and then suddenly engulfing it in a living trap. Such a line of specialization leads often to wide flat skulls and very shallow, widely-bowed jaws set with rather small teeth on the margins and a few larger piercing teeth on the roof of the mouth, as in the great labyrinthodonts or stegocephalians of the Permian and Triassic periods. Others, in which the jaws became very long and narrow, actively swam in pursuit of fishes. But those amphibians (*e.g.* Fig. 48 II) which were destined to give rise to the line of ascent to man, avoiding both these extremes, had jaws of only moderate length and a skull of moderate width and considerable depth, especially toward the rear end. At first they retained the teeth on the roof of the mouth (Fig. 53, II–IV) but in the series of reptiles (Fig. 53, V) that finally culminated in the cynodonts (Fig. 53, VI) and probably in the mammals (Fig. 53, VII), the teeth on the roof of the mouth, that is, on the primary upper jaw, were eliminated and the marginal teeth on the secondary jaws acquired the typical dog-toothed or caniniform type of predatory animals that pursue their prey on land.

From this condition there are intermediate stages

to the essentially mammal-like dentition of the cynodonts (Fig. 50 VI), in which the adult dentition, as in man and other mammals, consists of incisors, canines, premolars and molars, and in which the dentition was apparently reduced to two sets corresponding to our milk and permanent teeth. Moreover, each tooth in the cynodonts was set in a distinct socket as in the mammals. Hence these reptiles had already traveled far on the long road from fish to man.

We have followed some of the progressive changes in the jaws of these forms, in which the dentary bone finally became the predominant element and gained contact with the squamosal bone of the skull (Fig. 21), while the bones behind the dentary were reduced to slender proportions (Fig. 52). These changes, however they may have been initiated, were obviously associated with a great development of the temporal, masseter and pterygoid muscles of the jaws (Fig. 61), which have very strongly braced areas of origin and attachment. To the activity of the temporal muscle we apparently owe the first appearance of the temporal fossa (Fig. 48 IV) in the shell of bone that formerly roofed over the jaw muscles, while to the increase in size of the pterygoid muscles may safely be ascribed the pinching together of the opposite pterygoid bones and the development of a high bony crest on the mid-line of the base of the braincase (Fig. 53 V).

Turning again to the teeth, we may summarize their early history as follows: In some of the Silurian ostracoderms (*Lanarkia*) the teeth of later vertebrates are represented by thorny shagreen denticles embedded in the skin all over the surface of the body, but the ostracoderms themselves did not have teeth in the mouth. In the sharks the skin on the inside of the mouth and jaws carries the teeth, which represent only enlarged dermal denticles. In the sharks the tooth-bearing skin on the inner side of the jaws is rolled inward in a spiral manner and as the old teeth are broken off the new ones unwind or rotate into place.

In the lobe-finned or crossopt fishes, representing the ancestors of the amphibians, at least the larger teeth arise from pockets of bone sunk below the surface of the bony enamel-covered skin. In these forms the bases of the teeth are deeply and complexly infolded and the pockets of bony skin

117

are infolded into the bases of the teeth. The teeth succeed each other in an oblique series. In *Seymouria*, a fossil reptile from the Permo-Carboniferous of Texas, which is almost on the borderline between the primitive amphibians and all the higher levels of vertebrates, clear traces of the labyrinthodont method of tooth-attachment are still visible, but by the time of the higher mammal-like reptiles all traces of the older method had been lost and the teeth are set in sockets as in the mammals, including man.

ORIGIN OF THE MAMMALIAN PALATE

No less important in determining the course of future evolution in the mammals and in man were the progressive changes in the palatal region (Fig. 53). In the early amphibians the air taken into the olfactory chamber was passed through a pair of tubes opening by the choanæ (Fig. 53 II, *cho.*) or internal nostrils, into the fore part of the roof of the mouth, and from this point the inspired air was practically swallowed, or forced backward by the action of the throat muscles to the opening of the windpipe. In the early mammal-like reptiles (Fig. 53 V) the choanæ opened into a depression or chamber lying considerably above the general level of the tooth-bearing margins of the upper jaw and they may have been the beginning of a fleshy palate. In the higher mammal-like reptiles or cynodonts (Fig. 52 VI) a secondary palate or bony roof of the mouth was formed by horizontal ledges that grew out from the palatine (*pl*) and maxillary (*mx*) bones and formed a shelf below the chamber where the internal nostrils opened. Very possibly the increasing muscular power and mobility of the tongue, which pressed against the inner side of the upper tooth-bearing bones, may have favored the evolution of bony shelves from the palatine and maxillary bones. In the mammals (Fig. 52 VII–X) (including man) this process is carried much further so that in the adults the bony palate is prolonged much farther backward. To the rear end of this bony palate the soft palate was attached. In this way the naso-pharyngeal air passage was formed, by means of which the inspired air is delivered almost directly to the windpipe, instead of having to pass through the food-containing cavity of the mouth. All this is associated in the higher mammal-like reptiles and early mammals with the very active respiration of carnivorous animals.

The anti-evolutionists may be interested to learn that at a very early stage of its development the human embryo (Fig. 65) passes through a stage in which the olfactory capsules, like those of sharks, have no internal opening on the palate but are

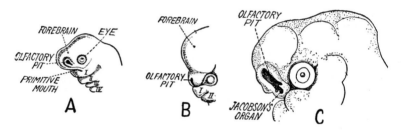

FIG. 65. EARLY EMBRYONIC STAGES IN THE DEVELOPMENT OF THE NOSE IN MAN (AFTER KEITH).

merely extended backward and downward toward the mouth. Later (Fig. 66) the choanæ, or internal openings of the olfactory capsules, develop in the fore part of the roof of the mouth, but there is only the beginning of a secondary palate and the conditions in the reptiles (Fig. 66B) are recalled (Keith, Corning).

In this connection Keith (1921, pp. 158, 159) summarizes the evolution of the human face as follows:

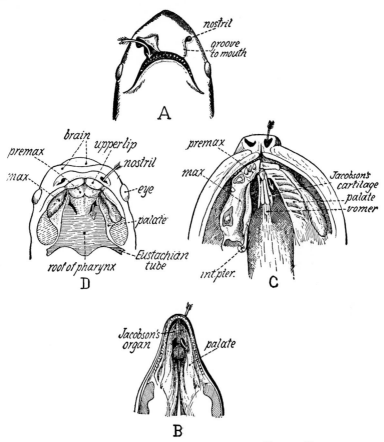

FIG. 66. COMPARATIVE ANATOMY OF THE HUMAN PALATE.

A. Recent shark, showing groove from nose to front of mouth. (After
      Keith.)
B. Lizard, in which internal opening (choana) from the nose opens in
      the forepart of the mouth cavity. (After Plate.)
C. Lion pup with cleft palate, recalling in form the palate of reptiles;
      showing internal opening of the nose (indicated by the arrow-
      point) in the forepart of the mouth cavity. In this abnormal
      specimen the secondary palate has failed to grow over to the
      midline. (After Keith.)
D. Human embryo at the end of the sixth week, showing the secondary
      palatal plates beginning to grow in toward the midline and the
      "primitive choanæ" (arrow-point) still exposed in the forepart
      of the roof of the pharynx. (After Keith.)
        (B, from *Allgem. Zool.*, Gustav Fischer.)

121

OUR FACE FROM FISH TO MAN

In our survey of the neural part of the human cranium we have seen that its outstanding features are the result of a great cerebral development. When, however, we turn to the facial and pharyngeal parts of the skull and head, we find that the factors which have determined their shape are related to the functions of smell, respiration and of mastication. It is unnecessary to again insist on the fact that the human embryo, in the latter part of the first month, shows a resemblance to a generalized type of fish; it possesses the basis of a branchial arch system. As in the fish, the olfactory organ is represented by a pair of pits or depressions, which at first have no communication with the mouth. In some forms of fish—certain rays and sharks—a channel is formed between each olfactory pit and the mouth. The functional meaning of such a channel is evident; the water imbibed is sampled by the nose before entering the mouth. When pulmonary breathing was introduced, as in Dipnoean fishes, the open naso-buccal channel became enclosed by the union of its bounding folds. In amphibians, reptiles and birds the naso-buccal channel becomes dilated to form a true respiratory nasal passage, and the parts bounding the passage unite on the roof of the mouth to form the **primitive palate**. In Fig. 152 the parts entering into the formation of the primitive palate are shown. They are three in number: (1) a premaxillary and vomerine part developed between the nasal passages; (2) a right and left maxillary part, laid down on the lateral or outer aspect of each passage. In mammals a fourth element is added to the primitive or reptilian palate, and in this way the mammalian mouth is separated from the nasal respiratory passage, and can serve the purposes of mastication and suction. Thus in the evolution of the face there have been three distinct stages: (1) a piscine, in which the nose and mouth were formed independently; (2) an amphibian stage, where the nasal respiratory passage opened on the roof of the mouth; (3) a mammalian stage, in which it opened in the nasopharynx. In the development of the human embryo we see these three stages reproduced.

EVOLUTION OF THE TONGUE AND RELATED STRUCTURES

In *Amphioxus* (Fig. 54) there is no tongue and in the lampreys and hags the so-called tongue with its enclosed cartilages probably represents the lower jaw of the shark (Stockard, Goodrich). In the shark the folding up of both the jaw cartilages and the gill cartilages causes the lower ends of the latter to project forward in a series of V's into the floor of the mouth (Fig. 7). These cartilages support the tongue proper, which at first is only a thickening of the floor of the mouth covered with epithelium containing the "taste" cells. In some of the amphibians the tongue becomes highly muscular and protrusile and by the time we reach the lower mammals the tongue is fundamentally the same as that of man. The early primates have a long narrow tongue with a well developed "under tongue" beneath it; in the higher primates, especially the orang, chimpanzee and gorilla, the tongue approaches the human type but is longer in proportion to its breadth. In the detailed number and arrangement of the papillæ

123

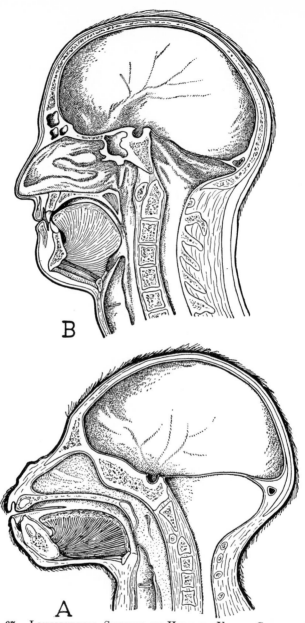

B

A

FIG. 67. LONGITUDINAL SECTION OF HEAD IN YOUNG GORILLA (A)
AND IN MAN (B), SHOWING RELATION OF TONGUE TO SURROUND-
ING PARTS (AFTER KLAATSCH).

vallatæ the orang agrees with man (Pocock, Sonntag).

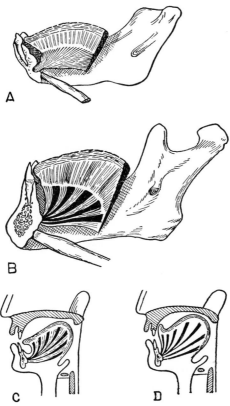

FIG. 68. LONGITUDINAL SECTION OF LOWER JAW OF MONKEY (A) AND IN MAN (B), SHOWING ATTACHMENT OF THE TONGUE MUSCLE TO THE BACK OF THE JAW (AFTER ROBINSON).

C. Diagram of the genioglossus muscle in pronouncing the sound "oo." D. Diagram of the genioglossus muscle in pronouncing the letter "T." (C, D, after Robinson.) For details, see pp. xxviii, xxix.

The muscles of the tongue are the same in the anthropoids and man (Figs. 67, 68) but in the latter

125

the geniohyoglossus muscles have acquired the ability to change the precise shape and position of the different parts of the tongue with extreme rapidity and in conjunction with movements of other parts of the voice-producing mechanism (Robinson).

The great size of the tongue in man and its important function as the leading organ of speech has doubtless partly conditioned the later stages in the evolution of the lower jaw, especially in the region of the chin, to the back of which the tongue muscles are attached (Fig. 68).

Meanwhile the remaining part of the branchial arches has given rise to the larynx with its highly elaborate voice mechanism, to the tonsils, thyroid and thymus glands, the last two being of vital importance in the normal growth and differentiation of the individual. Again the anti-evolutionist can offer no alternative scientific explanation of the fact that during the course of embryonic development the human tongue, larynx and adjacent structures reveal remarkably detailed resemblances to corresponding structures of lower vertebrates.[1] The "gill-slits" in the human

[1] For a clear presentation of the details see Keith, Arthur, 1921, *Human Embryology and Morphology*, London, pp. 240–252.

embryo (Fig. 69) have been heard of by multitudes, so that certain anti-evolutionists have tried to

FIG. 69. HUMAN EMBRYO OF THE THIRD WEEK (FROM EIDMANN, AFTER HIS).

Oblique front view of the head, showing mouth, primary upper and lower jaw buds, gill arches and gill slits.

(From *Entw. d. Zähne* . . ., Hermann Meusser, Berlin.)

offset their effect by arguing that they are not gill-slits since gills are not present. But this could only confuse people unfamiliar with the evidence that each of the so-called "gill-slits" of the human embryo of the fifth week may be compared directly with a corresponding one in

127

the fœtal and embryonic stages of other mammals, of reptiles, amphibians and primitive fishes, and that in the fishes these clefts are definitely associated with functional internal gills.

The anti-evolutionists should also be embarrassed by the fact that, leaving the embryonic stages aside, and considering only adult anatomy, the entire complex of the hyoid arch, larynx and associated parts in man corresponds in great detail with those of the anthropoids, differing only in the proportional development of certain parts. From the anthropoids down through the lower primates the homology of every segment of the hyoid arch and laryngeal complex can be completely established and from thence these structures can be traced backward step by step through the reptiles to the lower amphibians and thence to the elaborate branchial skeleton of the crossopt or lobe-finned ganoids. In fact the branchial skeleton of vertebrates, in all its complex relations with the muscles and nerves and in its successive stages of development, affords convincing evidence of the anatomical unity of the entire vertebrate series from shark to man. The human jaws, tongue, larynx and associated parts thus con-

stitute only a single manifestation of a morphological theme that has a thousand variations, but
is everywhere patently evolved from a shark-like
prototype. And in particular this region yields
most cogent evidence of man's unity of origin
with the anthropoid apes.

The salivary glands under the tongue and in
the sides of the cheek and throat afford another
example of the same kind. Huntington has shown
how even the variations in man are obviously
related to those of the higher primates.

ORIGIN AND EVOLUTION OF THE HUMAN LIPS

Let us return now to the outside of the mouth
and consider the origin and evolution of the
human lips. The mouth in the lowest existing
chordate *Amphioxus* (Fig. 54) is surrounded by
short stiff projections. Much the same condition
obtains in the larval lamprey (Fig. 59B). In the
adult lamprey the mouth cavity is surrounded by
a movable ring of cartilaginous plates beset with
thorn-like teeth, probably a very specialized
arrangement. In the ostracoderms (Figs. 4, 57)
of the Silurian the border of the capacious mouth
cavity was covered with small scales and plates.

129

In the modern sharks there is a fold of skin at the back of the upper border of the mouth that seems to foreshadow the maxillary or upper jaw bones of higher fishes (Allis). Underneath this fold of skin at the corner of the mouth are two labial cartilages embedded in muscles which apparently serve to draw forward the corner of the mouth (Fig. 6). A similar fold of tooth-bearing skin (Figs. 50, 53) in the lobe-finned ganoids, or crossopts, gives rise to the premaxillary and maxillary bones, which have every appearance of being homologous with the bones that bear the same name in the earliest amphibians, and from thence these two bones can be followed through the mammal-like reptiles to the earliest mammals, thence through the ascending grades of primates to man. In the earlier crossopts these bones were covered with enamel and lay right on the surface but in the more advanced crossopts the ganoine layer has disappeared and the outer surface of the bone is rough, indicating that it was covered with a thick tough skin. The dentary bone of the lower jaw was likewise covered.

In the early amphibians and reptiles the pre-maxilla, maxilla and dentary were likewise roughened for the attachment of the outer layers of the skin, of which they themselves formed the deeper layers. In some of the recent reptiles there is a small muscle at the corners of the mouth but the lips are not fleshy and the tough facial mask is not far below the surface. Probably the same conditions obtained in the entire series of mammal-like reptiles.

In the most archaic mammal living today, the Duckbill Platypus of Australia, the mouth is surrounded by a duck-like bill consisting of leathery skin well supplied with sense organs. Very possibly this condition is a specialized remnant of the tough skin that covered the mouth of the mammal-like reptiles. In the Spiny Anteater (*Echidna*) of Australia (Fig. 23C), the nearest living relative of *Ornithorhynchus*, the lips, although peculiarly specialized in connection with the ant-catching, protrusile tongue, approach the normal mammalian condition in so far as they are supplied with muscles that are innervated by the seventh or facial nerve and are covered with hair rather than scales.

Here we arrive at the most distinctive feature of the lips of mammals, in which the bony mask inherited from the primitive crossopts lies deeply covered by a mobile fleshy curtain. Doubtless the evolution of true lips was a part of the general transformation of reptiles with unstable body temperature and low grade metabolism, into mammals living at high pressure.

In an earlier chapter (pages 43, 44) it has been mentioned that the facial muscles of mammals represent a forward extension of a thin layer of muscle covering the neck of lower vertebrates and that when this muscle migrated forward beneath the skin it dragged its own nerve with it, which was subdivided into smaller branches as the muscle itself was differentiated into the facial muscles of the ears, eyes, nose and lips (Figs. 23, 24). The history of this invasion is now being traced in convincing detail by Huber. The invasion was facilitated by the fact that in the early stages of development (Figs. 65A, 69) the region of the mouth and lips arises quite close to the original territory of the facial nerve, which was on the side of the neck, so that forks of the parent mass in the neck could easily spread to the lips and forehead.

The researches of Ruge, Huber, Sonntag and

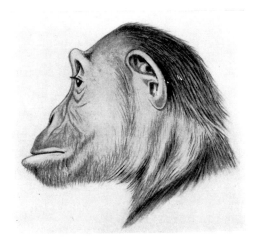

Fig. 70. Old Chimpanzee, Showing Extraordinary Protrusion of the Lips in
Anthropoids.

(From J. A. Allen, from a photograph
by Herbert Lang.)

others have shown that the anthropoids (as usual) are man's nearest living relatives in the anatomy of the facial muscles. The ability to move the ears is already reduced in the anthropoids but some men can still make a creditable showing of activity in these souvenirs of man's earlier mammalian ancestors.

In the lower primates the opposite upper lips, like those of carnivorous mammals, depend slightly at the sides and are barely, if at all, joined in front, but in the anthropoid apes and man the median flap of the fœtus, forming the philtrum of the lip in adult man, becomes very broad, so that the opposite halves of the orbicularis oris muscle become broadly continuous.

Thus the anthropoids acquired highly protrusile lips, useful in sucking up water and the juices of fruit (Fig. 70). *Man has inherited from the primitive anthropoids the ability to draw back his lips in anger, to open them in a laugh, or again, to protrude them into a funnel and so to confer kisses on the objects of his affection.* How much dour literature, ancient and modern, might be lightened by this thought!

All these muscles of the mouth and cheeks as

well as the muscles of swallowing were naturally of vital importance to the newborn mammal, enabling it to pump the mother's milk into its swelling cheeks. But how long it took mankind to realize the deep significance of the fact that even babies of bluest blood share this birthright with the beasts of the field.

LATER STAGES IN THE HISTORY OF THE TEETH

Thanks to the advertisers of tooth pastes all America knows the practical importance of beautiful teeth. But few indeed share the secret as to how we obtained these dazzling objects of charm, and fewer still ever give a thought to the humble creatures who slowly shaped them to our use. It is surprising that even today, after hundreds of millions of years' advancement beyond our shark-like ancestors, each human being, during the embryonic development of his teeth, starts at a shark-like stage (Fig. 71A). For at first the area of embryonic skin that is destined to give rise to the teeth lies on the surface of the mouth cavity, then it sinks down like a pouch (Fig. 71B), the bottom of the pouch is pushed upward (Fig. 71C) to form a pulp cavity and thus the germ of the

human tooth becomes essentially like the germ
of the shark's tooth.   However, in order to defend

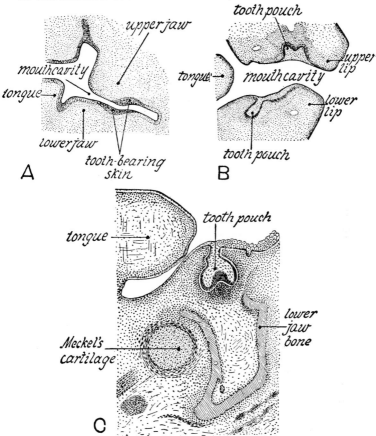

FIG. 71.   THREE EMBRYONIC STAGES IN THE DEVELOPMENT OF HUMAN
TEETH (A, B, FROM EIDMAN AFTER AHRENS; C, AFTER CORNING).

(A, B, from *Entw. d. Zähne* . . ., Hermann Meusser, Berlin; C, from *Lehrb. d.
Entw. des Menschen*, J. F. Bergmann.)

For details, see p. xxix.

the validity of these comparisons it is essential to
note that we are not leaping at once from shark

to man in the reckless manner of some of the older comparative anatomists, but that the same general process of tooth development may be traced in many successive grades in the ascent from fish to man.

Meanwhile (Fig. 71C) Meckel's cartilage, the descendant of the primary lower jaw of the shark, lies entirely free from the future dentary or lower jaw bone, which will later surround both the Meckel's cartilage and the developing tooth-germ, as in all the vertebrates above the shark.

In the earlier creatures that lie in or near the line of ascent to man the teeth were of the dog-tooth or canine type (Fig. 50). Some of the front teeth of man, especially the cuspids or canines, remain single-cusped to this day as souvenirs of our remote carnivorous ancestors; but the central incisors often exhibit a tendency to develop little cusps, mammillæ or subdivisions, along the flattened cutting edge of the crown (Fig. 72). The frequent presence of these mammillæ on the edges of the central incisors has sometimes been cited as evidence of a "triconodont" stage in the evolution of human teeth, in disregard of the fact that not even the extinct triconodont mammals of the

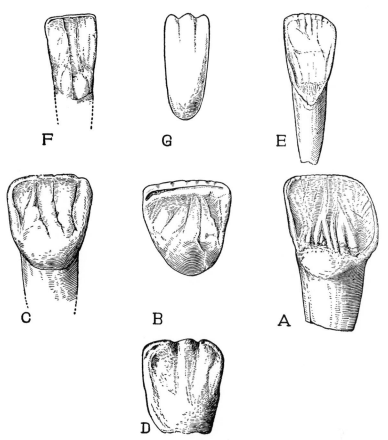

FIG. 72. CENTRAL INCISORS OF GORILLA (A, E) AND MAN (B, C, D, F). ENLARGED. (B, AFTER WEINERT, C. F, AFTER VIRCHOW; D, AFTER HRDLIČKA; G, FROM HRDLIČKA, AFTER ZUCKERKANDL.)

For details, see pp. xxix, xxx.

Triassic age themselves had "triconodont" incisors but only triconodont molars. In whatever way this tendency to subdivide the central incisor edges may have arisen, man shares it with many other mammals, especially with his relatives the anthropoid apes, whose central incisor crowns approach the human type. Remane (1921, Fig. 21E) has shown that in certain chimpanzees even the outer rim of the central upper incisor is vertical as in man.

Hrdlička has noted that on the rear surface of the central upper incisors of certain anthropoids and monkeys one finds the "rim and ridge" formation (Fig. 72) of many human incisors.

In the upper central incisors of recent Mongolians and many Indians the rims along the sides of the crown fold around toward the rear and the "shovel-shaped" incisor is developed. This arrangement was already foreshadowed in certain gorillas and is almost fully attained among the extinct Neanderthals of the Krapina race; it has also recently been discovered in a fossil human tooth from the Pleistocene of China. In its extreme form the shovel-shaped incisor represents a distinct specialization beyond that attained in the anthropoids. Dr. J. Leon Williams has observed among all races of mankind the presence of three types of central upper incisors (Fig. 73).

138

In the first type the inner and outer borders of the crown as seen from in front tend to be straight and vertical; in the second type the opposite borders diverge sharply toward the lower end of the crown; and in the third the outer border has a

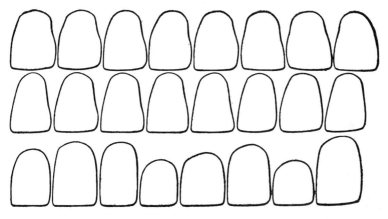

Fig. 73. The Three Types of Central Upper Incisors (after J. Leon Williams).

Lower row, first type; middle row, second type; upper row, third type.

marked double curve. Exactly these same three variants he found also in all the existing species of anthropoid apes and he rightly considers that this fact, taken in conjunction with hundreds of other items of similar purport, affords decisive evidence of close kinship between man and anthropoids.

The upper lateral incisors in anthropoids (Fig. 74) as a rule are more primitive in retaining the

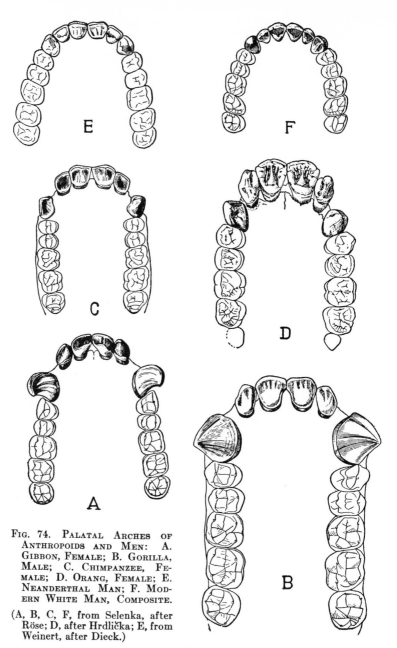

FIG. 74. PALATAL ARCHES OF
ANTHROPOIDS AND MEN: A.
GIBBON, FEMALE; B. GORILLA,
MALE; C. CHIMPANZEE, FE-
MALE; D. ORANG, FEMALE; E.
NEANDERTHAL MAN; F. MOD-
ERN WHITE MAN, COMPOSITE.

(A, B, C, F, from Selenka, after
Röse; D, after Hrdlička; E, from
Weinert, after Dieck.)

bluntly pointed tips, but Remane (1921, page 102) figures a certain chimpanzee in which the tip of the lateral upper incisor is submerged in a transverse incisal edge and even the outer rim is vertically developed, so that the crown as a whole is clearly approaching the human type.

The great outstanding difference between the dentition of man and that of his anthropoid cousins lies in the fact that in man the canine teeth, even in the milk set (Fig. 76) are much reduced in size, with rounded crowns and obtuse tips that project but little above the level of the adjacent teeth, while in the anthropoids, especially the males, the canines form large sharp-tipped tusks. If, however, the fossil lower jaw found at Piltdown, England (Fig. 45C), belongs with the human Piltdown skull, as nearly all authorities now believe, it affords a clear case of an ape-like canine belonging in a human jaw; only it should be noted that the Piltdown canine is much more like the lower canines of certain female gorillas, which have not attained the tusk-like stature of male canines. The human canines may indeed be most reasonably regarded as reduced and "infantilized" or "feminized" derivatives of a primitive anthropoid type and the process of reduction and infantilization may well have taken place during the millions of years of the Lower Pliocene epoch, at a period when the fossil record of human remains so far discovered is still blank.

The great mass of collateral evidence for the derivation of man from primitive anthropoids with well developed but not greatly enlarged canines, has been reviewed lately with great thoroughness by Remane, who finds no justification for the view that man has avoided the primitive anthropoid stage and has been derived from wholly unknown forms with the canine tips not projecting much beyond the level of the premolars.

When the skull of a chimpanzee (Fig. 35F) and the skull of a high type of man (Fig. 43D) are viewed from above, the ape is seen to differ widely from man in the marked projection of his muzzle. This projection is less in female anthropoids with smaller teeth and still less in early fœtal anthropoid stages before the tooth-germs are formed. On the other hand, savage types of man with very large teeth have a correspondingly prominent muzzle, especially if the molar and premolar teeth have large fore-and-aft diameters, as in the fossil

Talgai, Australia, skull (Fig. 42E), which has a strongly protruding muzzle. Again, the Piltdown lower jaw (Fig. 45C) with its "simian shelf" in front, its female anthropoid canine and its ape-like molar teeth (Fig. 41A), must indubitably have had a muzzle approaching that of an immature female gorilla. By the time we reach the Heidelberg and Neanderthal fossil men, however, the canines had become reduced to the level of the cheek teeth, the incisors and premolars were reduced in size and the lower molars were relatively wider than in the anthropoids; hence Professor McGregor's very thoroughly studied restorations show these men with only moderately developed muzzles and human lips.

The reduction of all the front teeth in man is foreshadowed in the fœtal stages in which the tooth-germs are smaller than those of apes; consequently the fœtal muzzle is likewise smaller than that of fœtal apes of corresponding stages.

The reduction in size of all the teeth, especially the canines, has been an important factor in shortening the palatal arch (Fig. 74) from the long ∩-shaped type of anthropoids, with a wide space between the canines, to the short human form of palate with narrow space between the canines. In the lower jaw the diminution of the lower canines and the backward retreat of the incisors finally brings the canines almost to the

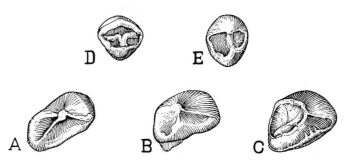

FIG. 75. LOWER FRONT PREMOLARS OF FOSSIL ANTHROPOIDS (A, B, C) AND MAN (D, E).

(A, B, after Gregory and Hellman; C, after Pilgrim; D, after Virchow; E, from Selenka, after Röse.)   For details, see p. xxx.

front of the jaw and into functional alignment with the incisors.

The upper premolars or bicuspids of man, which in the adult dentition are two in number on each side of both the upper and lower jaws, find their nearest relatives in the bicuspid upper and lower premolars of the anthropoid apes (Fig. 74).

The front lower premolars of the anthropoids show a wide range of forms, from types with a more compressed baboon-like crown to the almost human premolars of the extinct *Sivapithecus* (Fig. 75C)

144

and of certain modern chimpanzees. Remane records the fact that in certain human jaws the front lower premolar retains clear vestiges of the asymmetrical form of the outer surface of the crown, a condition that is far more accentuated in the typical anthropoids and is there associated with the large size and tusk-like form of the upper canines.

Neither the upper nor the lower molars of man show much resemblance to those of the cynodonts or pro-mammals of the far-off Triassic age (Fig. 77I); yet we owe to such lowly forbears the initial phases of the process by which the simple dog-tooth crowns of the cheek teeth began to subdivide and give rise to the accessory tips or cusps that are so characteristic of the cheek teeth of mammals.

Anti-evolutionists ask us to believe that even the hairs of our head are numbered, but we affirm only that our teeth are numbered: twenty in the milk set and thirty-two in the permanent sets of normal individuals; and that the same numbers occur in the anthropoid apes; that typical representatives alike of mankind and of the apes, have in the permanent dentition two incisors, one canine, two premolars, three molars, on either side in both the upper and lower jaws; and in the milk set, two incisors, one canine and two milk molars on either side above and below (Fig. 76).

The history of the human upper and lower premolar and molar teeth (Figs. 77, 78) has been

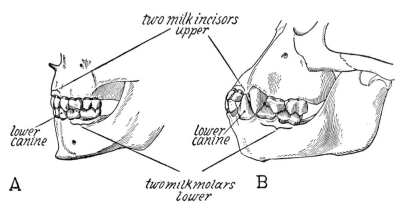

FIG. 76. MILK TEETH OF MAN (A) AND GORILLA (B). (BOTH FROM SELENKA, AFTER RÖSE.)

discussed at length by myself in the work on the *Origin and Evolution of the Human Dentition* and other papers and by Gregory and Hellman in our work on *The Dentition of Dryopithecus and the Origin of Man.* We have shown that notwithstanding the present profound differences in habits between man and the anthropoid apes, the lower molar teeth, especially of more primitive and more ancient races of man, retain the most

146

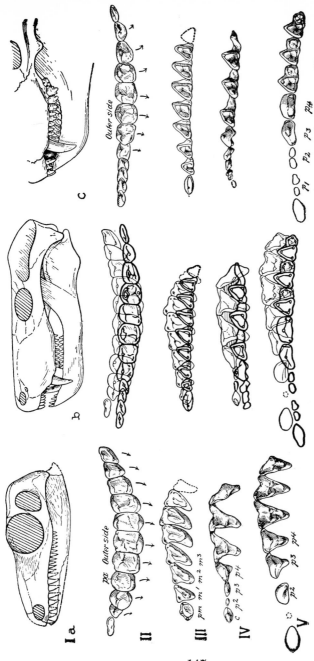

147

FIG. 77. TEN STRUCTURAL STAGES IN THE EVOLUTION OF THE HUMAN DENTITION FROM ASCENDING GEOLOGICAL HORIZONS.

Ia. Primitive theromorph reptile (after Williston). Ib. Primitive mammal-like reptile (after Broom). Ic. Advanced mammal-like reptile (after Seeley). II. Advanced mammal-like reptile (mainly after Seeley). III. Primitive pro-placental (kindness of Dr. Simpson). IV. Pro-trituberculate (from original specimen). V. Primitive placental (from original specimen).

For details, see p. xxxi.

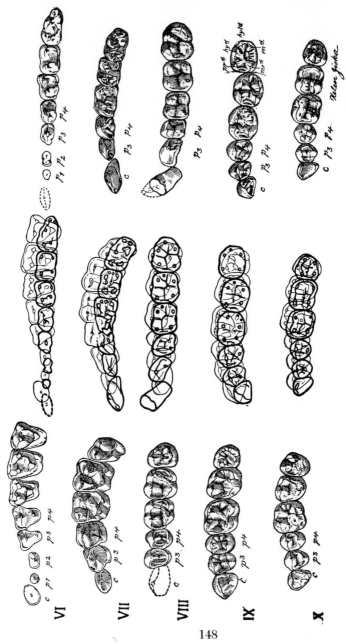

Fig. 78. Ten Structural Stages in the Evolution of the Human Dentition (*Continued*).

VI. Primitive primate (after Grandidier). VII. Advanced tarsioid primate (after Stehlin). VIII. Primitive anthropoid primate (upper molars mainly after Pilgrim). IX. Primitive man, Mousterian (from stereoscopic photographs by McGregor and published photographs by Weinert and by Virchow). X. Modern man, white (from original specimen).

For details, see pp. xxxi, xxxii.

148

indubitable marks of anthropoid kinship and derivation; the lower molar crowns displaying many intermediate stages from an almost perfect "*Dryopithecus* pattern" (Fig. 80C) with five main cusps and a complex, definite system of grooves and depressions, to a "cruciform," four-cusped form in which the *Dryopithecus* pattern is largely obliterated (Fig. 80F).

Similarly the upper molar crowns of the fossil Neanderthal skull known as "Le Moustier" (Fig. 78IX) may be compared cusp for cusp and ridge for ridge with those of such fossil anthropoids as *Dryopithecus rhenanus* of Europe and *Sivapi-thecus* of India, both of which even possess the peculiar depressions known as the fovea anterior and fovea posterior, which are characteristic of primitive human upper molars. Here again, as in the case of the lower molars, it is only the more primitive members of the human race that retain such indubitable traces of anthropoid kinship, the conditions of civilization tending to reduce the vigorous upper molar pattern of the primitives to an enfeebled type with less robust cusps and less salient angles (Fig. 78X).

Similarly the entire set of milk teeth of man

149

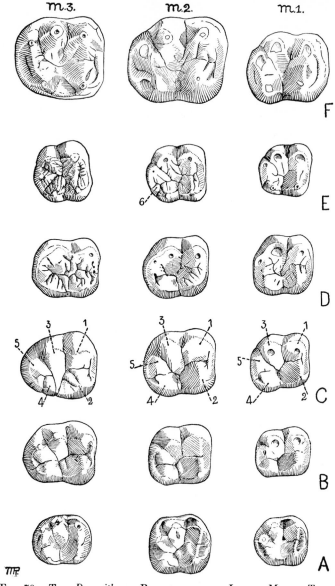

FIG. 79. THE *Dryopithecus* PATTERN IN THE LOWER MOLAR TEETH
OF FOSSIL (A, B, C) AND RECENT (D, E, F) ANTHROPOIDS.

For details, see p. xxxii.

150

m.3.   m.2.   m.1

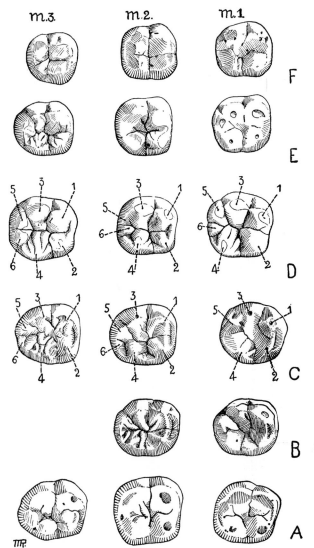

FIG. 80. PROGRESSIVE REDUCTION AND LOSS OF THE *Dryopithecus*
PATTERN IN THE LOWER MOLARS OF FOSSIL (A, B, C)
AND RECENT (D, E, F) MEN.

For details, see pp. xxxii, xxxiii.

151

must be regarded from a scientific viewpoint as derived by a few easily understandable modifications, from the type exemplified in the young of recent anthropoids (Fig. 76).

Against all this mass of evidence for man's evolution from a primitive anthropoid stock the modern schoolmen can only quibble that the corresponding parts of man and ape are "equivocable" but not "homologous."

CONCLUSIONS

Perhaps the most important and basic conclusion concerning the early history of the mouth and jaws in the remote ancestors and predecessors of man is, first, that however the mouth and jaws may have arisen in the first place, their subsequent history, from the grade of organization represented by the shark, may be traced through to man in its broad outlines with the greatest security; secondly, that whatever may have been the food habits of the invertebrate ancestors of the vertebrates, it is extremely probable that from the shark grade onward to the early mammalian ancestors of man, the mouth and jaws were adapted for the capture and disposal of sizable living prey and not for

the manipulation of any less nutritious form of food.

The amelioration of our features we owe not so much to the savage, furry little beasts that first bore the name of mammals, nor even to the earlier primates, who despite their large eyes and large brains still retained a fox-like snout and long jaws; but chiefly to the gentle pro-anthropoids who first took to a diet of fruit and buds and so acquired many modifications of the lips, jaws and dentition, which they transmitted to the earlier and less progressive races of men.

How much arrogance, deceit and wickedness would have been spared the world, if men had realized that even the most imposing human faces are but made-over fish traps, concealed behind a smiling mask but still set with sharp teeth inherited from ferocious pre-mammalian forbears.

HISTORY OF THE NOSE

Why do all men, anti-Darwinians included, have noses? Why does the human nose, both externally and internally, have precisely the same parts, only differently proportioned, as the noses of the gorilla and the chimpanzee? Why are man and ape, in this feature as in thousands of others, created so nearly in the same image? "Parallelism" say the anti-Darwinians; but physiology, comparative anatomy and allied sciences answer, "Blood kinship."

The story of the early evolution of the human nose would be strong reading for the delicate stomachs of our Mid-Victorian lady relatives. But in these Neo-Elizabethan days we will not shudder unduly at the thought that noses, at least of the vertebrate type, were first created in order to lead our shark-like ancestors straight to the feast—some nameless horror wallowing in the uneasy tide and alive with the writhing creatures that consumed it. Even to this day, odors cannot reach us except in water vapor.

The shark's smelling apparatus is comparatively simple—an extended surface of membrane sensitive to olfactory stimuli, folded into a rosette and packed neatly into the olfactory capsule, one on each side of the head. A small opening, the nostril, admits the water to be tested, and a groove, the oronasal groove of primitive sharks (Fig. 66A), connects the nose with the mouth cavity. In the embryo shark and embryo mammal the nasal sac

154

begins as an out-pushing of the mouth cavity, of which it thus appears to be only a specialized outgrowth for the detection and testing of food.

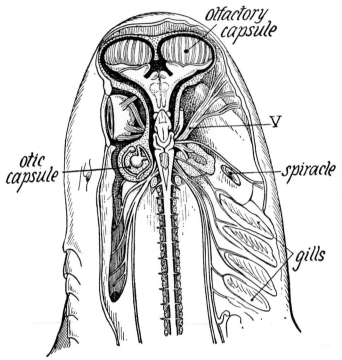

FIG. 81. DISSECTION OF HEAD OF SHARK, SEEN FROM ABOVE, TO SHOW RELATIONS OF OLFACTORY CAPSULES TO BRAIN, EYES AND INTERNAL EARS (MODIFIED FROM MARSHALL AND HURST).

The most essential parts of the nose are the olfactory sense organs and the olfactory nerve. The fibers of the latter are spread all over the olfactory membrane, from which, being collected into two great nerve cables (Fig. 81), they pass

155

backward into the forebrain, of which indeed they form the dominant part. If favorable signals are transmitted by the smelling nerves, the eyes turn toward the source of the odor and by means of the locomotor machinery the whole "ship" is steered in the right direction. The two olfactory capsules, rather widely separated from each other on either side of the head, not only double the chance of picking up a trail of olfactory value, but doubtless also serve as directional organs. The bilateral arrangement of the other sense organs may have a similar significance.

The resemblances of the shark nose to the human nose are fundamental and the subsequent changes in this organ are relatively not great. The ultimate mystery with regard to all the sense organs of vertebrates is decidedly not what are the broad stages of their evolution from fish to man, but what physical and chemical forces acting upon the primitive vertebrate skin caused one set of epithelial cells to become sensitive to olfactory stimulations, another set to respond to light, others to physical vibrations of different rates, and still others to be deaf and blind to all other stimuli except those coming from within the organism;

and what now causes other cells of the same primary outer layer to become a line of olfactory nerve cells, attached to the sense organ and arising from a nucleus in the central nervous system. Experimental embryology and physiology of the future may reveal some of the chemical changes involved, as the generalized ectoderm cell differentiates into the specialized one capable of only one class of reactions; but this will only widen our knowledge of the bewildering complexity of the single fertilized egg cell, which divides and subdivides so as to give rise to the olfactory organs as well as to all other parts of the body.

Meanwhile, as stated above, the main transitional stages in the evolution of the nose from fish to man are fairly well understood, and are well described in Keith's *Morphology and Embryology.* First the olfactory sac becomes folded up, and in sharks a groove (Fig. 66A) extends downward toward the corner of the mouth. Second, in the lung-fishes this lower extension of the sac has worked its way inside the mouth and there are thus two openings, a nostril on the outside and an internal narial opening in the roof of the mouth. Third, both in the air-breathing fishes and the

157

amphibians air may either be gulped in through the mouth or sucked in through the nose, which thus functions in breathing as well as in smelling.

By the time we reach the mammal-like reptiles of the Triassic of South Africa (Fig. 53VI) we find the paired olfactory capsules greatly elongated in a fore-and-aft direction, and in the highest members of this series, as shown by iron-stone casts of the interior of the nasal chamber, the median bony partition now supported scroll-like outgrowths like the delicate turbinate bones of mammals (Watson). The delicate olfactory membrane thus spread out on these scrolls, which in many mammals become complicated with secondary scrolls, thus secures a wide surface for testing the odors of the air drawn in.

In the living amphibians, reptiles and more primitive mammals there is also a pair of small cartilaginous scrolls near the bottom of the median cartilaginous partition, which contains a folded pocket of the olfactory membrane; from this pocket a very fine tube leads downward, opening into the cavity of the mouth. This whole arrangement is called Jacobson's organ. Primitively Jacobson's organ seems to have served for the testing by the olfactory membrane of the contents of the mouth, while the main portion of the olfactory membrane served to test the inspired air in the main chamber. In the marsupials and other lowly mammals Jacobson's organ is comparatively well developed but in the higher primates and especially in man it is either absent in the adult

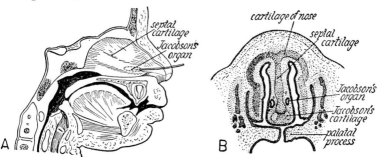

FIG. 82.   JACOBSON'S ORGAN IN THE HUMAN FŒTUS.
(AFTER CORNING.)
(From *Lehrb. d. Entw. des Menschen*, J. F. Bergmann.)
For details, see p. xxxiii.

stage or it exists in a vestigial and, so far as known, a useless condition. It is present, however, in the early fœtal stages of man (Fig. 82), degenerating later. Here then is another "poser" for anti-evolutionists. Is the fœtal human Jacobson's organ made after a divine prototype? And is the same true of the vestigial Jacobson's organ of the Old World monkey? Or have both man and monkey received this now vestigial or fœtal struc-

ture as part of their heritage from far earlier
mammals in which it was more fully developed?

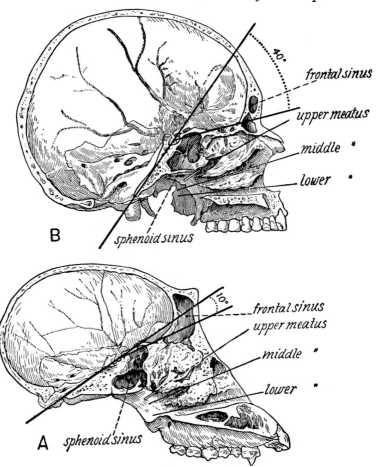

FIG. 83. LONGITUDINAL SECTION OF THE SKULL IN MAN (B)
(AFTER CUNNINGHAM) AND CHIMPANZEE (A).

A similar dilemma might politely be offered to
anti-evolutionists with regard to the whole anatomy

160

of the olfactory chamber. Why is it that man agrees with the Old World monkeys and anthropoid apes in the numbers and arrangement both of the turbinate scrolls that arise from the median partition or septum and of those that spring from the inner wall of the upper jaw bone? In man

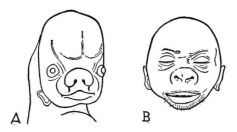

FIG. 84. BROAD FORWARDLY-DIRECTED NOSE OF HUMAN FŒTUS (A) (AFTER KOLLMANN) AND GORILLA FŒTUS (B) (FROM SCHULTZ, AFTER DENIKER).

these delicate bony scrolls, deeply buried in mucous membrane, are arranged in such a way that three air passages, the upper, middle and lower meati, pass between the scrolls and allow the air to pass downward and backward to and from the pharynx. In the Old World monkeys and anthropoid apes the same passages are present as in man, but in the chimpanzee and the gorilla the resemblance to man is even more striking, since the air cavities or sinuses in the frontal,

161

ethmoid and sphenoid bones have similar tubular connections with the nasal meati (Keith).

Nor should the anti-evolutionist be any less embarrassed by the history of the embryonic development of his own nose in comparison with that of other animals. For, broadly speaking, the human nose passes through an early stage in which the olfactory capsule is undeniably like that of a fish (Fig. 65); then the lower end of the capsule is prolonged downward in a tube which opens into the roof of the mouth; at this stage the morphology of this region is substantially like that of an amphibian or of a reptile; then horizontal plates (Fig. 66D) grow out from the upper jaw to form a secondary bony palate, so that the mammalian grade is reached in which the inspired air is delivered into the pharynx back of the palate.

Meanwhile the membranous Eustachian tube has sent off bubble-like outgrowths (Fig. 85), which invade the frontal, ethmoid, sphenoid and superior maxillary bones, forming in them the complex system of sinuses and antra which in its entirety is peculiar to man and the higher anthropoid apes (Keith).

With regard to the external nose, neither the

comparative anatomy nor the embryonic development of this region give the slightest support to
those who stress the isolation of man. On the
contrary, they show quite conclusively that man
and apes are merely the divergently modified
derivatives of a common pro-anthropoid stock and

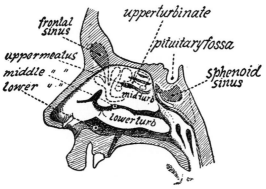

FIG. 85. CONNECTIONS OF THE FRONTAL, ETHMOID AND SPHENOID
SINUSES WITH THE NASAL MEATI (AFTER KEITH).

that with regard to this region civilized man has
become much further modified away from the
primitive ancestral condition than either the gorilla
or the chimpanzee.

In earlier human stages of development (Fig.
86) the nostrils are widely separated, almost as in
the South American monkeys. Later (Fig. 86E)
the opposite halves of the nose grow together.
At this stage the nose is very wide in proportion

163

to its height and as a whole is essentially indentical (Fig. 84B) with that of fœtal chimpanzees and gorillas. This fact, together with a multitude of similar ones, establishes the relatively close relationship between man and the existing anthropoids; it also indicates that in the shape of its nose the common ancestor of man and the anthropoids was far more like a gorilla than like a white man.

According to Professor Schultz, even unborn fœtuses show wide differences in the form of the nose, but in general, babies have wide short noses with very low bridges. In the negro pygmy represented in Fig. 89A the nose has remained in a low stage of fœtal development (*cf*. Fig. 86D). In the Mongolian race the infantile form of nose tends to be retained in the adults. How then does one baby grow up to have the famous figure-6 Jewish nose, another the V-shaped Alpine nose? How did that pretty British girl acquire a nose which has just the suspicion of an upturn at the tip? Why do exceedingly tall men have very long noses? Why do fat men often have inadequate juvenile noses? Of course it seems like a truism to say that in thin sharp noses the vertical components of growth of the nasal septum have

far outstripped the transverse components of the
nose as a whole; yet such no doubt are the most

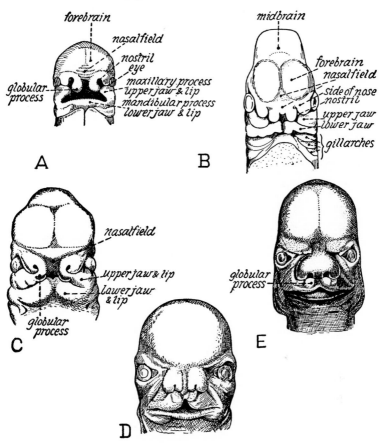

FIG. 86. EMBRYONIC DEVELOPMENT OF THE FACE IN MAN. (FROM
EIDMANN, A, B, AFTER HIS, C, AFTER RABL, D, E, AFTER RETZIUS).
(From *Entw. d. Zähne* . . ., Hermann Meusser, Berlin.)
For details, see p. xxxiv.

important factors in producing the excessively
different extremes shown in Fig. 89.

OUR FACE FROM FISH TO MAN

Let us consider further then the general course of embryonic development of the nose. In all mammals, including man and the anthropoid apes, the face in front of the eyes is formed during individual development (Fig. 86) by the growing

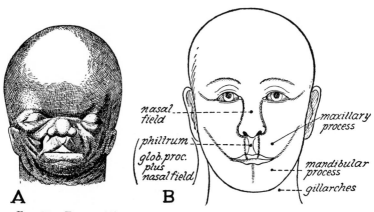

A   B

FIG. 87. FŒTAL (A) AND ADULT (B) DEVELOPMENT OF THE FACE IN
MAN. (A, FROM EIDMAN, AFTER RETZIUS;
B, MODIFIED FROM KEITH).
(A, from *Entw. d. Zähne* . . ., Hermann Meusser, Berlin.)
For details, see p. xxxiv.

together in the mid-line of a system of five flaps or rounded processes, four of which represent the opposite halves of the cheeks and upper and lower lips and jaws, while the fifth, a median area (the nasal field) forms the middle of the philtrum of the upper lip and the middle part of the nose. The sides of the nose are formed from the growing together in the mid-line of the nasal field and the enlarged olfactory capsules. The lateral or alar cartilages of the external nose represent a forward growth of the margins of the olfactory capsules.

According to Broom, the median cartilage or septum of the nose appears to have been derived originally from a forward prolongation of the base of the skull (presphenoid) and in the mammal-like reptiles, marsupials and some other orders of mammals it is still formed that way; but in man and other primates the forepart of the septum acquires a separate center of ossification and becomes the mesethmoid bone.

Schultz has shown (Fig. 88) that as development proceeds the middle cartilage (septum) grows forward and downward faster in man than in the anthropoids and faster in the white race than in the negro race; thus in the latter the everted lips and more protruding front teeth are associated with a less deep median septum and a lesser downgrowth of the nasal tip. In adults of all races the nose gets longer, narrower at the base and more raised at the bridge. Thus babies and young children have relatively shorter, less prominent noses than adults (Fig. 87).

The median partition (septum) that supports

the tip of the nose is tied to the bone above the
incisor teeth.   If then the front upper jaw bone

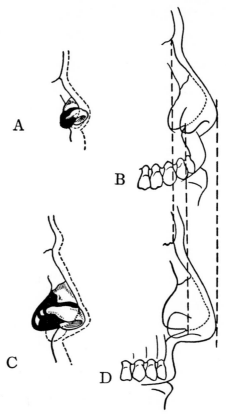

FIG. 88.   NASAL PROFILES AND RELATED PARTS IN MAN: A, NEGRO
CHILD; B, NEGRO ADULT; C, WHITE CHILD; D, WHITE ADULT.
(ALL AFTER SCHULTZ.)
For details, see pp. xxxiv, xxxv.

(premaxilla) has a feeble growth, it will not grow
far forward (as it does in the anthropoids) and
hence the anchorage of the median septum will be

relatively far back. This will tend both to increase the prominence of the nose as a whole and to give a downward inclination to the tip. In the typical Dinaric or Hittite nose (Fig. 89C) the resultants of all the horizontal, forward components and of all the downward components are very conspicuous.

If the transverse growth components of the palate are relatively weak, the bony palate may buckle up and the median septum may either bend on one side, producing a partial closure of the nasal passage, or possibly it may be displaced upward, producing a high-ridged or humped nose. If the bridge and the lower end of the nose as well as the median partition are all retarded in their growth, as in achondroplastic dwarfs, a marked repoussé or pug nose, with almost upturned tip, will result (see below, page 230). In the orang the median partition itself seems to lag in growth, while the orbits are crowded together and the nasal bones are extremely reduced.

The transverse components of growth are obviously in the ascendant in extremely wide noses with broad nostrils and low bridges, as in Australian and Tasmanian aborigines, Papuans, Melanesians, negritos and negros. Such conditions are apt to be associated with prognathous

169

jaws and large teeth (Fig. 89D). The reduction in size of the tooth row as a whole seems to have permitted or favored the vertical and forward growth of the nose, while the opposite tendency culminates in the gorilla, which has enormous teeth and an extremely broad nose. Doubtless other factors complicate the results, for instance, the lateral cartilages or alæ of the nose must in themselves have varying growth power, very feeble in the orang, vigorous in the gorilla, still more so in man.

The form of the nose bridge is likewise conditioned by many factors. The greater the volume of the brain in the fœtus, the sharper will be the bending of the brain upon itself, and the further forward will be pushed the greater wings of the sphenoid bone and the temporal region of the skull. All this has a tendency to push the face forward, especially the lateral angles of it, so that in extremely wide-headed forms the cheeks often protrude and the outer corners of the eye-orbits are far forward. This produces the Mongolian type of broad flat face, often with a wide space between the orbits and a low flat bridge and protruding eyes. The varying shape of the lower end of Mongolian noses is perhaps correlated with

170

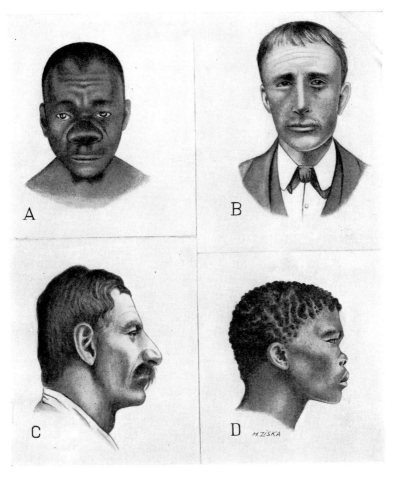

FIG. 89. EXTREMES OF NOSE FORM IN MAN: (A) AFRICAN PYGMY;
(B) TYROLESE; (C) ARMENIAN; (D) SOUTH AFRICAN BUSHMAN. (A, B,
FROM MARTIN, AFTER CZEKANOWSKI, D, AFTER SCHULTZ; C, AFTER
VON LUSCHAN).

(A, B, D, from *Lehrbuch der Anthropologie*. Gustav Fischer).

For details see p. xxxv.

other factors, such as the width of the palate.

Among other possible factors affecting the shape of the nose is the extent of upward growth of the frontal process of the superior maxillary bone (Fig. 50). This process is a small prong or fork, one on each side of the head, in contact with the frontal above and supporting the nasal bone. An increase in size of this process would tend to elevate the bridge of the nose. Similarly a down growth of the whole maxillary bone, as in acromegalic persons, produces a marked vertical lengthening of the nose.

Here we touch upon the question, what causes all these individual growth differences? The cretins and achondroplastic dwarfs, which have broad pug noses, have deficient thyroid glands, and the acromegalics with very long noses and protruding chins have diseased pituitary glands. For these and other reasons many authors are inclined to look upon the "hormones" that are thrown into the blood stream by the different endocrine glands as stimulators of differential growth or development; but it is also recognized that each growing part has its normal range of response or receptivity to the appropriate hormones. Consequently the mechanism of the development of any given part may be threefold: that is, it may involve first, its own inherent and probably hereditary growth power; secondly, the quality or amount of specific hormones produced by the endocrine glands; thirdly, the degree of receptivity of each part to the stimulation of the hormones.

The common saying, "As plain as the nose on one's face" is an unscientific recognition of the dominance of the nose in the human physiognomy. The studies of Schultz on the development and growth of the human nose, and of Stockard on the principles and factors of development and growth in general give us a slight hint of the complexity of the factors that mould the individual nose. Except in the case of identical twins no two persons will carry the same hereditary factors affecting nose form, while even in the case of identical twins the nutritional factors can hardly be exactly the same, especially after birth. The resulting diversity in nose form is as bewildering as the diversity in patterns of a kaleidoscope and, at least to some extent, is conditioned by the same law of chance associations of hereditary and environmental influences.

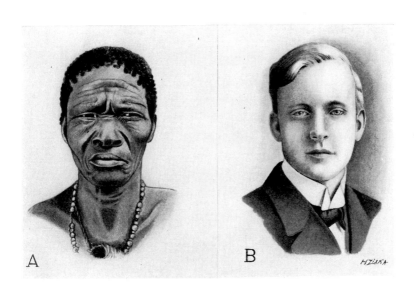

FIG. 90. EXTREMES IN FACE FORM AND COLOR: (A) HOTTENTOT WOMAN (FROM MARTIN, AFTER POECH, *Lehrbuch der Anthropologie*, GUSTAV FISCHER); (B) NORDIC SWEDE (FROM LUNDBORG AND RUNN-STRÖM, *The Swedish Nation*, H. W. TULLBERG.).

OUR BEST FEATURES

Optical Photography and its Results

THE HUMAN EYES AS INSTRUMENTS OF PRECISION

All sense organs are instruments of precision that register varying intensities of the pulsing streams of energy to which they are exposed. The paired eyes of man, together with their connections in the central nervous system, register even slight changes in the intensity of light, they respond to a wide range of its wave length, and hence discriminate colors, and they are extremely sensitive to the movement of images across the retina. Through their binocular adjustments they record extension, relative distances, and movements in a three-dimensional field, and by their biconjugate movements they can find a moving image and keep it in focus within wide limits.

THE EYES OF INVERTEBRATES

The anatomy and physiology of the eyes of invertebrates and vertebrates are the subjects of an enormous literature, which has been admirably summarized by L. Plate in his *Allgemeine Zoologie und Abstammungslehre*, Zweiter Teil, Jena, 1924, wherein are set forth more fully most of the facts cited in the present chapter.[1] The lower forms of animals exhibit a wide diversity of organs sensitive to light, in various stages of complexity. Too long exposure to the ultraviolet rays has an injurious or even fatal effect on many organisms, such as bacteria, infusoria, hydroids, rotifers, nematodes, etc. (Plate, 1924, p. 386), which hence shrivel up or shrink away from these rays, while as everyone knows, plants turn toward the sunlight and some animals love to bask in the sun. Hence in view of the importance of light to the organism in one way or another, it is not surprising that even in very simple one-celled forms such as certain protista there should be clear granules, like lenses, sometimes backed by dense pigment, which may in some way act as rudimentary eyes and contribute to the organism's different reactions to light of different intensities (Plate, 1924, pp. 424–427). At any rate, when we come to certain of the jellyfishes we find undoubted eyes or ocelli in the outer layer or

[1] Professor Plate (*in litteris*) calls attention to the fact that, considering the enormous range of electric waves (from almost zero to hundreds of kilometers), it is remarkable that the whole gamut of human sensation of light, color, form and movement, with all their derived pleasures, is caused by so relatively narrow a range of electric waves. "How different our picture of the world would be," he writes, "if we had more such regions!"

174

ectoderm of the cup-shaped body. In some cases (Fig. 91A) each ocellus consists only of a slightly raised patch of larger pigment-bearing epithelial cells alternating with smaller "light cells." The patch grades into the ordinary epithelial cells around it. In other cases (Fig. 91B) the patch

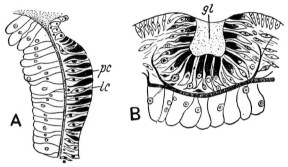

FIG. 91. THE BEGINNINGS OF EYES. (FROM PLATE, AFTER LINKO.)

A. Section of an ocellus, or eye spot, at the base of a tentacle of a jellyfish. B. Section of a "goblet eye" of a jellyfish.

(From *Allgem. Zool.*, Gustav Fischer.)

For details, see p. xxxv.

sinks below the surface, forming a pouch lined with pigment. Between the large deeply pigmented cells on the inside of the pouch are small "rods" at one end of the "light cells." Such an alternation of two kinds of cells foreshadows the alternation of the "rods" and "cones" of more advanced types of eyes, in which the "rods" are believed to detect light and darkness, form and movements, while the "cones" chiefly detect color differences (Plate, 1924, p. 705). In the jelly-fishes the cavity of the optic pouch is often filled with a transparent jelly-like substance corresponding to the "glass body" or vitreous humor of higher eyes, and functionally to the lens. That these organs are really eyes, says Plate (1924, p. 428), follows from the fact that if the animal is deprived of them it fails to react in its normal way to light.

In some of the flatworms the eyes consist of hollow capsules derived from an infolding of the epithelium and deeply lined with pigment. Each capsule has sunk beneath the epithelium, which has grown over it. It is open on one side and into its hollow interior project the flower-like ends of the "light cells," the outer ends of which pass into elongate nerve cells. Hesse (quoted by Plate, p. 433) notes that if two such capsules are symmetrically arranged on either side of the mid-line, then a light in front will give symmetrically placed shadows inside the capsules, a light on the left side will illuminate the left capsule and leave the interior of the right one in shadow, and so forth. Thus the nerves inside the capsules on

opposite sides of the body will be stimulated
differently according to the direction of the light

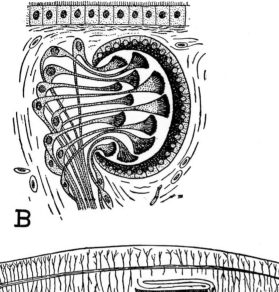

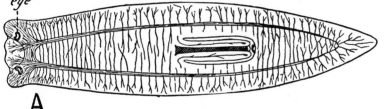

FIG. 92. EYE CAPSULES OF FLATWORM: (B) SECTION OF "GOBLET
EYE" (FROM PLATE AFTER HESSE); (A) LOCATION OF EYES
(AFTER PARKER AND HASWELL).

(B, from *Allgem. Zool.*, Gustav Fischer.)

For details, see p. xxxv.

and according to their own orientation in the
body. Here the function of paired eyes in enabling the organism to adjust its own axis of locomotion to the direction of the light comes into view.

Indeed, Plate (1924, pp. 738–742) cites much evidence for his view that *the paired eyes of vertebrates originated as directional organs, guiding the animal toward the light and that later by acquiring a lens they became true visual organs.*

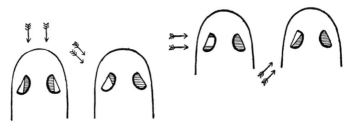

Fig. 93.   How the Eye Capsules of a Flatworm Serve as Directional Organs (from Plate, after Hesse).

The arrows show the varying directions of the light.   In each case only a particular part of each retina is stimulated, the rest being in shadow.

(From *Allgem. Zool.*, Gustav Fischer.)

The higher invertebrates exhibit eyes in all grades of evolution, from the simple types described above to the compound eyes of crustaceans and insects and to the elaborately constructed paired eyes of the higher molluscs.   Eyes occur in various parts of the body and sometimes in great numbers, as in certain deep-sea cephalopods.   The common scallop (*Pecten*) has numerous eyes along the scalloped edge of the mantle.   Thus in typical invertebrates the eyes are essentially derivatives of the skin and may occur almost anywhere on the surface of the body, but in the vertebrates the paired eyes are essentially an outgrowth of a definite part of the forebrain, only the outer parts of the eye (including the lens and cornea) being contributed by the epithelium; although eventually

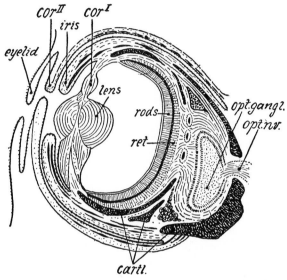

FIG. 94. EYE OF SQUID (HORIZONTAL MEDIAN SECTION). (FROM PLATE, AFTER HENSEN.)
(From *Allgem. Zool.*, Gustav Fischer.)

the brain itself has been derived from the same primary outer layer or ectoderm.

Among all the hosts of invertebrates the paired eyes which at first seem to approach the vertebrate type most nearly are found in some of the cephalopod molluscs, especially the squids and

179

octopuses. In these highly elaborate organs there are eyelids in front of the eyes, a contractile iris, muscles of accommodation, a highly complex retina of many layers, a large optic nerve and muscles to move the eyeball. But when we compare the parts of these cephalopod eyes with those of vertebrates we find many striking and profound differences. Thus in the squid (*Sepia*) the lids serve as a pupil, there are two corneas, the outer one perforated, the inner one dividing the lens into inner and outer parts; the so-called iris lies entirely outside of the retinal layer instead of next to it as in the vertebrates; and there is apparently no true choroid layer. More important still, in the cephalopods the optic nerve lies entirely behind the retina, while in vertebrates it pierces the retina and is then distributed over its front surface; finally, in the cephalopods the rods are on the front layer of the retina, pointing toward the light, while in the vertebrates they are on the back layer of the retina and point in the opposite direction.

Not all the cephalopods have eyes as compli- cated as the type described above and there is a gradation of forms leading back to the very simple eye of *Nautilus* (Plate, 1924, pp. 474–478). The retina and indeed the whole eye of cephalopods develops in the embryo as a pouch in the skin, and is thus comparable only to the lens of vertebrates; in the latter the retina is developed from the optic

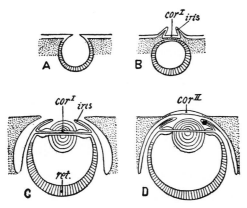

Fig. 95.   Development of the Eye in Cephalopod Molluscs.
(After Plate.)
(From *Allgem. Zool.*, Gustav Fischer.)
For details, see p. xxxvi.

cup, which is an outgrowth of the brain.   Thus at every important anatomical point the paired eyes of cephalopods and of vetebrates differ profoundly from each other.   From all this it is evident that the paired eyes of cephalopods and of vertebrates are not homologous with each other at all, that they have arisen from dissimilar beginnings and have come to resemble each other

181

by convergent evolution in adaptation to similar functional needs.

The paired eyes of the modern *Limulus* and the scorpions represent specialized offshoots of the annelid and primitive crustacean types (Plate, 1924, pp. 537–561). Patten and others have attempted to show how they might have been tranformed into the vertebrate eyes, but most authorities consider that there is no direct evidence in favor of this view and the profound differences between the eyes of arthropods and those of vertebrates have always been considered a grave objection to Patten's theory of the origin of the vertebrates from arthropods related to the eurypterids and to *Limulus*.

ORIGIN OF THE PAIRED EYES OF VERTEBRATES

We have seen above that a comparative study of the eyes of invertebrates shows several steps in the evolution of such elaborately constructed paired eyes as those of the cephalopods and therefore gives us a general idea how the somewhat similar paired eyes of vertebrates may have been produced. More direct evidence as to the origin of the vertebrate eye is wanting. The lancelet

Amphioxus, which, as all beginners in zoology learn, supplies us with an ideally simplified chordate, goes too far for our present purpose in the simplification of its eyes, which have either vanished entirely by degeneration or never developed.

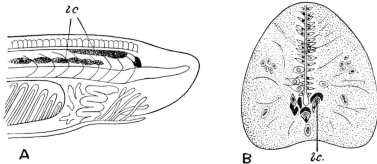

FIG. 96. LIGHT CELLS OF AMPHIOXUS: (A) FOREPART OF A YOUNG *Amphioxus*, ENLARGED; (B) CROSS-SECTION OF THE SPINAL CORD OF AMPHIOXUS (FROM PLATE, A, AFTER JOSEPH, B, AFTER HESSE.)
(From *Allgem. Zool.*, Gustav Fischer.)
For details, see p. xxxvi.

According to Plate (1924, p. 494) the lancelet (*Amphioxus*) when resting on the sandy bottom is supposed to sense the direction of the light by means of long rows of minute eye-like organs, which are deeply buried in the spinal cord and extend along each side of the back above the notochord. Each little eye consists of a single cell, supposed to be sensitive to light, backed by another cell which is concave and deeply pigmented. A much larger spot of pigment at the

183

front end of the brain tube is interpreted by
Plate (1924, p. 493) not as an eye at all, as it
lacks light cells, but as the last remnant of a
balancing organ. Thus the light-sensing apparatus
of *Amphioxus* is of the utmost simplicity and has
little obvious relation to the highly complex paired
eyes of vertebrates.

In the foregoing pages we have reviewed the
general construction of paired eyes, we have out-
lined the evolution of eyes from very simple
beginnings, we have considered the wide contrast
between vertebrates and invertebrates in the
structure of the paired eyes and we have seen that
according to present evidence the vertebrate
paired eyes do not appear to be inherited from
any of the more complex invertebrate types but
seem to have arisen in the very ancient and still
undiscovered pre-vertebrates. As direct evidence
from successive fossil stages illustrating the origin
of the paired eyes of vertebrates is meager or
wanting and as there are apparently no surviving
pre-vertebrate stages except possibly *Amphioxus*,
we must rely chiefly upon the evidence afforded by
embryology, and such evidence is often open to
the suspicion that we may be mistakenly inter-

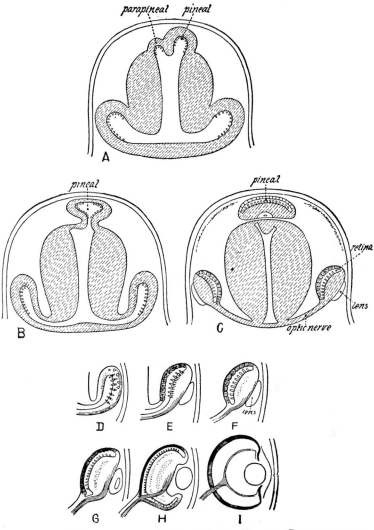

FIG. 97. EVOLUTION OF THE VERTEBRATE EYE AS CONCEIVED BY
STUDNICKA (FROM PLATE, AFTER STUDNICKA).

(From *Allgem. Zool.*, Gustav Fischer.)

For details, see pp. xxxvi, xxxvii.

preting as a repetition of long past adult stages such arrangements or conditions as may be merely adaptations of the growing embryo to its own physiological needs.

Studnicka (quoted by Plate), basing his theory chiefly on the embryology of the lampreys and their relatives (which may represent the degenerate descendants of the ostracoderms), holds that originally there were two pairs of paired eyes in the pre-chordates, one pair dorsal, on the top of the head, consisting of the pineal and parapineal organs, the second pair low down on the sides of the head, the eyes of later vertebrates. Both pairs were derived from patches of cells sensitive to light, located in the broad sensitive tract that later folded up to become the brain tube. Up to this time both sets of eyes had served merely to orientate the animal with reference to the direction of light. When as a result of its growing mass the primitive nerve tract swelled outward, its crests grew upward and curved over toward the mid-line, carrying the primary optic depressions on to its inner side, so that the future "rods" would now point away from the light, and their nerve fibers, formerly beneath them, would now be bent around toward the outer surface. Meanwhile the dorsal pair near the front edge of the brain tract were not turned over, so that their retina remained on the outer side of their nerve layer. As the brain swelling increased it pressed the future optic cups against the epithelium on the surface of the head; the epithelium sank inward, folded up into a lens, and the lens in turn increasing rapidly, conditioned the insinking of the optic swelling, which thus became the optic cup. The optic stalk or nerve is simply the constricted part between the brain and the cup. By this time the lateral paired eyes were becoming true organs of vision, while the dorsal pair gradually degenerated and their nerve stalks finally became the pineal and parapineal organs of the brain. It is important to remember that the retina apparently represents an inverted patch of epithelium and that the layer of nerve fibrils now covering it represents the former underside of the patch. Also that the optic cup was pushed in from the outside so that its primary cavity was squeezed out of existence.

The lens is at first connected with its parent epithelium by a slender stalk, which is soon lost. The lens thus finds itself protruding into the hollow side of the pushed-in ball, or optic cup. The space between the lens and the inside of the cup becomes filled with fibrillar tissue which gives rise to the transparent jelly-like substance called the vitreous humor.

The retina, derived from the inner layer of the cup, comprises the following series of layers: the innermost of these is a layer of nerve fibers and ganglion cells which are gathered together and pierce the center of the cup, issuing from it as the optic nerve; next follow various layers of large and smaller nerve cells, culminating in the layer of cones and rods, the latter being nearest the outer epithelial layer of the inner wall and directed away from the source of light. The outer layer of the optic cup gives rise to the pigmented layer of the retina, which doubtless provides the necessary opaque, light-proof layer, like the black inner surface of a camera. Next comes the network of blood vessels of the choroid, while outside of the choroid is the thick sclerotic layer, which is continuous in front with the cornea.

ORIGIN OF THE HUMAN EYES

Before attempting to trace the evolution of the human eye, let us recall its broader structural features. We know that it is essentially like a camera, with its dark chamber (the inside of the eyeball), its lens, its sensitive plate (retina), its iris-diaphragm for regulating the amount of light admitted through the pupil. We know also that it differs from an ordinary camera in altering the focus not by regulating the distance between the lens and the plate but by changing the curvature of the elastic lens through the pull of the ciliary muscles. We also know that the human eye differs from a single camera in being linked with its fellow of the opposite side so as to provide for a binocular, stereoscopic mental image and that the two eyes are biconjugate, that is, by means of its six eye muscles (Fig. 98), each eye can move in harmony with its fellow so as to keep a moving object in focus; also that the eye is a living mechanism provided with elaborate systems for the elimination of waste, for automatic renewal of all parts and for the lubrication, cleaning and protection of its exposed surface.

The retina carries a coloring matter named rhodopsin or visual purple,[1] which becomes rapidly bleached on exposure to sunlight. No doubt the

[1] Cunningham, D. J., 1902, *Textbook of Anatomy*, p. 689.

extent and intensity of the bleaching effect is in
some way proportional to the size of the aperture,
the intensity of the light and the length of exposure.
And no doubt also the innumerable rods and

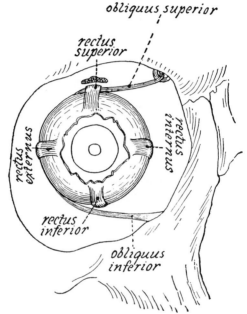

FIG. 98. THE RIGHT EYEBALL AND ITS SIX MUSCLES (FROM PLATE,
AFTER MERKEL AND KALLINS).
(From *Allgem. Zool.*, Gustav Fischer.)

cones of the visual field react differently to different
wave lengths (colors) and different intensities
(light and shade), so that an image made up of
innumerable points, like a half-tone picture, is
recorded on the retina. But whereas the photog-
rapher proceeds after an interval to fix the image

190

on the plate, the retina immediately proceeds to "televisualize" its images through the myriads of nerve fibers covering its surface. After passing through many microscopic relay and "booster" stations the disturbances pass along a vast cable route known as the optic nerve. Instantly reaching their first main destination, the visual cortex of the brain, the visual currents now incite millions of repercussions which are flashed and reflashed to the relay stations and great central systems in many parts of the brain, where they set off many triggers that control the secretory activities of glands or the contractility of muscle fibers.

The foregoing description holds in a general way for the eye of vertebrates of all grades from fish to man, the vertebrate eye, except in degenerate forms, being extraordinarily constant in its main features. Hence the basic features of the human eye date back to the beginnings of the vertebrates and are fully exemplified in such primitive forms as the sharks (Fig. 99). The six eye muscles of the human eye (Fig. 98) likewise date back at least to the shark-like stage. Here again the shark is vastly nearer to man in the essential features of its morphology than it is to any known invertebrate. In other words, while we can only surmise what the history of the eye may have been below the vertebrate stage, we have the most convincing evidence that once that grade of organization of the eye had

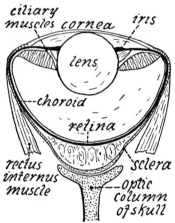

FIG. 99. THE RIGHT EYE OF A SHARK IN HORIZONTAL SECTION (FROM PLATE, AFTER FRANZ).
(From *Allgem. Zool.*, Gustav Fischer.)

been attained, it was transmitted by heredity with only minor improvements from fish to man.

Although the human eye is undoubtedly derived remotely from one that was in general like the shark type (Fig. 99), from which it has inherited even the principal layers of the retina, it shows also many progressive changes beyond that of the shark in adaptation to vision in the air rather than in water. Its lens, being relatively smaller and flatter than that of the shark, gives a longer focus, and accordingly the focal axis of the bulb is lengthened, the human bulb being spherical while that of the shark is flatter in front.   The cornea in

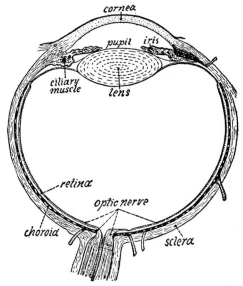

FIG. 100.   DIAGRAM OF HORIZONTAL SECTION OF THE RIGHT HUMAN EYE (SIMPLIFIED FROM PLATE, AFTER LUCIANI).

(From *Allgem. Zool.*, Gustav Fischer.)

man is more convex and widely separated from the lens, which is entirely behind the iris, whereas in many sharks it protrudes through the pupil and touches the cornea.   The human lens is much more delicate, less dense, more easily compressible than that of the shark and it readily responds to the pull of the ciliary muscles of accommodation.

193

As to the external accessories of vision, man retains a vestige of the nictitating membrane or third eyelid of lower vertebrates in his semilunar fold at the inner corner of the eyelid; but he has advanced far beyond the shark in possessing an elaborate lacrymal or lubricating apparatus, con-

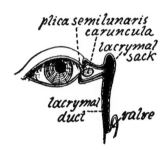

FIG. 101. TEAR-DRAINING CANALS OF THE EYE (AFTER KEITH).

sisting of tear-producing glands, with two collecting canals above and below the caruncula. These two canals converge toward and drain into the lacrymal sac, which is lodged in a pocket of the lacrymal bone on the inner wall of the orbit; the lacrymal sac is continued downward through the naso-lacrymal duct into the nasal chamber. Man also has fleshy, movable eyelids, which are provided with eyelashes and Meibomian glands.

Many similar details could be cited in which the human eye is superior to that of the shark; but the anti-evolutionist could find little justification for setting man apart from the rest of creation on this account, for we find that every one of the characters cited above is the common property of normal land-living mammals and that the evolution of some of these structures, such as the lacrymal apparatus and the third eyelid, can be traced with convincing detail through the various branches of the vertebrate tree lying between the human and the shark branches.

Moreover we are compelled to cause even further distress to the indomitable critics of the Darwinian theory of human origin by bringing forward again their special horror, the anthropoid apes and monkeys. For nowhere will more convincing morphological evidence of the relatively very close relationship of man to these animals be found than in a detailed comparison of the anatomy and physiology of the paired eyes. And when to these resemblances in the visual organs between man and anthropoid, we add the striking identity in the complex arrangements and connections of the optic tracts within the brain, as reported by the leading students of the human and anthropoid brains, the evidence for Darwin is heaped still higher.

OUR FACE FROM FISH TO MAN

The position of the eyes in the human head has likewise been inherited from the common man-anthropoid stock. In *Notharctus*, a primitive primate of the Eocene epoch (Fig. 35A) the eyes were directed partly outward as well as forward, the large muzzle extended far in front of the orbits and binocular vision was obviously impossible. The large size of the olfactory chamber in *Notharctus* also indicates that like other mammals and especially like its relatives the modern lemurs, the lowest existing primates, it still depended largely upon its olfactory sense, while the higher primates have a much reduced olfactory apparatus and a predominant visual apparatus. With regard to the direction of the orbital axes, these look partly outward also in most of the modern lemuroids (Fig. 35B) and even the greatly enlarged orbits of the modern *Tarsius* (Fig. 35C) are directed somewhat away from each other. In the South American monkeys (Fig. 35D) however, the outer angles of the orbits are shifted further forward and the muzzle is reduced; in the Old World monkeys and anthropoid apes (Fig. 35E, F), this process is completed and binocular vision is established. The binocular character of the vision of anthropoids and

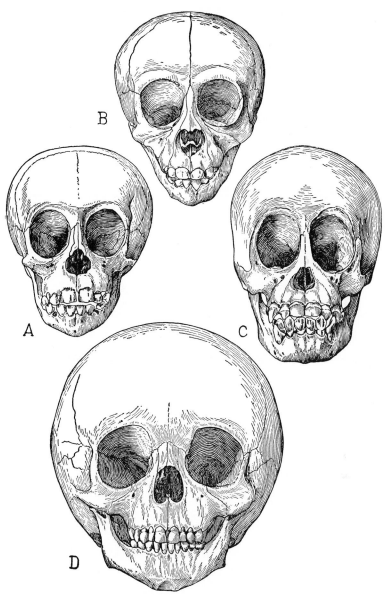

FIG. 102. FRONT VIEW OF INFANT AND YOUNG SKULLS OF
ANTHROPOIDS (A, B, C) AND OF MAN (D).
For details, see p. xxxvii.

197

man is especially evident in the front views of the young skulls (Fig. 102).

Meanwhile we observe a general progression in the character of the hands, which in the lemuroids are hardly more than forefeet, while in the gibbon, chimpanzee and gorilla the anterior extremities are true hands, adapted primarily for brachiation or leaping with the arms, a habit which requires the greatest quickness in adjusting the focus of the eyes and in correlating the locomotor activities with the rapidly changing visual data.

To the brachiating habit of his ancestors man doubtless owes much of his skill in discriminating the relative nearness of different objects. Brachiation would also seem to be greatly facilitated by biconjugate movements of the eyes. Broman and John I. Hunter have shown that in the chimpanzee the nucleus in the brain of the oculomotor nerves, which controls several of the eye muscles, has essentially the same pattern as in man and differs widely from that of the lower primates which have not attained biconjugate movement of the eyes.

The surface of the iris as seen through an ophthalmoscope differs widely in different kinds of animals. Lindsay-Johnson in his beautiful

198

monograph on the fundus oculi of vertebrates figures the retinal surface of the eye of many mammals, including a white man, a negro and a chimpanzee. The deeply pigmented iris of the chimpanzee shows the most striking resemblance to that of the negro, while its basic similarity to that of the white man is masked by the loss of pigment in the latter. Only man and the apes have a macroscopic "macula lutea" or spot of clearest vision on the retina (Plate, 1924, p. 690).

The lacrymal bone, in the inner corner of the eye, affords additional evidence of the close relationship of man and the anthropoids. Not only are its general form and connections strikingly similar in man and chimpanzee (save for the very small size of the "hamular process" in the apes) but Le Double notes[1] that in Deniker's gorilla fœtus the lacrymal bone begins to ossify in the same place that it does in the human fœtus toward the end of the fourth month, namely, in the covering membrane of the ethmoidal cartilage and on the inner side of the lacrymal sac; that, like the human fœtal lacrymal, it consists of an

[1] "Essai sur la Morphogénie et les Variations du Lacrymal et des Osselets péri-lacrymaux de l'Homme." *Bibliographie Anatomique,* 1900, T. VIII, p. 125.

oval plaque with its long diameter inclined obliquely from above downwards and from within outward. Le Double further notes[1] that during intrauterine life the human lacrymal is successively oval, triangular and quadrilateral in form, that the lacrymal of the gorilla is almost triangular, while those of the adult chimpanzee and orang, which show so much resemblance to the human lacrymal, are also subject to the same variations in form.

CONCLUSIONS

In conclusion, the human eyes owe their beginnings to the sensitivity of protoplasm both to the injurious and the beneficial effects of light. In their early pre-vertebrate stages they seem to have been merely directional organs to orientate the animal's locomotion with reference to the light, serving the same purpose at the lower sides of the head as the pineal and parapineal eyes did on the top of the head (Fig. 97A). At this stage the eyes were still on the inner side of the brain tube. When the brain grew outward into contact with the epithelium the optic cup acquired a lens

Ibid., pp. 128, 129.

and true vision resulted, greatly enhancing the organism's success in the pursuit of living prey and in the escape from its enemies. Then various accessory organs appeared, for regulating the focus of the lens, either by slightly changing its position with reference to the opening, or by altering its curvature. After the air-breathing fishes crawled out of the swamps their eyes had to become accustomed to functioning in the air and we find further improvements in the accessory devices for accommodation and for protecting and keeping in repair the whole delicate apparatus. These devices culminate in the mammals, in which however for the most part the olfactory apparatus rather than the eyes is still the dominant sense organ. The primates, alone, show a progressive reduction of the olfactory sense and a concomitantly increasing importance of the eyes, which is further emphasized in the arboreal brachiating anthropoids. In man, a secondarily terrestrial offshoot of the primitive anthropoid stock, the eyes retain not only all the advantages won by the vertebrates in their earlier predatory career, but also all the improvements resulting from a prolonged course of very active life in the trees. Starting with all this experience the eyes of the first true man not only cooperated with the hands, but filled the brain with memory pictures, and these, on the principle of conditioned reflexes, came to be associated in definite combinations with the memories of vocally produced sounds. *Thus man's eyes and ears, rather than his nose, provided him with the means of rising above the endless round of life known to his predecessors, of turning his observational powers upon himself, and eventually of foreseeing not only the immediate but also some of the distant effects of his own activities.*

PRIMITIVE SOUND RECORDERS

The human organ of hearing (Fig. 103) consists of three main parts: (1) the *external ear*, for collecting the sound waves; (2) the *middle ear*, including the tympanic or drum-membrane and the tympanum or middle-ear chamber, the latter containing the three auditory ossicles, the office of which is to transmit the vibrations of the drum membrane to the inner ear; (3) the *inner ear*, or labyrinth, comprising (a) the three semicircular canals with their basal connecting chamber or utriculus, the canals and utriculus being concerned

202

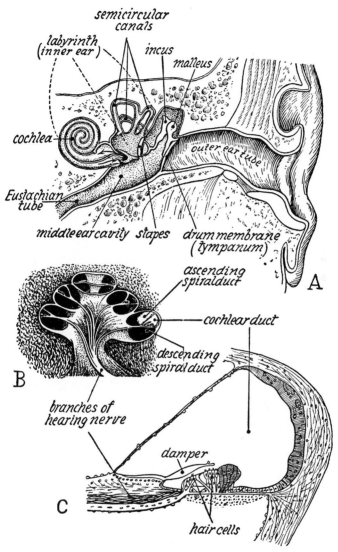

FIG. 103. THE HUMAN ORGAN OF HEARING AND BALANCE.

(A) Transverse section (after Cunningham); (B) Diagram section of
the cochlea; (C) Greatly enlarged view of the cochlear duct.
[For details, see pp. xxxvii, xxxviii.

203

with the sense of balance; (b) the cochlea, a spirally-wound double tube filled with liquid and containing between the upper and lower inner tubes the spirally-wound organ of Corti, the true organ of hearing. The sound waves in the air cause the drum membrane to vibrate, the ossicles magnify the movement and set up mechanical waves in the liquid of the cochlea. It is these mechanical waves and not the sound waves themselves that are picked up by the little rods of the organ of Corti and transmitted to the nerves of hearing.

In the more primitive fishes at the lower end of the vertebrate series there is no middle ear and the inner ear consists chiefly of the semicircular canals, which may be followed throughout the series without a break from fish to man.

The labyrinth arises in the embryo shark, as in the embryo man, by the formation of a sac or pocket in the ectoderm or outer cell layer on either side of the tube that gives rise to the hind brain. The sac later becomes surrounded by cartilage which finally ossifies. The nerves of the semi-circular canals appear to be part of the fore and aft series that innervates the "ampullæ" of the

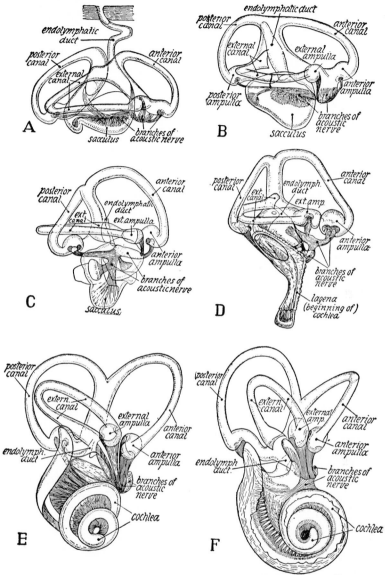

FIG. 104. SERIES SHOWING THE MEMBRANOUS LABYRINTH OR INNER
EAR FROM FISH TO MAN. RIGHT SIDE; OUTER
VIEW. (AFTER RETZIUS.)

A. Shark; B. Ganoid fish; C. Primitive reptile; D. Alligator; E. Rabbit;
F. Man. For details, see p. xxxviii.

205

shark (Fig. 6) and the lateral line organs in the skin of most fishes. These organs are sensitive to the disturbances caused in the water either by wind or by objects falling on the surface of the water (G. H. Parker). Below the semicircular canals there is a sac-like depression (Fig. 104A)

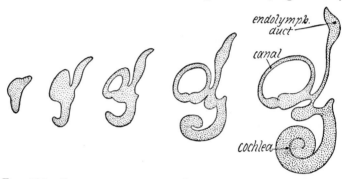

FIG. 105. DEVELOPMENT OF THE LABYRINTH OR INNER EAR OF MAN (AFTER STREETER).

frequently containing an otolith or calcareous secretion which may function in the sense of balance. The nerve that goes to the semicircular canals also sends off a branch which is attached to the otolith, and this lower branch, in the higher vertebrates, is the nerve of hearing (Fig. 104D–F).

It is doubtful whether fishes can really hear rather than feel sound waves in the water. The true organ of hearing equivalent to the cochlea of man has its inception apparently in the Amphibia in the shape of two small papillæ which grow out from the side of the sac below the semicircular canals. In the crocodiles and alligators one of these papillæ is prolonged into a curved tube (Fig. 104D) and in the mammals (Fig. 104E, F) the tube is wound into a spiral, the cochlea. Thus while the semicircular canals which are concerned with balance show only minor changes as we pass through the long series from shark to man, the organ of hearing in air has its beginnings in the Amphibia and culminates in the typical mammals, from which it is transmitted intact to the apes and man.

The chamber of the middle ear (Fig. 106) in the frog (which represents a comparatively little-modified survivor of the earliest amphibians) is derived in the embryo from an out-pocketing from the throat, corresponding to the first or hyoid gill pouch of fishes. This chamber is therefore lined with the entoderm, or primary inner cell layer. The Eustachian tube of the frog is the short passage connecting the cavity of the middle ear with the cavity of the throat. By this arrangement the outward pressure of the air inside the mouth and throat neutralizes the inward pressure of the air outside the ear-drum. Likewise in all higher vertebrates, including man, the cavity of the middle ear communicates with the throat through the Eustachian tube; this arises in the

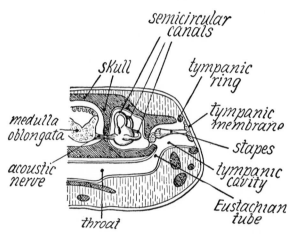

FIG. 106. TRANSVERSE SECTION OF THE HEAD IN A FROG, SHOWING THE RELATIONS OF THE MIDDLE EAR (THERE IS NO OUTER EAR) TO THE INNER EAR AND OF THE LATTER TO THE BRAIN (AFTER T. J. PARKER AND W. N. PARKER).

embryo as an outgrowth of the primitive throat cavity immediately behind the first or jaw arch (Frazer, quoted by Keith).

The tube of the outer ear of mammals corresponds in position partly to the spiracle or hyoid gill cleft of the shark. Both arise also in the embryo as a down-pocketing of the ectoderm, which meets an out-pocketing from the throat cavity called the hyoid gill pouch. In the sturgeon, a survivor of the primitive ganoids, W. K. Parker's plates of a very young embryo show the hyoid gill cleft lying in front of the upper part of the hyomandibula, or upper segment of the second gill arch. A spiracular cleft was also present in

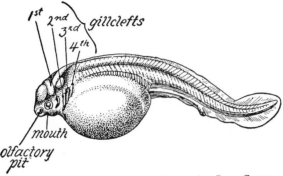

Fig. 107. Embryo Sturgeon, Showing Gill Clefts (after W. K. Parker).

the oldest fossil lobe-finned ganoid *Osteolepis* (Watson). In the earliest known amphibians and reptiles the spiracular cleft may be represented in part by the otic notch (Figs. 17, 19) upon which the tympanic membrane was stretched. In the fishes the gill chamber behind and below the spiracle was covered externally by the bony opercular flap, but in the oldest known amphibians this bony gill cover has disappeared, leaving the prominent otic notch open behind.

In the frog, a modern representative of the Amphibia, there is no external ear tube, since the tympanic membrane lies on the surface (Fig. 106). In the reptiles a ridge or fold of skin may guard the drum membrane and in the birds and typical mammals the latter has sunk so far below the surface that a deep tube is formed.

That the mammalian outer ear tube corresponds only at most in part with the spiracular pocket of the shark is indicated by the fact that the outer ear tube of mammals is formed below the Eustachian tube (which represents the lower part of the first internal gill pouch), while in fishes the spiracular pocket is formed from the upper part of the spiracular cleft and lies above the first internal gill pouch.

In *Echidna*, one of the egg-laying mammals, G. Ruge found that the cartilage of the external ear was continuous with the hyoid, or second gill arch, and hence the inference was drawn that the external ear cartilage was derived from the hyoid arch. But Gaupp's figures of the embryo *Echidna* show the hyoid cartilage entirely distinct from the external ear. And the relations of the ear tube to the tympanic ring both in *Echidna* and in other mammals indicate that its cartilage is a new local development in the mammals.

The outer ear in mammals takes on a great diversity of forms, from the trumpet-like ear of antelopes and other keen-eared, defenceless herbivores to the huge and imposing ear-flaps of the

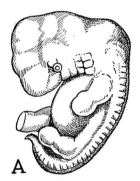 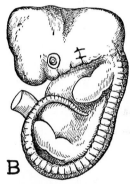

FIG. 108. HUMAN (A) AND MACAQUE (B) EMBRYOS, SHOWING ORIGIN OF THE EXTERNAL EAR FROM SIX TUBERCLES. (FROM LECHE, A, AFTER SELENKA, B, AFTER HIS, KEIBEL.)
(From *Der Mensch*, Gustav Fischer.)

African elephant. Some of the bats have large ears of extreme complexity, while the whales have only a thread-like tube beneath the skin that marks the last vestige of the external ears. Very little in detail is known either about the precise functioning of the different forms of external ear or about the origin and significance of its many subdivisions, such as the tragus, antitragus, crus of the helix and antihelix and the marginal fold or

211

descending helix and lobule. According to Keith (1921) in the human embryo of the sixth week all but the marginal fold arise from six tubercles that form around the first gill cleft depression.

> Three of these tubercles [writes Keith] grow from the mandibular or first arch and form the tragus, crus of the helix, and helix; three from the hyoid arch to form the lobule, antitragus and antihelix. The hinder margin of the ear, or descending helix, with the lobule, arise as a mere thickening or elevation of the skin behind the tubercles in the hyoid arch. Later in development the tubercles of the helix and antihelix send out processes which cross the upper part of the cleft and obliterate it, while the neighboring tubercles fuse to form the definite parts of the ear. The posterior margin and lobule rise up at the same time as a free fold.

A   B

FIG. 109. EARS OF FŒTAL MACAQUE (A) AND OF A SIX MONTHS HUMAN FŒTUS (B). (FROM PLATE, AFTER SCHWALBE.)
(From *Allgem. Zool.*, Gustav Fischer.)

The common lemur (*Lemur catta*) of Madagascar has very large pointed ears that can be directed forward. In the monkeys the ear tends to be flat with a rounded top, quite different from the trumpet-like ear and not capable of being thrust far forward. The ear of the Old

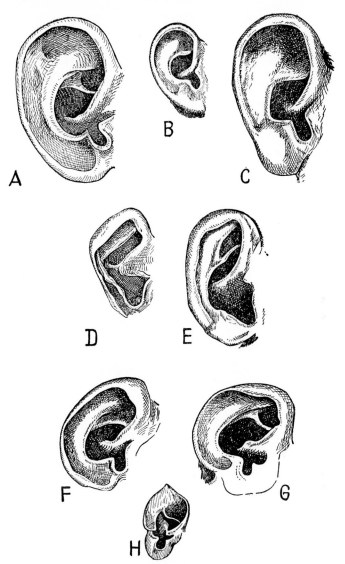

FIG. 110. EXTERNAL EARS OF ANTHROPOIDS AND MEN.
(AFTER KEITH.)

A. Chimpanzee; B. "Small chimpanzee type" (human); C. "Chimpanzee type" (human); D. Orang; E. "Orang type" (human); F. Gorilla; G. Gibbon; H. Lemuroid (*Nycticebus*).

World or catarrhine monkeys shows various stages in the reduction of the pointed tip (*cf.* Pocock, 1925, Fig. 36). The ear of a six-months' human fœtus (Fig. 109B) figured by Schwalbe has a truncate upper rim and vestigial tip and in general appearance approaches the Old World monkey type (Fig. 109A) as noted by Schwalbe. The un-rolled outer rim and Darwin's point, found as an occasional variant in man, is reminiscent rather of the monkeys than of the anthropoids, although indications of the Darwin's point are not lacking in certain chimpanzees (*cf.* Hæckel, 1903, Pl. 26) and in certain orangs (Pocock, 1925, Fig. 37D, E).

The ears of the great anthropoid apes, while highly variable in details, are substantially of the human type, especially those of the gorilla. All have the rolled-over upper rim, but in the chim-panzee the hinder rim, according to Pocock (1925) is "sometimes flat, sometimes slightly overfolded but never apparently so overfolded as is typically the case in *Homo*. The lower lobe, varying in size, is not so well developed as in Man." On the whole the external ears of the gorilla and chim-panzee are remarkably human in appearance and, like so many other features of anthropoid anatomy, they are literally one of the earmarks of man's relatively close relationship to the primitive brachiating ancestors of the chimpanzee-gorilla stock. If man had been derived from some entirely different stock of Primates there is no assignable reason why he should resemble the gorilla and the chimpanzee in so many external and internal characters in spite of his widely different habits and notwithstanding the millions of years that have passed since the human and gorilla-chimpanzee groups began to separate.

Since the time of Darwin the reduced ear muscles of man have been justly famous as indications of our derivation from mammals with more movable ears. Ruge's monograph (1887, Plates V, VI, VII) on the facial musculature shows very clearly the striking resemblance between the ear muscles of the chimpanzee and those of certain human embryos and children (*cf.* also Fig. 23D, E).

The evolution of the auditory ossicles (Fig. 111) has been referred to earlier in this book but may be summarized here as follows. The most ancient member of the ossicular chain is the stapes, or stirrup, which has probably been derived from one of the two upper segments of the second or

OUR FACE FROM FISH TO MAN

hyoid gill arch of fishes. In the oldest known
amphibians, as in the frog (Fig. 106) the stapes

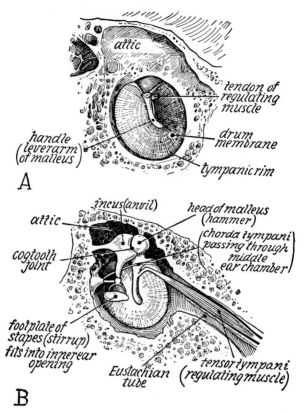

FIG. 111. THE MIDDLE EAR OF MAN, SHOWING THE AUDITORY
OSSICLES (AFTER CUNNINGHAM).

For details, see p. xxxix.

extends from the inner ear to the tympanum or
drum membrane. When the tympanum first appeared (in the Amphibia) it was fastened (Fig.

216

17B) to the back part of the squamosal bone, or bony shell over the back part of the primary upper

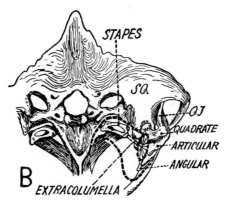

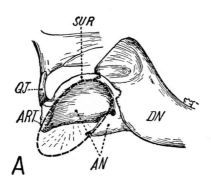

Fig. 112. Relations of the Parts of the Middle Ear in an Extinct Mammal-like Reptile (after Sushkin).

For details, see pp. xxxix, xl.

jaw. In the reptiles the tympanum is always associated with this same region and is also more or less connected with the angular bone of the

lower jaw. In the fossil mammal-like reptiles a
large notch (Figs. 112, 113) in the back of the

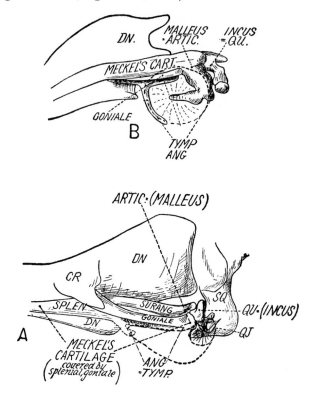

FIG. 113. ORIGIN OF AUDITORY OSSICLES.

(A) Back part of the lower jaw of an advanced mammal-like reptile
(based chiefly on a cast of the specimen combined with observations
and figures of Seeley and Watson); (B) Fœtal mammal (slightly
modified from R. W. Palmer). For details, see p. xl.

angular bone is thought for various reasons to
have served for the attachment of a pocket from
the membranous sac that encloses the cavity of

the middle ear. The stapes was connected with the inner ear on the inner side and by its double outer end (Fig. 112) with both the quadrate bone and the tympanic membrane. When the dentary bone became very large and formed the chief part of the lower jaw, the angular, articular and quadrate elements, which were still connected with the tympanum, became much smaller. When the dentary formed its new joint with the squamosal (pages 36–39) the lower jaw bones that were behind it (quadrate, articular and angular) gave up their function as jaw elements and intensified their auditory function, transforming sound waves into mechanical pulsations and thus transmitting the equivalents of the sound waves to the stapes; this in turn passed them on to the liquid in the inner ear.

In this way arose the marvellous delicate mechanism of the auditory ossicles, the tiny muscles of which (Fig. 111) are still innervated, even in man, by twigs from the main nerve of the jaw muscles. Meanwhile the first gill pouch, below the back part of the jaw, had grown upward and surrounded the now reduced angular, articular and stapes, forming the cavity of the middle ear (Fig. 112).

OUR FACE FROM FISH TO MAN

The human embryo, like that of mammals of all other orders, still shows in the clearest, most undeniable way, the origin of the malleus and incus from the reduced primary jaw elements (Figs. 114, 115).

ANCIENT AND MODERN PHYSIOGNOMY

The art of reading character from the human face is one of the things that every woman knows and every man prides himself upon. But the courts are crowded with the wrongs of deceived women and the prisons are filled with wolves in sheep's clothing who have hidden a ravenous heart behind faces that confident physiognomists, including practical men of business, have diagnosed as honest. What is the matter then with the popular "science" of physiognomy?

To the ancients, never embarrassed by facts, physiognomy was as easy as every other branch of science. Aristotle, according to the Encyclopædia Britannica (article on Physiognomy), taught that noses with thick bulbous ends belong to persons who are swinish; sharp-tipped noses belong to the irascible, those easily provoked, like dogs; large rounded, obtuse noses to the magnanimous, the lion-like; slender hooked noses to the eagle-like,

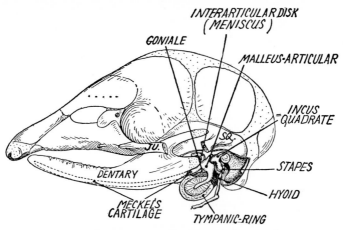

FIG. 114. RELATIONS OF OSSICLES TO LOWER JAW IN
FŒTAL ARMADILLO (*Tatusia hybrida*).

(Composed from two figures by W. K. Parker.)

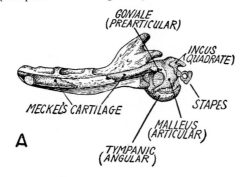

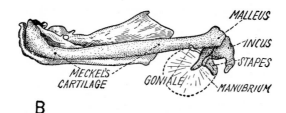

FIG. 115. THE REPTILIAN STAGE IN THE DEVELOPMENT
OF THE AUDITORY OSSICLES.

A. Lower jaw and attached auditory ossicles in a fœtal hedgehog
(after W. K. Parker).   B. Lower jaw and attached auditory ossicles in
a human fœtus (after Macklin).   For details, see p. xl.

221

the noble but grasping; round-tipped retroussé noses to the luxurious, like barnyard fowl. This is the kind of rubbish that passed under the name of science for more than two thousand years. Other self-appointed and equally successful teachers classified men and faces as mercurial, saturnine, jovial and so forth, according to the positions of the stars that ruled their fates from birth, so that physiognomy, like palmistry, was clearly linked with astrology.

The modern science of physiognomy, if it be a science, began when artists and sculptors tried to record the facial expressions of emotions and of moral character and when actors tried to reproduce these expressions on the stage. Much valuable descriptive material was thus accumulated and expressions intended to represent piety, devotion, suffering, anger, malice, joy and the like, may be seen in any collection of old masters or any antique treatise on physiognomy.

A great step in advance was taken in 1806 when Sir Charles Bell in his *Essay on the Anatomy of Expression* inferred the action of the mimetic or facial muscles in producing the characteristic expressions of the emotions.

222

FIG. 116. YOUNG CHIMPANZEE
SHOWING FACIAL EXPRESSION.

(From a photograph by Herbert Lang.)

OUR BEST FEATURES

The experimental method of studying physiognomy was founded by Duchenne (*Mechanisme de la physiognomie humaine*, Paris, 1862), who showed that by the use of electricity the action of the separate muscles could be studied and by the aid of photography accurately represented (*Encycl. Brit.*, XI Ed., Art. Physiognomy).

In Darwin's book on the *Expression of the Emotions* (1872) it was shown that man and the apes agreed in expressing equivalent emotions by means of homologous facial muscles (Figs. 23, 24, 116). Thus the subject of physiognomy was brought under the evolutionary point of view.

At the present time the general subject of physiognomy or the systematic investigation of the human face is being pursued according to the following methods. First, the evolutionary method, as in the present work, endeavors to answer the question, by what stages did the human face arrive at its present form? From the evolutionary viewpoint each type of face among the lower animals is associated with a definite pattern of behavior. Hardly a beginning has been made in tracing the evolution of behavior or in correlating the details of facial character with neuro-anatomy.

Second, the anthropological method studies the variations of the face in different races and endeavors to arrive at general concepts of pure and hybrid racial types. Third, the ontogenetic or embryological method describes the development and growth of the head as a whole and of its several parts. Fourth, the genetic method studies the heredity of facial characteristics, tracing through successive generations the results of homozygous and heterozygous matings with reference to particular features. Fifth, the physiological method studies the chemical factors of the growth and development of the face, including those growth-stimulating substances that the embryo derives from its parents and those that are produced by its own various endocrine glands. Sixth, the clinical method notes that certain types of face are frequently associated with low resistance to certain diseases and seeks to determine the causes of this association. Seventh, the psychologic or behavioristic method endeavors to determine whether there are measurable correlations between definite combinations of features and grades of intelligence. Can an expert predict from examining faces alone which individuals will score high and which low? Eighth, the student of crime and criminals endeavors to discover correlations between certain types of face and constitutional predisposition to crime. Ninth, the psychoanalyst will undoubtedly seek for traces in every face of the sore conflict between the "censor" and the rebellious subconsciousness. Tenth, the psychiatrist, studying pathologic types of mentality, may approach his material from any of the above described paths. Let us see now how much room there is for the old-fashioned physiognomy.

I undoubtedly inherit the general ground-plan of my face from my excessively remote shark-like ancestors who possessed paired olfactory capsules, paired eyes and paired internal ears, arranged in the order named, and who had a medium mouth below the nose and eyes. I also owe to these humble creatures the framework of my tongue and vocal organs, my jaw and throat muscles and many other features both useful and necessary.

Next, I owe to the primitive lobe-finned fishes or crossopts the complete bony scaffolding of the face and jaws, which in them lay on the surface but in my own face is deeply buried beneath the flesh.

Then I owe to the higher mammal-like reptiles

225

the fact that the right and left halves of my lower jaw are composed of a single piece and that I have a set of teeth limited to the margins of the jaws and differentiated into incisors, canines, premolars and molars. I also owe to these hitherto much neglected animals the "basic patents" for the delicate apparatus of my middle ear, together with my bony palate and several other important parts of my make-up.

In the earliest mammals the bony mask became covered with mobile, sensitive flesh; to them I owe also the very hairs of my head, my eyebrows, eyelashes and other facial accessories.

To my earliest primate ancestors I owe the large size of my eyes and a considerable part of my brains.

To my friendly anthropoid ancestors I am heavily indebted: for eyes that can focus on things near at hand, that give stereoscopic pictures and that follow closely the flight of a moving object; for a nose that is a real nose and not a snout; for lips that can smile and laugh or curl up in anger or kiss in love; from them I inherited all my baby teeth and my thirty-two adult teeth; the very shape of my ears is theirs.

OUR BEST FEATURES

To my early human ancestors I owe the reduction of my hitherto coarse muzzle and the first training of my tongue to speak.

To my later human ancestors I owe the improvement of my forehead, the general refinement of my features and my rather weak jaw.

To the Nordic strain in my ancestry I ascribe my fair skin and blue eyes, while to both the Nordic and the Mediterranean strains I owe my narrow head and a nose of moderate dimensions, conforming neither to the figure-6 type nor to the alpine V, nor to any of the concave varieties, but fairly straight and presentable.

However, when I have determined all this and much more of the same kind I am still far from giving a description of my face that would satisfy the requirements of Scotland Yard, for most of the features mentioned have been true of millions of men of all ages. There remains then not only the exact measurements and proportions but also the individual history of my face.

Fortunately my development proceeded without undue mental stress or sudden prenatal shock. Hence I escaped being a Mongolian idiot. My ancestors do not seem to have had deficient thyroids and there must have been a fair sufficiency of iodine in my food, for I missed being a cretin. After birth I never developed any notable deficiency in either the hypophysis, the thyroids, the thymus or other glands, so on all these counts I missed obesity, and on account of the fair state of the pituitary I escaped gigantism and acromegaly; as the adrenals functioned properly, excessive pigment was not deposited in the skin and so I escaped Addison's disease by a wide margin.

Thus owing to all the favorable circumstances of my prenatal development I did not "come into the world scarce half made up" but all the various parts of my face joined together in the right order, with no undue accelerations or delays, and so I escaped many distressing inconveniences such as a hare lip or a cleft palate. At the right time before birth I lost the "Mongolian fold" in the inner corner of my eye; nor was my face marked with a nævus. But after birth I had to run the gamut of children's diseases and no doubt they checked growth to some extent, leaving me with a temporarily impaired heart and a little below the average in stature and weight. On the deficit side also there was a defective turbinate bone and a slightly warped septal cartilage of the nose, together with slight malocclusion of certain teeth and a failure of two wisdom teeth to erupt.

Thus I may explain my face although I cannot improve it. A specialist in this subject could afflict the reader with many pages of this sort of thing; but the chief object here is to raise this point. Suppose I asked my grocer to open a credit account on short acquaintance; upon which, if any, of the features listed above would he decide to trust me? Would he not trust equally well many other customers with entirely different types of face? And do we not see similar artistic talent, musical talent and traits of leadership, moral courage, etc., embodied in widely different types of face? In short, does not scientific physiognomy and even intuitive physiognomy discount all these and many other such before coming to the small residue of features that may conceivably be correlated with particular mental and temperamental qualities? And in order to detect the abnormal must one not know at sight the normal range of variations in all the features in all the races for both sexes from infancy to old age?

The studies of Keith, Stockard and others on

abnormal human types and of Stockard on the parallelism between abnormal human and animal types are all leading to a new understanding of the causes of racial and individual types of faces. The bulldog and a certain type of human dwarf with a broad face and retroussé nose equally owe their peculiar features to a derangement of the normal functioning of the hypophysis, one of the growth-regulating glands. This condition is called achondroplasia and is largely hereditary. In both the bulldog and the achondroplastic dwarf the base of the skull ceases to grow and becomes ossified at an early stage. The rest of the growing head, being confined at the base, grows out at the side and the head thus becomes short in proportion to its width, or brachycephalic. Similarly the median cartilaginous septum of the nose is not pushed forward by the base of the skull, the bridge of the nose therefore fails to rise up and the nose remains flat or actually sunken, giving a marked depression below the forehead. The maxilla, or upper jaw bone, like the base of the skull, fails to grow forward and this causes the lower jaw to protrude beyond the upper, giving a characteristic "undershot jaw."

OUR BEST FEATURES

The opposite condition to achondroplasia is known as acromegaly and is due to an opposite disturbance of the normal functioning of the hypophysis-pituitary complex. It is characterized by excessive growth of bone in the linear direction. Human acromegalics are apt to become excessively tall, their faces growing exceedingly long and their chins very protruding. Acromegaly is often but not always associated with gigantism, which presumably results from an abnormally active thyroid gland. Among the dogs, writes Stockard, the St. Bernard, the mastiff and some others show symptoms of acromegaly along with gigantism. The bloodhound, on the other hand, is a splendid example of the acromegalic type without gigantism and his facial expression and general appearance are closely similar to the human acromegalic.

The opposite condition to gigantism, known as ateleosis, is responsible for the production of true midgets, which typically grow normally for five or six years after birth and then stop growing. They may or may not become sexually mature and often retain infantile faces. Among dogs the King Charles spaniel is in "shape, outline and expression almost a picture of the human midget" (Stockard).

231

Quite recently Stockard has classified all human faces under two general types, into which almost all ordinary persons fall, the "linear" and the

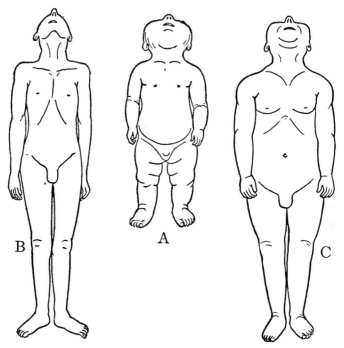

FIG. 117.   STOCKARD'S LINEAR AND LATERAL GROWTH
TYPES (AFTER STOCKARD).

A. Infant; B. "Linear" adult; C. "Lateral" adult.

"lateral" (Fig. 117).   His linear type is that in which, owing to a high rate of metabolism induced by a highly active thyroid gland, growth along the long axis of the body (from the tip of the nose down the back) greatly predominates over growth

232

in the transverse plane. The linear type is the faster-growing, thin but not necessarily tall group. His lateral type, owing to the slower metabolism of low thyroid activity, is slower in maturing and is stocky and rounder in form; that is, the transverse growth components are relatively greater than in the linear type. Stockard's recognition of these two types was a result of his long experimental work on the factors of growth during the embryonic development of animals. His descriptions of the types are of such fundamental importance for an understanding of racial and individual differences in faces that it is necessary to quote them quite fully:

Taking the tip of the nose as the extreme anterior point of the body and viewing the figure laterally, as seen in figure 1 [118] we may draw a line which would indicate the morphological lateral line. This line on each side of the body separates the truly dorsal from the truly ventral surface regions. When these lines on the two lateral surfaces of the head and body are thought of in space we may imagine that the nearer they come together the more linear is the individual, and the wider apart they diverge the less linear and more lateral the individual type will be. Figure 2 [117] illustrates this in the growth and development of the two types from the infant condition.

Examining figure 2B [117B] it is seen that when the lateral lines are near together the head is of course narrow or dolichocephalic. The interpupillary distance is short and the eyes are close together, the nose bridge is narrow and therefore generally high, the mouth arch is narrow and for the same reason generally high, the lower jaw is small and narrow and usually not strongly developed.

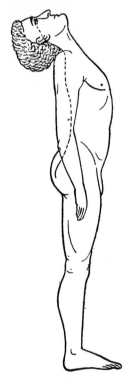

FIG. 118. SIDE VIEW OF HUMAN FIGURE, TO INDICATE THE ANTERIOR TIP AND THE GENERAL DIRECTION OF THE LATERAL LINE (AFTER STOCKARD).

The teeth are usually crowded and somewhat ill-set. The neck is long and small in circumference, the shoulders are square, high and angular, the extremities are long and slender with long slender muscles and slender bones, the trunk is short and narrow, tapering to the waist. The intercostal angle is quite acute. The stomach in such a person is long and narrow and rather vertical in position, extending to low in the abdomen and the liver is generally small.

The shape of the eye in this type is such that it is usually physiologically far-sighted though not pathologically so. They need no glasses on the street unless for astigmatism or some pathological condition. They are under weight for height according to the crude average tables now in use, and are often so as children. They arrive at puberty rather early than late and differentiate rapidly so that the males develop a large strong larynx and a low-pitched bass or baritone voice. Their skin is thin and sensitive as is also the epithelial lining of their alimentary tracts. When in normal health they rarely laugh aloud and when suddenly shocked they resist the reflex jump and never scream. In this way they pass for cool, calm individuals with steady nerve, but as a matter of fact the body is almost constantly held under nerve control and they are actually nervous, usually suffering more after a shock than on the occasion.

The lateral type when fully expressed is the antithesis of the linear type in all of the respects mentioned. The lateral lines are far apart and the head grows wide and not long (Brachycephalic), the interpupillary distance is wide and the eyes are far apart, the nose bridge is wide and often, though not necessarily, low. The mouth arch is wide and low, the teeth are not crowded and are usually smoothly set. The lower jaw is large and strongly developed. The neck is short and large in circumference. The shoulders are round and sloping. The extremities are not long and are stocky with large bones and thick short muscles. The trunk is inclined to be long and full, not constricted but bulging at the waist. The intercostal angle is quite obtuse. The stomach in such a person is large and tends to be transverse and high in position, the liver is generally large.

The eye in the lateral type is so shaped as to be anatomically near-sighted instead of far and such persons frequently wear glasses on the street. This type is well rounded and over weight for height and also shows great fluctuations in weight, often gaining or losing as much as 15 or 20 pounds in a short space of time. Those of the linear type on the contrary do not experience rapid weight changes but maintain a very constant weight, and may during the twenty years from about nineteen to thirty-nine vary a small number of pounds. The lateral type arrives at puberty a little late and is slow differentiating, the larynx of the male does not develop so suddenly as in the linear type and does not usually grow so large. The voice is thus high or tenor instead of bass. When men are under thirty years old the heaviest bass voices are almost always found among the thin linear individuals and these are very rarely tenors. The finest tenor voices are those of the round lateral type. Everyone recalls that the fine tenor is a fat man while the heaviest bass is a tall thin man.

The two types are more clearly expressed in men than in women since the growth and glandular reactions are more decided in the male than in the female and are also freer from physiological disturbances. Many more physical points of difference and contrast could be cited for the groups but the above list is sufficient to make the differences clear.

The balance between these two opposite growth tendencies is very delicate and during individual development environmental stimuli may deflect the results now in one direction and later in the other, the exact median between the extremes being seldom realized.

As to the inheritance of individual features, Von Luschan, Hooton and other anthropologists have shown that in respect to adult head length and head breadth, nose length and nose breadth and

many similar measurements, the individual tends
to resemble either one parent or the other and not
an average between the two.

The results of crossing the linear and the lateral
types with their opposites are described by Stockard (1921–22, p. 62) as follows:

> Again there are persons who do not properly fall into
> either type, nor are they typical intermediates, or blends
> of the two types. These individuals may possess well
> marked fully expressed features of the linear type along
> with typically developed lateral features. They may be
> dolichocephalic with near-sighted eyes, wide palate arches,
> and tenor voices. Combinations that are at once out of
> harmony. Such individuals are almost invariably found to
> be derived from parents of opposite types, and they are
> very common among the offspring of race mixtures.

Environmental influences may tend either to
emphasize or neutralize hereditary tendencies.
According to Stockard, Keith and others, a person
may inherit from his parents a highly active thyroid gland which under favorable conditions would
cause a high rate of metabolism and produce
features of the linear type. But owing to disease
or deficiency in iodine this person's thyroid may
be checked in its activity and he may to that
extent acquire lateral features. On the other hand,
another person may tend to inherit a more sluggish

thyroid gland, which would give him lateral features, but owing to some environmental stimulus, such as treatment with thyroxin, his thyroid gland may be stimulated to greater activity and to that extent his features may approach the linear type.

Another complication arises from the circumstance that the growing parts themselves show different degrees of response or receptivity to the hormones or growth-stimulating substances secreted by the ductless glands. In the dachshund, for example, the bent legs resemble those of the achondroplastic bulldog, while the long muzzle is like those of ordinary large hounds (Stockard, 1923, pp. 269, 273). Whatever influence produced the achondroplastic limbs would have produced a bulldog-like head, if the growing head itself had been receptive to it.

One goal of scientific physiognomy would be the ability to control and regulate the environmental factors of growth to such an extent that hereditary defects in the facial make-up could be overcome; while a eugenic ideal would be to encourage the increase of strains tending to produce beautiful faces linked with high intelligence and moral worth.

OUR BEST FEATURES

In conclusion, the labors of Keith, Stockard, Davenport, Bolk and of the endocrinologists are slowly bringing modern physiognomy toward the goal of ancient physiognomy, in so far as they tend to the discovery of correlations between particular facial characteristics and psychologic reactions. Thus Stockard, for example, writes as follows, giving his impressions of various physical and mental traits associated with the linear and the lateral growth types:

The basic psychology of an individual is probably associated with his structural type. Two persons of the same race and region that chance to be of opposite types show contrasted mental reactions. The lateral type is careful and painstaking, observing details and valuing them and making little effort to get at the meaning of things or draw conclusions until a mass of detail has been accumulated. This type is emotional and expressive, laughs aloud and shows impulses and feeling towards things, the eyes easily fill with tears and the point of view is rarely concealed. The linear type on the other hand has great difficulty in accumulating detail or in working a subject out thoroughly. These individuals have mild respect for details and tend to draw conclusions and see the meaning of things after only a hurried survey. They are not emotional and do not laugh aloud since their reactions are generally under control and their reflexes are suppressed. They conceal their impulses and would be ashamed to shed a tear. This type is self-conscious and nervous, while the lateral type is not self-conscious and not really nervous in the common sense of the word. The linear type has great self-control and among savage tribes the chief is almost always of this type, but among civilized peoples the lateral type with near sight and emotion are often rulers of great ability. The lateral type rulers are popular and aware of the details of the immediate situation but are not apt to perceive the great principles of the future. So the linear type Presidents of the United States are honored long after their terms of service, but are often not popular during office, on the other hand, lateral type Presidents perchance of equal ability and equal greatness have been the idols of their time but leave nothing to be remembered in the future.

THE FACE OF THE FUTURE

In the United States the Indians as a whole have not readily adopted the ways of the white man and with few exceptions have not been absorbed into the general population. Hence by outside political and economic pressure they have been forced into relatively small reservations where a great increase in their numbers seems improbable. Except in very limited regions Indians have seldom been able to compete for a livelihood with a more or less antagonistic white population. It is hardly likely therefore that a thousand years from now the Indian features will be very common in the population of the United States as a whole. The negro population, on the other hand, is much larger. But the negro is peculiarly liable to certain fatal diseases and particularly in rural districts infant mortality has hitherto been high. In the cities where mixed bloods occur in large number the constant accession of darker features from the country may more than offset the relatively slow infiltration of white blood. Moreover the white population is so enormously greater than the negro and has such great economic and social advantages and there is such a widespread and deep antipathy to the marriage of full-blooded whites and "negroes" of any shade that it seems highly improbable that the white population will soon absorb the black population *en masse*. Hence it seems unlikely that the *average* white man's face a thousand years from now will show much trace of negroid admixture in the United States as a whole. In many parts of Africa, on the contrary, the whites are so far out-numbered and the climatic conditions are so unfavorable that it seems probable that a thousand years from now the negro, with perhaps some infiltration of white blood, will still be in the vast majority. Thus we see at once that the average face of the future in any given locality will naturally depend first of all upon the relative increase of one or another racial type in the general population.

OUR FACE FROM FISH TO MAN

As to the changes in the face of the white race, Sir Arthur Keith has adduced evidence tending to show that a thousand years ago the average Englishman had a wider face, a shorter nose, a broader palatal arch and better teeth than the typical Englishman of today, who tends toward a narrow face and a narrow-vaulted dental arch. Keith ascribes this in part to the coarser diet and outdoor life of a thousand years ago, which gave the ductless glands that control growth more chance to produce better teeth and better dental arches. Nevertheless there is reason to believe that in spite of the many unfavorable influences today, especially in the cities, living conditions are on the whole more sanitary, as shown by the decreasing mortality. But while there are better conditions for producing healthy children, more of the weaklings are also kept alive to perpetuate their troubles. In any event, it is not unlikely that in the long run eugenic counsels will prevail in the more enlightened countries of the world, at least to a noticeable extent.

Possibly the people of those days may extract all their teeth before they begin to give trouble, or they may be fed with endocrine and other extracts to combat the ills that we now suffer. In any case it seems not improbable that at least for a long time conscious effort will be directed toward correcting unbalanced departures from the types of face that for thousands of years past have been considered good-looking. From all this it appears probable that a thousand years from now the average adult white person's face will not be profoundly different from what it is today.

But what of the human face a million years from now?—a short period compared with its entire history. If present tendencies continue unchecked the white people of those days will for the most part have lost all four of their wisdom teeth so that their total number of teeth will be twenty-eight. This will tend to make their jaws somewhat slender. If they no longer eat meat and vegetables but take prepared extracts as food, their jaw muscles and jaws may be further weakened. Their brain capacity on the average may be considerably larger. Even under the operation of restrictive eugenic principles there may be at least as great a diversity in normal white faces then as there is today. While some of those people might look strange to us, others would remind us at least of certain types we had seen in our own times.

In short, the only conservative prediction to make is that the people a million years from now may be far less unlike ourselves than we had at first imagined. But as the determination of the dominant type of human face in the remote future will depend partly upon unpredictable economic and political movements and upon the success in spreading and enforcing eugenic principles, prophecy of any kind is obviously rash.

If, as many geologists suspect, we are now living in an interglacial period and the continental ice-sheet again covers the northern parts of Europe and North America, then a large part of the white population may be driven to the southern United States and Mexico, with consequent tendency to absorb the more or less colored strains of those regions; but on the other hand, many of the white race may persist along the southern borders of the glaciers. Such speculation is only excusable in order to make the point that prediction of the distant future is far less reliable than deciphering the remote past.

OUR BEST FEATURES

LOOKING BACKWARD

The mobile mask in front of men's brains began to attract our attention when we were babies and continues to fascinate us as long as we live.

Its signals have vital meanings to us: we variously respect, admire, love, hate or are bored by it.

But we cannot escape it. It dominates literature and with its mystical symbolism it broods over religion.

Let Science interrogate the sphinx, let her expose the intricate and delicate mechanism by which the mask is operated, let her even show that the human face, with all its charms, is but the end of a long series of useful improvements upon simple beginnings.

Yet the transformation of the face from fish to man will lose none of its wonder.

Our hearts will still move to the flashing glances of youth; nor will we cherish less the serene, beloved countenance of old age.

LITERATURE CITED

ADAMS, L. A. 1919. "A Memoir on the Phylogeny of the Jaw Muscles in Recent and Fossil Vertebrates." *Anns. N. Y. Acad. Sci.*, Vol. XXVIII, pp. 51–156, Pls. I–XIII.

ALLEN, J. A. 1926. "Primates Collected by the American Museum Congo Expedition." *Bull. Amer. Mus. Nat. Hist.*, Vol. XLVII, Art. IV, pp. 283–499, Pls. LXXIX–CLXVII.

ALLIS, EDWARD PHELPS, JR. 1923. "The Cranial Anatomy of *Chlamydoselachus anguineus.*" *Acta Zoologica*, Bd. IV, pp. 123–221, Pls. I–XXIII.

BARRELL, JOSEPH. 1917. "Rhythms and the Measurements of Geologic Time." *Bull. Geol. Soc. Amer.*, Vol. XXVIII, pp. 745–904, Pls. XLIII–XLVI.

BELL, SIR CHARLES. 1806. "Essay on the Anatomy of Expression." London.

BINGHAM, HAROLD C. 1928. "Sex Development in Apes." *Comparative Psychology Monographs*, Vol. V, No. 1, Serial No. 23, pp. 1–165.

BOLK, L. 1921. "The Part Played by the Endocrine Glands in the Evolution of Man." *The Lancet*, Sept. 10, 1921, pp. 588–592.

BOULE, M. 1911. "L'Homme fossile de la Chapelle-aux-Saints." *Ann. de Paléontologie*, T. VI, pp. 111–172, Pls. I–IV; 1912, T. VII, pp. 85–190, Pls. V–XVI.

1915. "La Paléontologie Humaine en Angleterre." *L'Anthropologie*, T. XXVI, Nos. 1–2, pp. 1–67.

1921. "Les Hommes Fossiles." 8vo, Paris.

BROILI, F. 1904. "Permische Stegocephalen und Reptilien von Texas." *Paläontographica*, Bd. 51, pp. 1–120, Pls. I–XIII. [*Seymouria.*]

LITERATURE CITED

BROOM, R. 1911. "On the Structure of the Skull in Cynodont Reptiles." *Proc. Zool. Soc. London*, pp. 893–925, Pl. XLVI.

— 1914. Croonian Lecture: "On the Origin of Mammals." *Philos. Trans. Roy. Soc. London*, Series B, Vol. 206, pp. 1–48, Pls. 1–7.

— 1926. "On the Mammalian Presphenoid and Mesethmoid Bones." *Proc. Zool. Soc. London*, April 26, pp. 257–264.

BRYANT, W. L. 1919. "On the Structure of *Eusthenopteron*." *Bull. Buffalo Soc. Nat. Sci.*, XIII, No. 1, pp. 1–23, Pls. I–XVIII.

BUDGETT, J. S. See Kerr, J. Graham.

CLARK, W. E. LE GROS. 1924. "On the Brain of the Tree-Shrew (*Tupaia minor*)." *Proc. Zool. Soc. London*, Part 4, pp. 1053–1074, Pls. I–III.

— 1925. "The Visual Cortex of Primates." *Journ. Anat.*, Vol. LIX, Part IV, pp. 350–357, Pl. I.

— 1926. "The Mammalian Oculomotor Nucleus." *Journ. Anat.*, Vol. LX, Part IV, pp. 426–448, Pl. I.

— 1926. "On the Anatomy of the Pen-tailed Tree-Shrew (*Ptilocercus lowii*)." *Proc. Zool. Soc. London*, Part 4, pp. 1179–1309, Pls. I–V.

CORNING, H. K. 1925. "Lehrbuch der Entwicklungsgeschichte des Menschen." Munich, 4to, 1902.

CUNNINGHAM, D. J. 1902. "Text-Book of Anatomy." New York, 8vo.

DART, RAYMOND, A. 1925. "*Australopithecus africanus*: The Man-Ape of South Africa." *Nature*, No. 2884, Vol. 115, pp. 195–199.

— 1926. "Taungs and its Significance." *Nat. Hist.*, Vol. XXVI, No. 3, pp. 315–327.

DARWIN, CHARLES. 1872. (Ed. by Francis Darwin Second edition, 1890.) "The Expression of the Emotions in Man and Animals." London, 8vo.

DAVENPORT, C. B. 1923. "Body-build and its Inheritance." *Carnegie Inst. of Washington, Publ.* No. 329.

LITERATURE CITED

DEAN, BASHFORD. 1909. "Studies on Fossil Fishes (Sharks, Chimæroids, and Arthrodires)." *Mem. Amer. Mus. Nat. Hist.*, Vol. IX, Part V, pp. 211–287, Pls. XXVI–XLI.

DELAGE, IVES, et HÉROUARD, EDGARD. 1898. "Traité de Zoologie Concrète." Tome VIII: Les Procordés. Paris.

DENIKER, J. 1885. "Recherches Anatomiques et Embryologiques sur les Singes Anthropoides." *Arch. de Zool. Exper. et Gén.*, 2e Série, T. iii *bis*, Suppl. 1885–1886, 3e Mém., 265 pp., 8 Pls.

DUBOIS, EUGEN. 1894. "*Pithecanthropus erectus.* Eine Menschenachnliche Uebergangsform aus Java." Batavia, 4to.

DUCHENNE, G. B. 1862. "Mechanisme de la physiognomie humaine ou Analyse Electro-Physiologique de l'expression des passions." Paris. (Quoted in *Encycl. Brit.*, XI Ed., Art. Physiognomy.)

EIDMANN, HERMANN. 1923. "Die Entwicklungsgeschichte der Zähne des Menschen." Berlin.

ELLIOT, D. G. 1912. "A Review of the Primates." *Monograph Series*, Vols. I–III, *Amer. Mus. Nat. Hist.*

FÜRBRINGER, MAX. 1900. "Zur vergleichenden Anatomie des Brustschulterapparates und der Schultermuskeln." *Jenaischen Zeitsch. f. Naturw.*, XXXIV Band, pp. 215–718, Pls. XIII–XVII.

FRAZER, J. E. 1914. "The Second Visceral Arch and Groove in the Tubo-Tympanic Region." *Journ. Anat.*, Vol. XLVIII (3rd Ser., Vol. IX), pp. 391–408.

GARMAN, SAMUEL. 1885. "*Chlamydoselachus anguineus* Garm.—A living Species of Cladodont Shark." *Bull. Mus. Comp. Zoöl.*, Vol. VII, No. 1, pp. 1–35, Pls. I–XX.

—— 1913. "The Plagiostomia (Sharks, Skates, and Rays.)" *Mem. Mus. Comp. Zoöl.*, Vol. XXXVI, pp. 1–515, Pls. I–LXXVII.

GAUPP, E. 1911. "Beiträge zur Kenntnis des Unterkiefers

LITERATURE CITED

der Wirbeltiere." III. *Anat. Anz.*, Vol. XXXIX, Band Nos. 23, 24, pp. 609–666.

1913. "Die Reichertsche Theorie." *Archiv. f. Anat. u. Entw.*, *Jahrb.*, 1912, pp. 1–416.

GEGENBAUR, CARL. 1872. "Untersuchungen zur Vergleichenden Anatomie der Wirbelthiere." Drittes Heft:— Das Kopfskelet der Selachier, ein Beitrag zur Erkenntniss der Genese des Kopfskeletes der Wirbelthiere. 4to, Leipzig.

GIDLEY, J. W. 1923. "Paleocene Primates of the Fort Union, with Discussion of Relationships of Eocene Primates." No. 2469, *Proc. U. S. Nat. Mus.*, Vol. LXIII, Art. 1, pp. 1–38, Pls. I–V.

GOODRICH, E. S. 1909. "A Treatise on Zoology." (Ed. Sir Ray Lankester), Part IX: Vertebrata Craniata (First Fascicle: Cyclostomes and Fishes), London.

GRANDIDIER, G. 1905. "Recherches sur les Lémuriens disparus et en particulier sur ceux qui vivaient à Madagascar." Ext. des *Nouvelles Archives du Museum*, 4e Série, Tome VII, pp. 1–42.

GREGORY, WILLIAM K. 1916. "Studies on the Evolution of the Primates." *Bull. Amer. Mus. Nat. Hist.*, Vol. XXXV, Art. XIX, pp. 239–355, Pl. I.

1920. "On the Structure and Relations of *Notharctus*, an American Eocene Primate." *Mem. Amer. Mus. Nat. Hist.*, N. S. III, Part II, pp. 49–243, Pls. XXIII–LIX.

1920. "Studies in Comparative Myology and Osteology." No. IV: A Review of the Evolution of the Lacrymal Bone of Vertebrates with Special Reference to that of Mammals. *Bull. Amer. Mus. Nat. Hist.*, Vol. XLII, Art. II, pp. 95–263.

1922. "The Origin and Evolution of the Human Dentition." Baltimore.

1926. (With Milo Hellman.) "The Dentition of *Dryopithecus* and the Origin of Man." *Anthropological Papers, Amer. Mus. Nat. Hist.*, Vol. XXVIII, Part I, pp. 1–123 Pls. I–XXV.

LITERATURE CITED

1926. "The Palæomorphology of the Human Head: Ten Structural Stages from Fish to Man." Part I: The Skull in Norma Lateralis. *Quart. Rev. Biol.*, Vol. II, No. 2, pp. 267–279.

1926. (With G. G. Simpson.) "Cretaceous Mammal Skulls from Mongolia." *Amer. Mus. Novitates*, No. 225, Oct. 8, pp. 1–20.

1926. "Palæontology of the Human Dentition: Ten Structural Stages in the Evolution of the Cheek Teeth." *Amer. Journ. Phys. Anthrop.*, Vol. IX, No. 4, pp. 401–426.

1927. "The Origin of Man from the Anthropoid Stem—When and Where?" Bicentenary No., *Proc. Amer. Philos. Soc.*, Vol. LXVI, pp. 439–463.

1927. "How Near Is the Relationship of Man to the Chimpanzee-Gorilla Stock?" *Quart. Rev. Biol.*, Vol. II, No. 4, pp. 549–560.

1928. "The Lineage of Man." (Creation by Evolution. Ed. Frances Mason.) Macmillan, New York.

1928. "Were the Ancestors of Man Primitive Brachiators?" *Proc. Amer. Philos. Soc.*, Vol. LXVII, No. 2, pp. 129–150, Pls. I–IV.

1929. "The Palæomorphology of the Human Head: Ten Structural Stages from Fish to Man." Part II: The Skull in Norma Basalis. *Quart. Rev. Biol.*

HÆCKEL, ERNST. 1903. "Anthropogenie." Zweiter Teil: Stammesgeschichte des Menschen. Leipzig.

HARRIS, WILFRED. 1904. "Binocular and Stereoscopic Vision in Man and other Vertebrates." *Brain*, Vol. XXVII, p. 105.

HAUGHTON, S. H. 1920. "On the Genus *Ictidopsis*." *Ann. Durban Museum*, Vol. II, Part 5, pp. 243–246.

1924. "On Cynodontia from the Middle Beaufort Beds of Harrismith, Orange Free State." *Ann. Transvaal Mus.*, Vol. XI, Part I, pp. 74–92, Pls. III–VI.

HOOTON, E. A. 1925. "The Ancient Inhabitants of the

LITERATURE CITED

Canary Islands." *Harvard African Studies*, Vol. VII, *Peabody Mus. of Harvard Univ.*, 401 pp., 39 Pls.

HRDLIČKA, A. 1920. "Shovel-shaped Teeth." *Amer. Journ. Phys. Anthrop.*, Vol. III, No. 4, pp. 429–465, Pls. I–VI.

1921. "Further Studies in Tooth Morphology." *Amer. Journ. Phys. Anthrop.*, Vol. IV, No. 2, pp. 141–176, Pls. I–VI.

HUBER, ERNST. 1922. "Uber das Muskelgebiet des Nervus facialis beim Hund, nebst allgemeinen Betrachtungen über die Facialis-Muskulatur." I. Teil. *Sonderabdruck aus dem Morphologischen Jahrb.*, Bd. LII, Heft 1, pp. 1–110.

1923. "Uber das Muskelgebiet des Nervus facialis beim Hund, nebst allgemeinen Betrachtungen über die Facialis-Muskulatur." II. Teil. *Sonderabdruck aus dem Morphologischen Jahrb.*, Bd. LII, Heft 4, pp. 353–414.

1926. (With Walter Hughson.) "Experimental Studies on the Voluntary Motor Innervation of the Facial Musculature." *Journ. Comp. Neurology*, Vol. XLII, No. 1, pp. 113–163.

HUNTER, JOHN I. 1923. "The Oculomotor Nucleus of *Tarsius* and *Nycticebus*." *Brain*, Vol. XLVI, Part 1, pp. 1–11.

HUNTINGTON, G. S. 1913. "The Anatomy of the Salivary Glands in the Lower Primates. Studies in Cancer and Allied Subjects." *Contributions to the Anatomy and Development of the Salivary Glands in the Mammalia*, etc., Vol. IV, pp. 73–113, Pls. XXI–XXXIII, Columbia University Press, New York, 4to.

HUXLEY, T. H. 1863. "Evidence as to Man's Place in Nature." London.

JONES, F. WOOD. 1916. "Arboreal Man." New York, 8vo.

1918. "The Problem of Man's Ancestry." *Soc. for Promoting Christian Knowledge*, pp. 1–48, London, 12 mo.

LITERATURE CITED

1920. "Discussion on the Zoological Position and Affinities of *Tarsius*." *Proc. Zool. Soc. London*, pp. 491–494.

1923. "The Ancestry of Man." *Douglas Price Memorial Lecture*, No. 3, pp. 1–35. Brisbane.

KEITH, ARTHUR. 1921. "Human Embryology and Morphology." London, 8vo.

1921. (With George G. Campion.) "A Contribution to the Mechanism of Growth of the Human Face." *The Dental Record*, Feb. 1, 1922.

1923. "The Adaptational Machinery Concerned in the Evolution of Man's Body." Supplement to *Nature*, No. 2807.

1923. "Man's Posture: its Evolution and Disorders." *British Medical Journal*, March and April.

KERR, J. GRAHAM. 1907. "The Development of *Polypterus senegalus* Cuv." In *The Works of John Samuel Budgett*, pp. 195–283, Pls. XIII–XV. Cambridge.

KIÆR, JOHAN. 1924. "The Downtonian Fauna of Norway." I: Anaspida. Videnskapsselskapetskrifter I, *Mat.-Naturv. Klasse*, No. 6, pp. 1–139, Pls. I–XIV.

KLAATSCH, HERMANN. (No date.) "Entstehung und Entwickelung des Menschengeschlechtes." *Weltall und Menscheit* (Hans Kræmer), Bd. II, Abschnitt IV, pp. 1–138, Berlin, Leipzig, Wien, Stuttgart, 4to.

KOEHLER, W. 1925. "The Mentality of Apes." (Trans. by E. Winter), New York.

KOLLMANN, J. 1907. "Handatlas der Entwickelungsgeschichte des Menschen." Erster Teil: Progenie, Blastogenie. . . . Embryologia musculorum. 340 figs.

LANKESTER, E. RAY. 1868. "The Cephalaspidæ." *A Monograph of the Fishes of the Old Red Sandstone of Britain*, Part I, pp. 1–33, Pls. I–V.

LECHE, WILLIAM. 1911. "Der Mensch." Jena.

LE DOUBLE, A. F. 1900. "Essai sur la Morphogénie et les Variations du Lacrymal et des Osselets péri-

LITERATURE CITED

lacrymaux de l'Homme." *Bibliographie Anatomique,* T. VIII, Fas. 3, pp. 109–182.

LUNDBORG, H. 1921. (With J. Runnström.) "The Swedish Nation." 4to, Stockholm.

LUSCHAN, FELIX V. 1911. "The Early Inhabitants of Western Asia." *Journ. Roy. Anthropol. Inst. Great Britain and Ireland,* Vol. XLI, pp. 221–224, Pls. XXIV–XXXIII.

MACKLIN, CHARLES C. 1921. "The Skull of a Human Fetus of 43 Millimeters Greatest Length." Publ. 273, Carn. Inst. Washington, *Contributions to Embryology,* No. 48, pp. 58–103, Pls. I–IV.

MARSHALL, A. M., and HURST, C. H. 1895. "Practical Zoology." Fourth Edition, New York.

MARTIN, R. 1914. "Lehrbuch der Anthropologie." Jena.

MATTHEW, W. D. 1915. (With Walter Granger.) "A Revision of the Lower Eocene Wasatch and Wind River Faunas." Part IV.—Entelonychia, Primates, Insectivora (Part). *Bull. Amer. Mus. Nat. Hist.,* Vol. XXXIV, Art. XIV, pp. 420–483.

1916. "A Marsupial from the Belly River Cretaceous. With Critical Observations upon the Affinities of the Cretaceous Mammals." *Bull. Amer. Mus. Nat. Hist.,* Vol. XXXV, Art. XXV, pp. 477–500.

MIHALKOVICS, V. "Entwickelungsgeschichte des Gehirns." 4to, Leipzig.

MILLER, G. S. 1920. "Conflicting Views on the Problem of Man's Ancestry." *Amer. Journ. Phys. Anthrop.,* Vol. III, No. 2, pp. 213–245.

MINOT, CHARLES S. 1892. "Human Embryology." New York, 815 pp., 463 figs.

MORTON, D. J. 1927. "Human Origin. Correlation of Previous Studies of Primate Feet and Posture with other Morphologic Evidence." *Amer. Journ. Phys. Anthrop.,* Vol. X, No. 2, pp. 273–203.

OSBORN, HENRY FAIRFIELD. 1907. "Evolution of Mammalian Molar Teeth to and from the Triangular Type." (Ed. William K. Gregory.) New York, 8vo.

LITERATURE CITED

1910. "The Age of Mammals in Europe, Asia and North America." New York, 8vo.

1915. "Men of the Old Stone Age." New York, 8vo.

1927. "Man Rises to Parnassus." New York, 8vo.

1928. "The Influence of Bodily Locomotion in Separating Man from the Monkeys and Apes." *Scientific Monthly*, Vol. XXVI, pp. 385–399.

PALMER, R. W. 1913. "Notes on the Lower Jaw and Ear Ossicles of a Fœtal *Perameles*." *Anat. Anz.*, 43 Band, No. 19–20.

PANDER, C. H. 1856. "Monographie der Fossilen Fische des Silurischen Systems." St. Petersburg, 4to.

1858. "Ueber die Ctenodipterinen des Devonischen Systems." St. Petersburg (Kais. Akad. d. Wiss.), 4to.

PARKER, G. H. 1902. "Hearing and Allied Senses in Fishes." *Bull. U. S. Fish Commission*, pp. 45–64, Pl. IX.

PARKER, T. J. 1897. (With W. A. Haswell.) "A Text-Book of Zoology." Vols. I, II, London and New York, 8vo.

1900. (With W. N. Parker.) "An Elementary Course of Practical Zoology." London and New York, 8vo.

PARKER, W. K. 1881. "On the Structure and Development of the Skull in Sturgeons (*Acipenser ruthenus* and *A. sturio*)." *Philos. Trans. Roy. Soc.*, pp. 139–185, Pls. XII–XVIII.

PATTEN, WILLIAM. 1912. "The Evolution of the Vertebrates and their Kin." Philadelphia, 8vo.

PILGRIM, G. E. 1915. "New Siwalik Primates and their Bearing on the Question of the Evolution of Man and the Anthropoidea." *Rec. Geol. Surv. India*, Vol. XLV, Part 1, 1–74, Pls. I–IV, A.

1927. "A *Sivapithecus* Palate and other Primate Fossils from India." *Mem. Geol. Surv. India*, N. S., Vol. XIV, pp. 1–24, Pl. I.

PLATE, L. 1924. "Allgemeine Zoologie und Abstammungslehre." Zweiter Teil: Die Sinnesorgane der Tiere. Jena, 8vo.

LITERATURE CITED

Pocock, R. I. 1925. "The External Characters of the Catarrhine Monkeys and Apes." *Proc. Zool. Soc. London*, Part 4, pp. 1479–1579.

Remane, A. 1921. "Beiträge zur Morphologie des Anthropoiden gebisses." *Archiv. für Naturgeschichte*, 87 Jahrg., Abt. A, 11 Heft, pp. 1–179.

1921. "Zur Beurteilung der fossilen Anthropoiden." *Centralblatt f. Min.* . . , Jahrg. 1921, No. 11, pp. 335–339.

1927. "Studien über die Phylogenie des Menschlichen Eckzahns." *Zeitschr. f. Anat. u. Entw.*, I. Abt., 82 Band, Heft 4–5, pp. 391–481.

Retzius, Gustaf. 1881. "Das Gehörorgan der Wirbelthiere." I: Das Gehörorgan der Fische und Amphibien. II: Das Gehörorgan der Reptilien, der Vögel und der Säugethiere. Stockholm, 4to.

Robinson, L. 1913. "The Story of the Chin." *Knowledge*, Vol. XXXVI, pp. 410–420, 4 Pls.

Rohon, J. V. 1892. "Die obersilurischen Fische von Oesel." I: Thyestidæ und Tremataspidæ. *Mém. Acad. Sci. St. Pétersburg*, 7 sér., Vol. 38, No. 13.

1893. "Die obersilurischen Fische von Oesel." II: Selachii, Dipnoi, Ganoidei, Pteraspidæ and Cephalaspidæ. *Mem. Acad. Sci. St. Petersburg*, 7 sér., Vol. 41, No. 5.

Ruge, Georg. 1887. "Untersuchungen über die Gesichtsmuskulatur der Primaten." Leipzig.

Schmalhausen, J. J. (No date.) "Fundamentals of the Comparative Anatomy of Vertebrates." *Government Publication*, Moscou and Petersburg.

Schoetensack, O. 1908. "Der Unterkiefer des *Homo Heidelbergensis* aus den Sanden von Mauer bei Heidelberg. Ein Beiträge zur Paläontologie des Menschen." Leipzig, 4to.

Schultz, A. H. 1918. "Relation of the External Nose to the Bony Nose and Nasal Cartilages in Whites and Negroes." *Amer. Journ. Phys. Anthrop.*, Vol. 1, No. 3, pp. 329–338.

LITERATURE CITED

"The Development of the External Nose in Whites and Negroes." Publ. 272, Carn. Inst. Washington, *Contr. to Embryol.*, No. 34, pp. 173–190.

1924. "Growth Studies on Primates Bearing upon Man's Evolution." *Amer. Journ. Phys. Anthrop.*, Vol. VII, No. 2, pp. 149–164.

1927. "Studies on the Growth of Gorilla and of Other Higher Primates, with Special Reference to a Fetus of Gorilla, Preserved in the Carnegie Museum." *Mem. Carn. Mus.*, Vol. XI, No. 1, pp. 1–70, Pls. I–VIII.

SCHWALBE, G. 1889. "Das Darwin'sche Spitzohr beim menschlichen Embryo." *Anat. Anz.*, IV. Jahrg., No. 6, pp. 176–189.

1923. "Die Abstammung des Menschen und die Ältesten Menschenformen." *Anthropologie*, Abt. 5, pp. 223–338, Pls. I–XIII.

SELENKA, EMIL. 1898. "Menschenaffen." I: Rassen, Schädel und Bezahnung des Orangutan. Wiesbaden, pp. 1–91, figs. 1–108.

1899. "Menschenaffen." II: Schädel des Gorilla und Schimpanse. Wiesbaden, pp. 95–160, figs. 109–194 (incl. 10 Pls.)

SIMPSON, G. G. 1928. "A New Mammalian Fauna from the Fort Union of Southern Montana." *Amer. Mus. Novitates*, No. 297, Feb. 2, 1928, pp. 1–15.

1928. "A Catalogue of the Mesozoic Mammalia in the Geological Department of the British Museum." London: Printed by Order of the Trustees of the British Museum. 215 pp., 12 Pls.

SMITH, G. ELLIOT. 1904. "The Morphology of the Occipital Region of the Cerebral Hemisphere in Man and the Apes." *Anat. Anzeiger*, XXIV Band, No. 16 u. 17, pp. 436–451.

1912. "Address to the Anthropological Section." *British Assoc. Adv. Sci.*, Trans. Section H, pp. 1–24.

1919. "A Preliminary Note on the Morphology of the

LITERATURE CITED

Corpus Striatum and the Origin of the Neopallium."
Journ. Anat., Vol. LIII, Part IV, pp. 271–291.

1924. "The Evolution of Man." Oxford University
Press, 8vo.

SMITH, STEWART A. 1918. "The Fossil Human Skull
Found at Talgai, Queensland." *Philos. Trans. Roy.
Soc. London*, Ser. B, Vol. 208, pp. 351–387, Pls. XII–
XVIII.

SOLLAS, W. J. 1925. "The Taungs Skull." *Nature*,
No. 2902, Vol. CXV, pp. 908, 909, July 13.

SONNTAG, CHARLES F. 1924. "The Morphology and
Evolution of the Apes and Man." London, 8vo.

STEHLIN, H. G. 1912. "Die Säugetiere des schweizer-
ischen Eocaens." Siebenter Teil, erste Hälfte: Ein-
leitende Bemerkungen zum Genus *Adapis* und zu der
Gruppe des *Adapis parisiensis* Blainville. *Abhandl.
d. schweiz. paläont. Gesellsch.*, Vol. XXXVIII, pp.
1165–1298.

STENSIÖ, ERIK A: SON. 1921. "Triassic Fishes from Spitzbergen." Part I. Vienna, 4to.

1924. "Triassic Fishes from Spitzbergen." Part II.
Kungl. Svenska Vetenskapsakademiens Handl., Tredje
Serien, Band 2, No. 1, pp. 1–261, Pls. I–XXXIV.

1927. "The Downtonian and Devonian Vertebrates of
Spitsbergen." Part I: Family Cephalaspidæ. A. Text.
B. Plates. *Skrifter om Svalbard og Nordishavet:
Resultator av de Norske Statsunderstoittede Spitsber-
genekspeditioner. No. 12.* Det Norske Videnskaps-
Akademi i Oslo.

STOCKARD, CHARLES R. 1923. "The Significance of Modifications in Body Structure." *The Harvey Society
Lectures*, 1921–1922, Philadelphia.

STREETER, G. L. 1907. "On the Development of the
Membranous Labyrinth and the Acoustic and Facial
Nerves in the Human Embryo." *Amer. Journ. Anat.*,
Vol. VI, pp. 140–165, Pls. I, II.

STUDNICKA, F. K. 1918. "Das Schema der Wirbeltieraugen." *Zool. Jahrb., Abt. f. Anat. u. Ont. d. Tiere*, Band XL, pp. 1–48.

SUSHKIN, PETER P. 1927. "On the Modifications of the Mandibular and Hyoid Arches and their Relations to the Brain-case in the Early Tetrapoda." *Sonderabdr. aus der "Palæontologischen Zeitschr,"* Band VIII, Heft 4, pp. 263–321.

TRAQUAIR, R. H. 1877. "The Ganoid Fishes of the British Carboniferous Formations." Part I. Palæoniscidæ. *Monogr. Palæontogr. Soc.*, Pls. I–VII.

1879. "On the Structure and Affinities of the Platysomidæ." *Trans. Roy. Soc. Edinburgh*, Vol. XXIX, pp. 343–391, Pls. III–VI.

1881. "On the Structure of *Rhizodopsis sauroides.*" *Trans. Roy. Soc. Edin.*, Vol. XXX.

1910. "Les poissons Wealdiens de Bernissart." *Mem. Mus. roy. Hist. nat. Belgique*, pp. 1–65, Pls. I–XII.

TILNEY, F. 1921. (With H. A. Riley.) "The Form and Functions of the Central Nervous System." New York.

1928. "The Brain from Ape to Man." New York.

VERNEAU, R. 1916. "Les grottes de Grimaldi (Baousse-Rousse)." Tome II, Fasc. I, *Anthropologie*, Imprimerie de Monaco, 4to.

WATSON, D. M. S. 1916. "Notes on some Palæozoic Fishes." *Mem. and Proc. Manchester Literary and Philosophical Society*, Vol. LX, Part I, pp. 1–48, Pls. I–III.

1919. "On *Seymouria*, the Most Primitive Known Reptile." *Proc. Zool. Soc. London*, pp. 267–301.

1919. "The Structure, Evolution and Origin of the Amphibia. . . ." *Philos. Trans. Roy. Soc. London*, Series B, Vol. 209, pp. 1–73, Pls. I, II.

1926. Croonian Lecture: "The Evolution and Origin of the Amphibia." *Philos. Trans. Roy. Soc. London*, Series B, Vol. 214, pp. 189–257.

WEBER, MAX. 1904. "Die Säugetiere." (Zweite Auflage, 1927), Jena, 8vo.

LITERATURE CITED

WEINERT, HANS. 1925. "Der Schädel des Eiszeitlichen Menschen von Le Moustier. . . ." Berlin, 8vo.

WEISSE, F. D. 1899. "Practical Human Anatomy." New York, 8vo.

WILLIAMS, J. LEON. 1914. "A New Classification of Human Tooth Forms . . ." *Journ. Allied Dental Societies*, Vol. IX, pp. 1–52.

WILLISTON, S. J. 1911. "American Permian Vertebrates." Chicago University Press, 8vo.

    1911. "A New Genus and Species of American Theromorpha, *Mycterosaurus longiceps.*" *Journ. Geol.*, Vol. XXIII, No. 6, pp. 554–559.

    1914. "Water Reptiles of the Past and Present." Chicago University Press, 8vo.

    1916. (1) "The Osteology of some American Permian Vertebrates," II. (2) "Synopsis of the American Permo-Carboniferous Tetrapoda." *Contrib. Walker Museum*, Vol. I, No. 9, pp. 165–236.

    1925. "The Osteology of the Reptiles." Edited by William K. Gregory, Harvard University Press, 8vo.

WOODWARD, A. SMITH. 1913. (With Charles Dawson.) "On the Discovery of a Palæolithic Skull and Mandible in a Flint-bearing Gravel overlying the Wealden (Hastings Beds) at Piltdown, Fletching (Sussex)." *Quart. Journ. Geol. Soc.*, Vol. LXIX.

    1914. (With Charles Dawson.) "Supplementary Note on the Discovery of a Palæolithic Human Skull and Mandible at Piltdown (Sussex)." *Quart. Journ. Geol. Soc.*, Vol. LXX.

    1917. "Fourth Note on the Piltdown Gravel, with Evidence of a Second Skull of *Eoanthropus dawsoni.*" *Quart. Journ. Geol. Soc.*, Vol. LXXIII.

YERKES, ROBERT M. 1925. "Almost Human." New York, 8vo.

INDEX

Acanthias, labyrinth of, Fig. 104, 205

Achondroplastic dwarf, nose of, 169, 171; development of skull in, 230

Acorn-worm (*Balanoglossus*), theory of relation to ancestors of vertebrates, 93; larva of (*Tornaria*), Fig. 55, 93

Acromegaly, causes and effects of, 171, 231

Adapidae, feet compared with those of lemur, 54

Adapis, skull of, Fig. 53, 85

African pygmy, nose of, 164, Fig. 89, facing 170

Alar cartilages, of mammalian nose, 167; growth power of, 170

Alligator, labyrinth of, Fig. 104, 205; ear of the, 207

Alligator-gar, resemblance to Devonian ganoids, 23

Allis, Edward Phelps, Jr., head of shark figured by, 13

Amblystoma punctatum, embryo of, Fig. 14, 26

Armenian, nose of, Fig. 89, 170

Amphibia, in coal-beds of Great Britain, 27; restoration of *Eogyrinus*, Fig. 15, 28; Watson's studies of early, 28; disappearance of bony plates over gill-chamber, 29, Fig. 17, 30, 89, 114; middle ear of earliest, 29; lower jaw of, 29; teeth of, 31; teeth similar to those of lobe-finned ganoids, 31; enlargement of parasphenoid, 31; breeding habits of, 32; development of, 32; period of dominance of, Fig. 25, 46; man's debt to, 89; primary upper jaw becomes attached to skull, 104, Fig. 62,

105; covering of primary jaws in early, 106; skull compared with that of crossopt, 107, Fig. 63, 108; close relatives of osteolepid crossopts, 114; elimination of internal gills in adult stage, 114; feeding habits of, 114; unspecialized, nearest to line of ascent to man, 115; respiration of, 118, 158; naso-buccal channel of, 122; tongue of, 123; first true ear in, 207; section of head of, Fig. 106, 208; otic notch of, 209; stapes of, 216; tympanum of, 216, 217; Jacobson's organ in, 158

Amphioxus, entire animal and transverse section of, Fig. 54, 92; as descendant of ancestral stock of vertebrates, 93; ingestion in, 95; "ciliated groove" of pharynx, 98; mouth of, 129; light cells of, Fig. 96, 183; spinal cord (section), Fig. 96, 183

"Ampullæ" of shark, Fig. 6, 13, 16, 204, 206

Anaspida, Fig. 4, 11, 96

Andrews, Roy C., discovery of Cretaceous mammals by, 51

Angular bone, evolution of, Fig. 52, 82; of *Trimerorhachis*, Fig. 64, 111; of *Megalichthys*, Fig. 64, 111; of mammal-like reptiles, 218

Animalcule, slipper (*Paramœcium*), Fig. 1, 5

Anteater, Spiny (*Echidna*), mouth of, 131

Anthropoid, human dentition derived from that of, 57; development of the eye in, 65; face influenced by erect posture of, 66; date of man's

Anthropoid—(*Continued*)
separation from primitive, 74; genesis of temporal bone in, 88; lips of, 133; incisors of, 138, 139; affinities of Piltdown canine tooth to that of, 141; difference between human and anthropoid dentition, 141; muzzle of fœtus, 142; fœtal muzzle compared with that of man, 143; palatal arch of, 143; premolars of, 144; dental formula of man and of, 145; type of milk teeth ancestral to that of man, 149; comparison of molar teeth with those of man, 146, 149; nasal chambers of, 161; rate of growth of nasal septum, 167; human eye compared with that of, 195; orbital axes of, 196, Fig. 35, 58; external ears of, 214

Antihelix, development of, 212

Antra, of nasal chamber, 162

Arachnids, theory of vertebrates derived from, 7

Arboreal life, all primates passed through stage of, 54; favored development of eye, 55; man bears traces of, 63; skull changes in pro-anthropoids brought about by, 91

Archæozoic era, origin of plant life in, 27

"Arches, visceral," 102

Arctocebus, top view of skull, Fig. 35, 58

Aristotle, on physiognomy, 220, 222

Armadillo, fœtal, Fig. 114, 221

Articular bone, development of, 112; of *Megalichthys*, Fig. 64, 111; of *Trimerorhachis*, Fig. 64, 111; of turtle embryo, Fig. 64, 111

Arthropods, theory of vertebrates derived from branch of, 7; eyes of, 182

Asia, as home of early mammals, 52

Auditory ossicles, of human ear, 202; Fig. 103, 203; Fig. 111, 216; origin of, Fig. 113, 218; of fœtal *Perameles*, Fig. 113,

218; of *Cynognathus*, Fig. 113, 218; innervation of muscles of, 219; of fœtal armadillo, Fig. 114, 221; of fœtal hedgehog, Fig. 115, 221; of human embryo, Fig. 115, 221

Auricularia, (larva of sea-cucumber), Fig. 55, 93

Australian aboriginal, skull of (under side), Fig. 53, 85; lower molar of, Fig. 80, 151; nose of, 169

Australopithecus, skull, side view, Fig. 42, 68; Fig. 46, 72; brain of, 72; restoration of, Fig. 47, 73

Autostylic attachment, of primary upper jaw to skull, Fig. 62, 105

Balance, the sense of, 202

Balanoglossus, theory of relation to ancestors of vertebrates, 93; larva of (*Tornaria*), Fig. 55, 93

Bandicoot, *See Perameles*

Baphetes, under side of skull of, Fig. 53, 85, Fig. 63, 108

Bass, striped, braincase of, Fig. 10, 22

"Becheraugen," of *Amphioxus*, Fig. 96, 183

Behavioristic method of study of physiognomy, 224

Behring Straits, as land-bridge for early mammals, 52

Bell, Sir Charles, "Essay on the Anatomy of Expression," 222

Bichir (*Polypterus*), 24; embryo of, Fig. 14, 26

Biconjugate, eyes of man and apes, 67, 189; movement not attained by lower primates, 198

Bilateral symmetry, supersedes radial symmetry, 6

Binocular, eyes of man and apes, 67; vision in man, 189; not possible in *Notharctus*, 196; established in Old World monkeys and anthropoid apes, 196

Bipinnaria, larva of starfish, Fig. 55, 93

INDEX

Birds, inconspicuous during Age of Reptiles, 45; period of dominance of, Fig. 25, 46; nasobuccal channel of, 122

Bloodhound, acromegaly in, 231

Bone-cell, in cross-section of skull of fossil ganoid, Fig. 9, 20; as basic element of skull, 21

Bony mask, in *Labidosaurus*, Fig. 23, 42; sunk beneath skin in mammals, 43

Brachiation, and quickness of vision, 198; and biconjugate movement of eyes, 198

Branchiostegals, elimination of, 114

Brain, rudimentary, of flatworms, 6, Fig. 2, facing 6; of sandflea, Fig. 2, facing 6; of annelid worms, 6; forebrain of shark, 14; of the tarsier, 53; progressive series in evolution of primate, 63; primates characterized by enlargement of, 64; of chimpanzee, 66; of *Australopithecus*, 72; skull changes consequent upon enlargement of, 87; enlargement of, in pro-anthropoids, 91; forebrain as olfactory center, 156; fœtal growth of, its effect on skull shape, 170; as derived from ectoderm, 179; eyes of vertebrates as outgrowths of forebrain, 179; origin of pineal and parapineal organs in tract that became brain tube, 186; visual cortex of, 191; oculomotor nerves of, in chimpanzee and man, 198

Braincase, of shark, Fig. 7, 17; of fish, Fig. 10, 22; as thrustblock, 22; evolution of primate, 63; bony crest on base of, of *Scymnognathus*, 117

Brain tube, relation of primitive eyes to, 186

Branchial arches, of shark, Fig. 7, 17; constrictors of, Fig. 8, 18; as origin of larynx, tonsils, thyroid and thymus glands, 126

Branchial chamber, loss of bones covering, 89

Branchial skeleton, of man compared with that of other vertebrates, 128

Broili, F., contributions to palæontology, 86

Broom, R., contributions to palæontology, 86

Brown, Barnum, discovery of *Eodelphis* by, 47

Bryant, W. L., contributions to palæontology, 86

Bulldog, as abnormal animal type, 230

Bursa (meniscus), origin of, 38, 39; Fig. 22, 38

Calamoichthys, 24

Calcium carbonate, in skeleton of shark, 23

Canals, semicircular, *see* Semicircular canals

Canine teeth, human, origin of, 90; of primitive man, 76; of human ancestor, well developed, 142; human and anthropoid, 141; of Piltdown man, 141, 143; alignment of, 144; of cynodonts, 116

Caniniform teeth, 115

Captorhinus, skull of, Fig. 53, 85

Carnivorous ancestors of man, 136

Cartilage, alar, of mammalian nose, 167; growth power of, 170; labial, early form of, 104, of shark, Figs. 7, 8, 17, 18; Meckel's, *see* Meckel's cartilage; median, of nose, origin of, 167; oral, of sharks and embryo vertebrates, 102; palatoquadrate, of primary upper jaw, 102

Cartilaginous skeleton, of head of shark, Fig. 7, 17

Caruncula, of human eye, Fig. 101, 194

Chapelle aux Saints, La, skull of, *see* Man, Neanderthal

Cheek arch, of *Scymnognathus* and *Ictidopsis*, 35, 36

Cheek bone, human, foreshadowed in *Mycterosaurus*, 34

Cheeks, embryonic development of the, 166

Ceratohyal, of the shark, 18

Cebus, face of, Fig. 34, facing 56

INDEX

Cephalaspis, Fig. **4, 11**; mouth of, Fig. 57, 96

Cephalaspid ostracoderms, Stensiö on, 94

Cephalopods, eyes of, 178, 179; development of eye in, Fig. 95, 181

Catarrhine monkeys, *see* Monkeys, catarrhine

Catablema, ocellus of, Fig. 91, 175

Chimpanzee, facial expression of, Fig. 116, facing 222; female and male, Fig. 40, facing 65; female with young, Fig. 39, facing 64; brain of, compared with that of *Notharctus* and of man, 65, 66; external ear of, Fig. 110, 213, 214; face of, compared with that of early man, 76; hands of, 198; palatal arch of, Fig. 74, 140; incisors of, 138; iris of, 199; jaw muscles of, Fig. 61, 103; lacrymal bone of, 200; lower jaw of, Fig. 45, 71; molar of, Fig. 79, 150; muzzle of, 142; nasal meati and sinuses of, 161; oculomotor nerves of, 198; protrusile lips of old, Fig. 70, 132; skull of, 65 (young), Fig. 102, 197; (female), Fig. 36, 59; (top view), Fig. 35, 58; Fig. 43, 69, (front view), Fig. 44, 70, (under side), Fig. 53, 85; tongue of, 123

"Chimpanzee type" of human ear, Fig. 110, 213

Chin, effect of development of tongue on, 126; of early man, 76

Chlamydoselachus, face of, Fig. 5, facing 12; instruments of precision in head of, Fig. 6, 13; jaw muscles of, Fig. 61, 103; development of teeth of, 109

Choanæ, in palate of lion pup, Fig. 66, 121; of lizard, Fig. 66, 121; of human embryo, 120, Fig. 66, 121

Chondrocranium, its component parts, 83

Chordate, earliest type of vertebrate, 10; *Amphioxus*, most primitive living, Fig. 54, 92

Choroid, of shark, Fig. 99, 192; of man, Fig. 100, 193

Choroid layer, lacking in cephalopod eye, 180

Cilia, as means of ingestion in *Amphioxus*, 95; in ostracoderms, 95

Ciliary muscles, of eye of shark, Fig. 99, 192; of human eye, Fig. 100, 193

"Ciliated groove" of *Amphioxus*, Fig. 54, 92; of pharynx of larval lamprey, 98

Circumorbital bones, Evolution of the, Fig. 51, 81

Civilization, its effect upon human teeth, 149

Clark, W. E., Le Gros, on evolution of primate brain, 63

Cladoselache, frontispiece

Clinical study of physiognomy, 224

Coal measures, *see* Carboniferous

Cochlea, human, development of, Fig. 105, 206; its equivalent first in amphibia, 206; of human ear, Fig. 103, 203; spiral ducts of, Fig. 103, 203

Constrictor muscles of gill arches, 104

Cornea, human, Fig. 100, 193; in shark and man, 193; of molluscan eye, development of, Fig. 95, 181; of shark, Fig. 99, 192

Coronoid bones, of *Megalichthys*, Fig. 64, 111; of *Trimerorhachis*, Fig, 64, 111; of turtle embryo, Fig. 64, 111

Corti, the organ of, Fig. 103, 203, 204

Cotylosaurian reptiles, *see* Reptiles

Cranial nerve, seventh, 43

Cretinism, cause and effect of, 171

Criminological study of physiognomy, 225

Cro-Magnon man, *see* Man, Cro-Magnon

Crossopterygii, related to Carboniferous amphibia, 114; comparison of skull with early Amphibia, 107, Fig. 63, 108; composition of skeleton, 23; characteristics of, 24; living representatives of, 24; dentary

INDEX

Crossopterygii—(*Continued*)
bone of, 108, 130; maxillae
and premaxillae of, 107, 130;
mouth of, 130; nearest to
direct line of ascent, 26;
origin of teeth of, 109; tooth
structure of, 112, Fig. 18,
following, 30; teeth of, 117;
possibly possessed a lung, 24;
Eusthenopteron (upper Devonian), *frontispiece;* Fig. 12,
facing 23; skull of, under side,
Fig. 53, 85; Fig. 63, 108;
Megalichthys, lower jaw of,
Fig. 64, 111; *Rhizodopsis,*
skull of, Fig, 17, 30; Fig. 48,
78; *Osteolepis,* cross section of
skull, Fig. 9, facing 20;
Polyplocodus, teeth of, Fig.
18, following 30; *Polypterus,*
jaw muscles of, Fig. 61, 103;
embryo of, Fig. 14, 26
Cruciform pattern of lower molars,
149; Fig. 80, 151
Crustacea, compound eyes of, 178;
mouth-legs of, 6
Crus helicis, development of the,
212
Cusps, characteristic of the cheek-
teeth of mammals, 145
Cyclostomes, as possible descendants of ostracoderms, 98, 186;
embryology of the, 186; feeding habits of the, 97, 98;
lamprey, adult, Fig. 59, 97;
lamprey, larval, Fig. 59, 97;
mouth-pouches in, Fig. 56,
94; "tongue" of, 123; tooth-
germs of, (section), Fig. 60,
99
Cynodonts, skulls of, Figs. 48–53,
78–85; dentition of, 115, 116;
secondary palate of, 119;
comparison of molar teeth
with those of man, 145;
middle ear of, Fig. 112, 217
Cynognathus, dentition of, Fig. 77,
147; middle ear of, Fig. 113,
218; jaw muscles of, Fig. 61,
103; skull of, Fig. 53, 85

Darwin, on the origin of mankind,
65
Dawn man, *see Eoanthropus dawsoni*

Deltatheridium, **D.** *pretrituberculare,* skull and head restored, Fig. 29, 50; dentition
of, Fig. 77, 147
Dental formula, of the primates,
Fig. 37, 61; of man and
anthropoids, 145
Dentary bone, its development in
mammal-like reptiles, 108;
evolution in series from fish
to man, Fig. 50, 80; contact
with squamosal in mammals,
87; not dominant in crossopts,
108; covered with skin in
early amphibia and crossopts,
130; crowded out posterior
elements, 36; evolution of,
87; progressive dominance of,
116
of armadillo, fœtal, Fig. 114,
221
of crossopts, 110, 130
of *Ictidopsis,* Fig, 21, 37
of *Megalichthys,* Fig. 64, 111
of *Mycterosaurus,* 35
of *Scymnognathus,* 36; Fig. 21, 37
of *Thylacinus,* 36; Fig. 21, 37
of *Trimerorhachis,* Fig. 64, 111
of turtle, embryo, Fig. 64, 111
Denticles, constitution of shagreen,
100; in skin of ostracoderms,
117
Dentition, evolution of human,
Fig. 77, 147; Fig. 78, 148;
origin of human, 90; reduced
to two sets in cynodonts, 116
Dermal plates (prevomers) of
Devonian crossopts, 109
"Derm-bones," development of,
21; of fossil crossopts, 112
Dermocranium derived from skin,
21; its component parts, 83
Dermo-supraoccipital bone, evolution of, Fig. 49, 79
Development and growth, Stock-
ard's studies of, 172
Development of the human face,
Fig. 86, 165; Fig. 87, 166
Diadectes (Permo-Carboniferous),
skull of, Fig. 62, 105
Diademodon, dentition of, Fig. 77,
147
Diaphragm, its origin and func-
tion, 41; Sir Arthur Keith on
the primate d., 63

INDEX

Didelphodus, dentition of, Fig. 77, 147

Didelphys, Fig. 26, facing 46; jaw muscles of, Fig. 61, 103; skull of, Fig. 28, 49; skull compared with *Eodelphis*, Fig. 27, 48

Diet, changes in diet of primitive man, 75; probable carnivorous diet of man's ancestors, 152; characters of early primates adapted to, 67; of prevertebrates, 95; later dietary habits of man, 70

Dinaric type of nose, Fig. 89, facing 170

Dipnoi, modern survivors of, 24; removed from main line of ascent, 25; embryonic development of, 25; nose of, 157; respiration of, 122, 157; *Dipterus* (Devonian), Fig. 13, facing 24

Dipterus (Devonian), Fig. 13, facing 24

Disharmonic types of human face, 237

Dogs, acromegaly in, 231; ateleosis in, 231

Dryopithecus, dentition of, Fig. 78, 148; derivation of human dentition from, 58; lower jaw of, Fig. 45, 71; *D. cautleyi*, premolars, lower front, Fig. 75, 144; molars, lower, Fig. 79, 150; *D. fontani*, premolars of, Fig. 75, 144; molars of, Fig. 79, 150; *D. frickæ*, molars of, Fig. 41, facing 66, Fig. 79, 150; *D. rhenanus*, molars of, Fig. 38, 62; comparison of upper molars with human, 149

"*Dryopithecus* pattern," 149, Fig. 41, facing 66; in teeth of anthropoids, Fig. 79, 150; in teeth of man, Fig. 80, 151

Duchenne, G. B., his study of physiognomy, 223

Dwarf, achondroplastic, nose of, 169; skull of, 230

Ear, evolution of the primate, 63; evolution of auditory ossicles, 215, Fig. 115, 221; innerva-

tion of the muscles of, 219; movement of, 133

External ear, of antelope, 211
of bat, 211
of chimpanzee, Fig. 110, 213
of *Echidna*, 210
of elephant, 211
of gibbon (*Hylobates*), Fig. 110, 213
of gorilla, Fig. 110, 213
of lemur (*Lemur catta*), 212
of lemuroid (*Nycticebus*), Fig. 110, 213
of macaque, fœtal, Fig. 109, 212
of mammals, 211
of monkeys, 212
of primates, lower, 57
of orang, Fig. 110, 213
of whale, 211
origin of, Fig. 108, 211; development of, 211; aid in development of man, 202; types of mammalian, 211; function of human, 202; approach to monkey type of fœtal human, 214; "chimpanzee type" of human, Fig. 110, 213; resemblance of human and anthropoid, 214

Inner ear
of alligator, Fig. 104, 205, 207
of frog, Fig. 106, 208
of ganoid (*Lepidosteus*), Fig. 104, 205
of man, Fig. 103, 203, Fig. 104, 205, Fig. 105, 206
of rabbit, Fig. 104, 205
of reptile, primitive (*Hatteria*), Fig. 104, 205; see also *Sphenodon*
of shark (*Acanthias*), Fig. 104, 205
derivation from ectoderm of, 204; components of, 202, 204; functions of, Fig. 103, 203, 204; evolution of, fish to man, Fig. 104, 205

Middle ear
of ancient and modern Amphibia, 29
of frog, 207; Fig. 106, 208
of mammal-like reptiles, Figs. 112, 113, 217, 218

266

Ear—(*Continued*)

Middle Ear—(*Continued*)

of fœtal mammal, Fig. 113, 218

of man, Fig. 111, 216

components of, 202; function of, 202; communication with throat of, 208

Ear muscles, reduced in man, 215

Ear drum, *see* Tympanum

Echidna, external ear of, 210; head of, Fig. 23, 42; mouth of, 131

Echinodermata, *Auricularia*, larva of sea-cucumber, Fig. 55, 93; *Bipinnaria*, larva of starfish, Fig. 55, 93

Ectoderm, derivation of brain from, 179; of mouth from, 94; of mouth-pouches from, Fig. 56, 94; of inner ear from, 204; origin of eyes of jellyfish in, 174; specialization of cells of, 157

Egg cell, complexity of the fertilized, 157

Egyptian, upper incisor of old, Fig. 72, 137

Ehringsdorf man, *see* Man, Neanderthal

Elasmobranchs, *see* Sharks, Rays, etc.

Embryo, Jacobson's organ in, Fig. 82, 159; muzzle of, 142; nose of, 162, Fig. 65, 120; palatal region of, Fig. 66, 121; teeth of, 134, Fig. 71, 135; gill-slits of, 127, Fig. 69, 127; fish-like stage of, 122; tongue and larynx of, 126

of *Amblystoma punctatum*, Fig. 14, 26

of macaque, Fig. 108, 211

of man, Fig. 108, 211

of *Perameles*, 38, Fig. 22, 38

of *Polypterus*, Fig. 14, 26

of rabbit, Fig. 56, 94

of sturgeon, Fig. 107, 209

of turtle, Fig. 64, 111

of vertebrates, Fig. 56, 94

Embryonic development

of cyclostomes, 186

of *Polypterus*, 24

of *Neoceratodus*, 25

Embryology, its evidence on origin of vertebrate eye, 186

Endocrine glands, as producers of hormones, 171

Endocranium, derived from cartilage, 21

Eoanthropus dawsoni, jaw and teeth ape-like, 72; lower jaw of, Fig. 37, 61; lower jaw of, Fig. 45, 71; left lower molars of, Fig. 38, 62; left lower molars of, Fig. 41, facing 66; skull, side view, Fig. 42, 68

Eocene, mammalian remains from, 53; early placental mammals in, 52; development of eye in primates of, 55; European Adapidæ from, 54

Eodelphis (Cretaceous), restoration of face of, *frontispiece;* skull compared with *Didelphis*, Fig. 27, 48; skull compared with *Notharctus*, 55; skull of, Fig. 48, 78

Eogyrinus (Lower Carboniferous), Fig. 15, 28; restoration of face of, *frontispiece*

Epipterygoid bone, of *Diadectes*, Fig. 62, 105

Epipterygoid process, of fœtal salamander, Fig. 62, 105

Epithelial cells, differentiation of, 156

Epithelium, derivation of primitive eye from, 176; as origin of parts of the vertebrate eye, 179

Erinaceus, auditory ossicles of embryo, Fig. 115, 221

Eryops, jaw muscles of, Fig. 61, 103

Ethmoid sinus, 162; its connection with nasal meati, Fig. 85, 163

Ethmoidal cartilage, ossification of, 199

Eurypterids, derivation of vertebrates from forms related to, 182

Eustachian tube, of frog, 207; Fig. 106, 208; of man, Fig. 111, 216; in human embryo, 162

Eusthenopteron (Devonian), Fig. 12, facing 23; face of, *frontispiece;* skull of, under side, Fig. 53, 85; skull of, under side, Fig. 63, 108

INDEX

Evolution, proceeds by loss of superfluous parts, 114; of human face, Sir Arthur Keith on, 120; of primates, divergent, 57; of the circumorbital bones, Fig. 51, 81; of human dentition, Fig. 77, 147; *also* Fig. 78, 148; of the human jaw bones, Fig. 50, 80; of human jaw muscles, Fig. 61, 103; of human skull roof, Fig. 49, 79; of human skull, under side, Fig. 53, 85; of the temporo-mandibular series, Fig. 52, 82; of the vertebrate eye, Fig. 97, 185

Eyes, beginnings of, Fig. 91, 175; biconjugate movement and the oculomotor nerves, 198; ciliary muscles of, 193; circumorbital bones, evolution of the, 88; Fig. 51, 81; clearness of vision and the brachiating habit, 198; correlation of vision with smell, 156; as directional organs, 178, 200; dorsal eyes, Fig. 97, 185, 187, 200; elements of primitive, and their functions, 175; choroid of vertebrate, 188; evolution of vertebrate, Fig. 97, 185; evidence of embryology on origin of vertebrate, 186; function of paired, 177; Plate cited on paired eyes of vertebrates, 178; paired eyes essentially an outgrowth of brain, 179; meagre fossil evidence of origin of vertebrate paired eyes, 184; vertebrate and invertebrate, compared, 178, 180, 181; summary of development of vertebrate, 200; human, as a camera, 189; development of human eyes favored by arboreal life, 55, 90; function of human, 173; comparison of human, and shark, 192; comparison of human, and anthropoid, 195; position of, inherited from pro-anthropoid stock, 196; pineal and parapineal, Fig. 97, 185, 200; caruncula of

human, 194; fundus oculi of human, 199; horizontal section of, Fig. 100, 193; iris of human and anthropoid, 198; lacrymal glands and canals of human, Fig. 101, 194; macula lutea of human and anthropoid, 199; muscles of human, Fig. 98, 190, 191; of cephalopod mollusca, development of Fig. 95, 181

of flatworm (*Planaria*), Fig. 92, 177, Fig. 2, facing 6
of jellyfish (*Catablema*), Fig. 91, 175
of jellyfish (*Sarsia*), Fig. 91, 175
of *Amphioxus*, Fig. 96, 183
of deep-sea cephalopods, 178
of crustacea and insects, 178
of flatworms, 6, 176
of Galago, 60
of invertebrates, 174
of advanced lemuroids, 60
of *Limulus*, 182
of higher mollusca, 178
of *Nautilus*, 181
of *Notharctus*, position in, Fig. 35, 196
of *Pecten*, 178
of *Planaria*, as directional organs, Fig. 93, 178
of *Planaria*, section, Fig. 92, 177
of pre-chordates, 186
of primates, development of, 65; progressive declination of the, Fig. 36, 59
of protista, 174
of sand-flea (*Orchestia*), Fig. 2, facing 6
of scorpion, 182
of shark (*Chlamydoselachus anguineus*), Fig. 6, 13, 15
of shark, horizontal section, Fig. 99, 192
of shark nearer to human than to invertebrate, 191
of squid, section of, Fig. 94, 179
of *Tarsius*, Fig. 31, facing 53, 60

Eye stalks, formation of the, Fig. 97, 185
Eyeball, muscles of the human, Fig. 98, 190; muscles of the, of shark, Fig. 6, 13, 15
Eyelids, of man, 194; of *Sepia*, 180

268

INDEX

Face, as index of character, 220; changes in arboreal proanthropoids, 91; changes in primitive man, 76; embryonic development in mammals, 166; extremes in form and color of, Fig. 90, facing 172; primary functions of the, 3; shape of anthropoid f. conditioned by erect posture, 64, 66; Mongolian type, 170; human, of same elements as in gorilla, 91; Sir Arthur Keith on evolution of, 120; three stages in evolution of, 122; Stockard's classification of the, 232
   of young chimpanzee, Fig. 116, facing 222
   of chimpanzee, Figs. 39, 40, facing 64, 65, 66, 76
   of lemur (*Lemur variegatus*), Fig. 34, facing 56
   of man, see Man, face of
   of catarrhine monkey (*Lasiopyga pygerythrus*), Fig. 34, facing 56
   of platyrrhine monkey (*Cebus capucinus*), Fig. 34, facing 56
   of shark *Chlamydoselachus*, Fig. 5, facing 12
Facial armor of *Osteolepis*, Fig. 11, facing 22
Facial expression, methods for the study of, 223–5
Facial muscles,
   of *Echidna*, Fig. 23, 42
   of gorilla, Fig. 23, 42
   of *Labidosaurus*, Fig. 23, 42
   of man, Fig. 23, 42
   of *Sphenodon*, Fig. 23, 42
Facial nerve, chief branches of, Fig. 24, 44; original territory of the, 132
Features, inheritance of individual, 236
Feeding habits of some Amphibia, 114
Feet, correlated use of, in Primates, 64; evolution of primate, 63
Fishes, lobe-finned, ancestral to land vertebrates, 26; comparison of skull with that of amphibian, 29; theories of

origin of, 7, 8, 92, 93; ears of primitive, 204; jaws of, primary, 104; jaw muscles and jaws of, 104–6; lateral line organs of, 206; man owes ground-plan of face to early, 89; methods of ingestion of, 104; resemblance of human embryo to, 122; shoulder girdle of, compared with that of early amphibia, 28
Crossopterygii
   bony plates on primary jaws of, 106; Fig. 12, facing 23; chemical composition of skeletion of, 23; structure of teeth, 112; Fig. 18, following 30
   Eusthenopteron, Fig. 12, facing 23; face of, *frontispiece*; skull of, under side, Fig. 53, 85; skull of, under side, Fig. 63, 108
   Osteolepis, skull of, top view, Fig. 11, facing 22; cross section of skull, Fig. 9, facing 20
   Polyplocodus, teeth of, Fig. 18, following 30
   Polypterus, jaw muscles of, Fig. 61, 103; embryo of, Fig. 14, 26
   Rhizodopsis, skull of, Fig. 17, 30; skull of, side view, Fig. 48, 78; skull, roof of, Fig. 49, 79
Dipnoi (Dipneusti)
   Dipterus, the nose of, Fig. 13, facing 24, 157; respiration of, 122
Elasmobranchii, *see* Shark, passim
Ganoidei, skeleton, composition of, 23
Flatworm (*Planaria*), Fig. 2, facing 6; apparently descendant of jellyfish group, 5; eyes of the, 176, Fig. 92, 177, eyes as directional organs in the, Fig. 93, 178; illustrates evolution of primitive head, 6, Fig. 2, facing 6
Foot, of tree-grasping type in all primates, 54
Fore-brain, as olfactory center, 156

Forests of the Devonian period, 27
"Fossil, living," opossum as a, 47
Fovea anterior, 149; in molar of
    Ehringsdorf man, Fig. 80, 151
Fovea posterior, 149
Frog, development of ear in, 207;
    Eustachian tube of, 207;
    head of, transverse section of,
    Fig. 106, 208; stapes of,
    216
Frontal bones, 83; become one of
    dominant elements in vault
    of human skull, 87; evolution
    shown in series of ten skulls
    from fish to man, Fig. 49, 79;
    joint process of frontal and
    malar replaces reptilian post-
    orbital bones, 90; their rela-
    tion to superior maxillary in
    mammals, 87; retained from
    fish to mammals, 86; sinus of,
    161
    of chimpanzee, female, Fig. 49,
        79
    of Didelphys, 50; Fig. 49, 79
    of Ictidopsis, Fig. 49, 79
    of man, Fig. 49, 79
    of Mycterosaurus, Fig. 49, 79
    of Notharctus, Fig. 49, 79
    of Seymouria, Fig. 49, 79
Frontal sinus, its connections with
    nasal meati, Fig. 85, 163
Fundus oculi in man and anthro-
    poids, 199

Galago, eye and orbits of, 60
Ganoids, possessed a lung, 24;
    skull compared with that of
    amphibian, 29, 107; com-
    position of skeleton, 23;
    mouth of, 130; relation to
    human ancestry, 24; hyoid
    gill cleft in, 209; teeth of
    earliest amphibia similar to
    those of, 31
Ganoine, 23; covers bony jaw-
    plates of higher fishes and
    early amphibia, 106; on max-
    illæ and premaxillæ of early
    crossopts, 130; on teeth of
    fossil crossopts, 112
Gaupp, E., cited on the origin of
    the meniscus, 38
Genetic study of physiognomy,
    224

Genioglossus, see Geniohyoglossus
    muscle
Geniohyoglossus muscle, of gorilla,
    Fig. 67, 124; of man, Fig. 67,
    124; Fig. 68, 125, 126
Gibbon (Hylobates) external ear
    of, Fig. 110, 213; habit of
    climbing upright, 64; hands
    of, 198; palatal arch of
    female, Fig. 74, 140; skull of,
    top view, Fig. 35, 58
Gidley, J. W., on mammalian
    teeth from Basal Eocene, 53
Gigantism and acromegaly in
    dogs, 231
Gill arches, see Branchial arches
Gill cartilages, folding of, in
    shark, 123
Gill chamber, bony covers of the,
    23; changes of, from crossopts
    to Amphibia, 29
Gill clefts, in embryo sturgeon,
    Fig. 107, 209
Gills, internal, eliminated by
    Amphibia in adult stage, 114
Gill openings, homologous with
    mouth-pouches, 94
Gill region
    of Cephalaspis (restored by
        Stensiö), Fig. 57, 95
    of Kiæraspis, Fig. 57, 95
Gill slits, in human embryo of
    third week, Fig. 69, 126, 127
Glands, endocrine, as producers
    of "hormones," 171; hypo-
    physis, 230; hypophysis-
    pituitary complex, 231; lacry-
    mal, human, 194; Meibomian,
    in human eyelids, 194; pineal
    and parapineal, 186, 200;
    pituitary, effect of diseased,
    171; salivary, of man and
    apes, 129; sebaceous, origin
    and function of, 41; sudori-
    parous, origin and function
    of, 41; thyroid, and gigan-
    tism, 231; effects of deficient,
    171; effects of deranged, 237;
    effect on growth of face,
    232
"Goblet eye" of flatworm, section
    of, Fig. 92, 177; of jellyfish
    (Sarsia), Fig. 91, 175
Goniale, of armadillo, fœtal, Fig.
    114, 221; of hedgehog (Erin-

INDEX

Goniale—(*Continued*)
aceus) fœtal, Fig. 115, 221; of human embryo, Fig. 115, 221
Gorgonopsian reptiles, *see* Reptiles
Gorilla, external ear of, Fig. 110, 213,214; facial muscles of, Fig. 23, 42; facial nerve of, Fig. 24, 44; hands of, 198; head, longitudinal section, Fig. 67, 124; lacrymal bone, 200; lachrymal bone of fœtal, 199; nose of, 164, 170; nose of, fœtal, Fig. 84, 161; palatal arch of male, Fig. 74, 140; nasal meati and sinuses of, 161; skull compared with Piltdown, 143; skull of young g., front view, Fig. 102, 197; teeth foreshadow "shovel shaped" incisors, 138; teeth, lower molar, Fig. 79, 150; teeth, canine, resemblance to Piltdown, 141; central incisors of young, Fig. 72, 137; milk teeth of young, Fig. 76, 146; tongue of young, 123
Gregory, William K., his contributions to palæontology, 86; places separation of man and anthropoids in Lower Miocene, 74; on hind-feet of primates, 54; "Origin and Evolution of the Human Dentition," 146
Gregory, William K., and Milo Hellman, 146; "The Dentition of *Dryopithecus* and the Origin of Man," 146
Gregory, William K., and Simpson, G. G., describe Cretaceous mammals, 51
Growth, glandular factors affecting, 237; mechanism of, 172; stimulation of, by "hormones," 171; types of, in man, Fig. 117, 232
Gular plates, elimination of, Fig. 17, 30; *also* 114

Hagfishes (Cyclostomata), compared with ostracoderms, 97; ostracoderms ancestral to, 10; tongue of, 123
Hair, origin and function of, 41; possibly possessed by mammal-like reptiles of Trias, 42
Hands, correlated use of eyes, hands and feet, by primates, 64; evolution of primate, 63; progressive changes of, 198
Hatteria, labyrinth of, Fig. 104, 205
Hatteria, see also Sphenodon
Haughton, S. H., his contributions to palæontology, 86
Head, evolution of primitive, Fig. 2, facing 6; inheritance of head shape, 236; nature and function of, 12;
of arachnids, 7
of *Australopithecus*, restored, Fig. 47, facing 73
of *Deltatheridium*, restored, Fig. 29, 50
of *Echidna*, Fig. 23, 42
of flatworm (*Planaria*), Fig. 2, facing 6
of frog, transverse section, Fig. 106, 208
of gorilla, young, longitudinal section, Fig. 67, 124
of *Labidosaurus*, Fig. 23, 42
of lamprey, larval, longitudinal section, Fig. 56, 94
of man, longitudinal section, Fig. 67, 124
of man, embryo, third week, Fig. 69, 127
of ostracoderms, 11
of rabbit, longitudinal section, Fig. 56, 94
of sand-flea (*Orchestia*), Fig. 2, facing 6
of shark, cartilaginous skeleton of, Fig. 7, 17
of shark, dissection of, Fig. 81, 155
of shark (*Chlamydoselachus*), Fig. 5, facing 12
of shark (*Chlamydoselachus*), diagram, Fig. 6, 13
of *Sphenodon*, Fig. 23, 42
of *Zalambdalestes lechei*, restored, Fig. 29, 50
Hearing, the mechanics of, 204
Hedgehog (*Erinaceus*) fœtal, auditory ossicles of, Fig. 115, 221
Heidelberg man (*Homo heidelbergensis*), chin of, 72; lower

271

INDEX

Heidelberg man—(*Continued*)
jaw of, Fig. 37, 61; Fig. 45,
71; lower molar of, Fig. 80,
151; teeth of, 143
Helix, development of, 212
Hellman, Milo and William K.
Gregory, "The Dentition of
Dryopithecus and the Origin
of Man," 146
Herbivorous vertebrates, could
not have given rise to carnivorous forms, 101
Heredity, the shape of the head,
236; and the shape of the
nose, 172
Hesse, on the primitive eye, 176
Hindu, lower molar of, Fig. 80, 151
Hittite, type of nose, 169; Fig. 89,
facing 170
Homo heidelbergensis (Heidelberg
man), chin of, 72; lower jaw
of, Fig. 37, 61; Fig. 45, 71;
lower molar of, Fig. 80, 151;
teeth of, 143
Homo neanderthalensis, lower jaw
of, Fig. 45, 71; left upper and
lower molars of, Fig. 38, 62
Homo neanderthalensis (La Chapelle aux Saints), skull of, side
view, Fig. 42, 68; skull of,
top view, Fig. 43, 69; skull of,
front view, Fig. 44, 70
Homo neanderthalensis (Ehringsdorf), central incisors of, Fig.
72, 137; lower jaw of, Fig. 45,
71; lower molar of, Fig. 80,
151; lower front premolars of,
Fig. 75, 144
Homo neanderthalensis (Le Moustier), dentition of, Fig. 78,
148; characters of teeth of,
Fig, 45, 71, 72; central
incisors of, Fig. 72, 137;
lower molar of, Fig. 80, 151;
palatal arch of, Fig. 74, 140
Homo sapiens, see Man
Hooton, Earnest A., his work on
inheritance, 236
Hormones, the function of, 171
Hottentot, male, the face of, Fig.
90, facing 172
Hrdlička, Ales, on incisors of
anthropoids and monkeys, 138
Huber, Ernst, on facial muscles,
44, 132

Human characters, point at which
primates assumed, 64
Human Dentition, Evolution of
the, Fig. 77, 147; Fig. 78,
148
Human Ear, Evolution of the,
Fig. 104, 205
Human Circumorbital Bones,
Evolution of the, Fig. 51,
81
Human Temporomandibular
Series, Evolution of, Fig. 52,
82
Human Face, Development of the,
Fig. 86, 165; Fig. 87, 166
Stockard's classification of the,
232
Human Jawbones, Evolution of
the, Fig. 50, 80
Jaw muscles, Evolution of the,
Fig. 61, 103
Nose, Embryonic stages of the,
Fig. 65, 120
Skull roof, Evolution of the,
Fig. 49, 79
Human types, abnormal, studies
of, 229
Humor, vitreous, 188
Hunter, John I., on evolution of
primate brain, 63, 198
Huxley, T. H., his views con-
firmed, 51
Hydroids, effect of ultra-violet
rays on, 174
Hylobates, external ear of, Fig.
110, 213; skull of, top view,
Fig. 35, 58; male, palatal
arch of, Fig. 74, 140
Hyoid arch, of man homologous
with that of primates, 128;
primary upper jaw suspended
from, 104; stapes derived
from, 215; cartilage, of
Echidna, 210; gill pouch, ear
derived from, 208
Hyoid, of shark, Fig. 7, 17
Hyomandibular cartilage, of
shark, Fig. 62, 105; Fig. 7,
17; Fig. 8, 18
Hyostylic attachment, of jaw in
shark, Fig. 62, 105
Hypophysis of larval lamprey,
Fig. 56, 94
Hypophysis-pituitary complex, in
acromegaly, 231

INDEX

Ictidopsis, dentary of, Fig. 21, 37; restoration of face of, *frontispiece;* skull of, Fig. 20, 35; Fig, 28, 49; Fig. 48, 78

Incisors, of anthropoids and monkeys, 138; mammillæ on, 136; Fig. 72, 137; of chimpanzees, 138; of cynodonts, Fig. 50, 80, 116; central, of gorilla, Fig, 72, 137; of Neanderthal man (Le Moustier), Fig. 72, 137; of Neanderthal man (Ehringsdorf), Fig. 72, 137; of old Egyptian, Fig. 72, 137; of white boy, Fig. 72, 137; upper central, of man, three types of, 138; Fig. 73, 139; "shovel-shaped," of the Krapina race, Mongolians and Indians, 138; retreat of human, 144; of fossil man, 143; origin of, 90

Incus, human embryo shows origin of, 220
    of armadillo, fœtal, Fig. 114, 221
    of *Cynognathus*, Fig. 113, 218
    of hedgehog (*Erinaceus*), fœtal, Fig. 115, 221
    of man, Fig. 111, 216
    of man, fœtal, Fig. 115, 221
    of *Perameles*, fœtal, Fig. 113, 218

Indians, "shovel-shaped" incisors of, 138

Indrodon, left upper molar of, Fig. 38, 62

Infusoria, effect of ultra-violet rays on, 174

Inheritance, of individual characters, 236

Insectivores, ancestors of man were, 52

Insectivorous dentition, traces of, in early primates, 57

Insects, compound eyes of, 178

Interarticular disc, formation of, in *Perameles*, Fig. 22, 38

Interoperculum, elimination of, Fig. 17, 30, 114

Interorbital space, in advanced lemuroids, 60

Interparietal bones, retained from fish to man, 86

Intertemporal bone, its changes from fish to man, Fig. 49, 79;

loss of, in reptiles, 89; reduction of, 88

Invertebrates, well established before vertebrates, 8; eyes of, 173; eyes compared with vertebrate, 178; eyes of higher, 178

Iris, of man, Fig. 100, 193; of mollusca, development of, Fig. 95, 181; of *Sepia*, 180; of shark, Fig. 99, 192

Jacobson's organ, description of 158; in man, fœtal, Fig. 65, 120; Fig. 82, 159

Jaw, conclusions from history of the, 152; elements traced from earliest Amphibia to man, 107; evolution of the bones of the, 87; Evolution of the Human, Fig. !50, 80; evolution of the primate, 63; mammalian joint of, its formation, 39; the interarticular disc in (*Perameles*, fœtal), Fig. 22, 38; its elements homologous in crossopts and early Amphibia, 107; labyrinthodont method of attachment of teeth in, 112; points of advancement in crossopt jaws, 113; prognathous jaws and shape of nose, 170; Fig. 89, facing 170; primate, tabular history of, Fig. 37, 61; origin uncertain below ostracoderms, 101; of dipnoan fishes, 25; of fossil ganoids, 23; of *Osteolepis*, Fig. 11, facing 22; architecture of "visceral arches," 104; progressive changes associated with development of musculature of, 116; of shark nearer to those of man than to invertebrate, 102; specialized jaws of some Amphibia, 115

Primary, completely masked by secondary jaws in higher vertebrates, 104, 106; of crossopts, 106, 110, 113; of higher fishes and early Amphibia, covered with ganoine-coated bony plates, 106; of

Jaw—*(Continued)*
Primary—(Continued)
shark, 106, Fig. 7, 17; Fig. 8, 18; of primitive sharks, 109; of lower primates, in relation to eyes, 60; buds of, in human embryo, Fig. 69, 127
Primary Upper, elimination of teeth in, 115; methods of attachment of, 104, Fig. 62, 105; palatoquadrate cartilage, 102; traces of, in mammalian embryo, 106; retained teeth in Amphibia, 115; of *Baphetes*, Fig. 63, 108; of Devonian crossopts, 109; of *Eusthenopteron*, Fig. 63, 108
Primary Lower, coronoid bones of, in crossopts, 110; develops into articular bone, 112; Meckel's cartilage, 102
Secondary, definition and description, 107; elements of the, 107; shows unity of origin of higher vertebrates, 107: in sharks, represented only by skin, 106
of armadillo, fœtal, relation of ossicles to, Fig. 114, 221
of crossopts, 109; *also* 113
of *Dryopithecus*, section of, Fig. 45, 71
of *Eodelphis*, Fig. 27, 48
of *Leipsanolestes siegfriedti*, Fig. 37, 61
of man, influenced by size and function of tongue, 126
of man, longitudinal section, Fig. 68, 125
of man, Cro-Magnon, section of, Fig. 45, 71; Ehringsdorf, section of, Fig. 45, 71; Heidelberg, section of, Fig. 45, 71; Neanderthal, section of, Fig. 45, 71; Piltdown, Fig. 41, facing 66, 142; Piltdown, section of, Fig. 45, 71
of *Megalichthys*, Fig. 64, 111
of monkey, longitudinal section, Fig. 68, 125
of *Mycterosaurus*, 34
of *Pelycodus trigonodus*, Fig. 37, 61
of *Seymouria*, 32
of *Trimerorhachis*, Fig. 64, 111
Jaw muscles
of *Chlamydoselachus*, Fig. 61, 103; *also* Fig. 8, 18
of *Cynognathus*, Fig. 61, 103
of *Didelphys*, Fig. 61, 103
of *Eryops*, Fig. 61, 103
of fishes, their evolution, 104
of man, evolution of, Fig. 61, 103
of *Notharctus*, Fig. 61, 103
of chimpanzee, Fig. 61, 103
of *Polypterus*, Fig. 61, 103
of *Scymnognathus*, Fig. 61, 103
of shark, their derivation, 104
Jellyfish, mouth of the, 4, 5; eyes of, 174; eye of, (*Sarsia*), section of, Fig. 91, 175; *Tessera*, Fig. 1, 5
Jugal bone (malar), 83; series of skulls showing evolution of, Fig. 51, 81; Fig. 53, 85; joint process of frontal and malar replaces reptilian postorbital, 90

Karroo (Africa), mammal-like reptiles of, Fig. 20, 35–36
Keel bone, *see* Parasphenoid bone
Keith, Sir Arthur, on the development of the human ear, 212; his studies of abnormal human types, 229; "Morphology and Embryology," 157; on the primate diaphragm, abdomen and pelvic floor, 63; his study of growth, 237; on the evolution of the human face, 120; on the hind feet of primates, 54
Kiaer, J., on ostracoderms, 10
King crab (*Limulus*), 7
Kinsfolk, Some of Our Earliest, Fig. 4, 11
Krapina race (Neanderthal), "shovel shaped" incisors of, 138

Labial cartilages, of shark (*Chlamydoselachus*), Fig. 6, 13; Fig. 7, 17; Fig. 8, 18; 130
Labidosaurus, head of, Fig. 23, 42
Labyrinth, embryonic development of, 204
of alligator, Fig. 104, 205

INDEX

Labyrinth—(*Continued*)
  of ganoid (*Lepidosteus*), Fig. 104, 205
  of man, 202; Fig. 103, 203, Fig. 104, 205, Fig. 105, 206
  of rabbit, Fig. 104, 205
  of reptile (*Hatteria*) (*Sphenodon*) Fig. 104, 205
  of shark (*Acanthias*), Fig. 104, 205
Labyrinthodont, attachment of teeth, 112; pattern in teeth of fossil crossopts, Fig. 18, following 30, 112; teeth of Devonian fish (*Polyplocodus*), Fig. 18, following 30; traces in teeth of *Seymouria*, 118
Labyrinthodonts, teeth of the, 113, 115
Lacrymal apparatus of human eye, Fig. 101, 194
Lacrymal bone, 83, 194; development of, 199; relation to superior maxillary and jugal in mammals, 87; series of ten skulls showing evolution of, Fig. 51, 81; similar in man and anthropoids, 199; survives in man, 88
Lacrymal glands and canals in human eye, 194
Lacrymal sac, in human eye, 194
Lagena, of alligator, Fig. 104, 205
Lampreys (Cyclostomata), ostracoderms ancestral to, 10; compared with ostracoderms, 97; adult, Fig. 59, 97; embryology of, 186; feeding habits of, 98; mouth of adult, 129; tongue of, 123; section of tooth germ of, Fig. 60, 99; "ciliated groove" of pharynx (*Ammocœtes* stage), 98; longitudinal section of larval, Fig. 59, 97; mouth of larval, 129; mouth pouches in larval, Fig. 56, 94
Lanarkia, shagreen denticles of, 100; teeth represented by denticles, 117
Lancelet, *see Amphioxus*
Laryngeal complex, of man and other vertebrates, 128
Larynx, in human embryo, 126;

origin in branchial arches, 126
Lasiopyga kolbi, side view of skull, Fig. 36, 59
Lateral line organs of fishes, 206
Lateral type, in man, Fig. 117, 232; result of crossing with linear, 237
"Lateral line," of Stockard, Fig. 118, 234
Le Double, his work on lacrymal bone, 199
Legs, hind, of the tarsier, 53; Fig. 31, facing 53
Leipsanolestes, left lower molar of, Fig. 38, 62; jaw of, Fig. 37, 61
Lemur, African (*Arctocebus*), top view of skull, Fig. 35, 58
Lemur (*Lemur catta*), ears of, 212; face of, 56; Fig. 34, facing 56; *L. variegatus*, face of, Fig. 34, facing 56; olfactory sense of, 196; rhinarium of, 56
Lemuroids, eyes of advanced, 60; *Adapis* (Eocene) skull of, under side, Fig. 53, 85; *Notharctus*, skull, side view, Fig. 36, 59; *Notharctus*, skull, top view, Fig. 35, 58; hands of, 198; orbital axes of, Fig. 35, 58, 196; *Nycticebus*, external ear of, Fig. 110, 213; *Pelycodus*, left upper and lower molars of, Fig. 38, 62; jaw of, Fig. 37, 61; *Propithecus*, restoration of face of, *frontispiece*
Lens, in eye of *Sepia*, 180; lens, in development of molluscan eye, Fig. 95, 181; formation of the, in vertebrate eye, Fig. 97, 185, 187; in eye of man, Fig. 100, 193; in eye of shark, Fig. 99, 192
"Light cells," of the primitive eye, 175, 176; Fig. 91, 175; of *Amphioxus*, Fig. 96, 183
Limulus, 7; eyes of, 182; Patten derives vertebrates from relatives of, 92
Lindsay-Johnson, his work on the fundus oculi, 198
Linear type of human growth, Fig. 117, 232; results of crossing with lateral, 237

275

INDEX

Lips, embryonic development of the, 166; origin and evolution of human, 129; mammalian, their most distinctive feature, 131; philtrum of, 133; of anthropoids, 133; of old chimpanzee, Fig. 70, facing 132; of Lemur, 56, Fig. 34, facing 56; of catarrh in monkeys, 56, Fig. 34, facing 56; of platyrrhine monkeys, 56, Fig. 34, facing 56; of lower primates and man, 133; of Spiny Ant-eater, 131; uses of protrusile, 133; muscles of, their importance to newborn mammal, 133, 134

Lizard, palate of, Fig. 66, 121

Lobe-finned fishes (see also Crossopterygii, Fishes), Eusthenopteron, Fig. 12, facing 23, Fig. 53, 85, Fig. 63, 108; Osteolepis, Fig. 11, facing 22, Fig. 9, facing 20; Polyplocodus, Fig. 18, following 30; Polypterus, Fig. 14, 26, Fig. 61, 103; Rhizodopsis, Fig. 17, 30, Fig. 48, 78, Fig. 49, 79

Lobule, development of the, 212

Locomotion, of primitive man, changes in, 75; skull changes related to habits of, 88

Loxomma allmani (Carboniferous), skull of, Fig. 16, facing 28; teeth of, Fig. 18, following 30

Lung-fishes (Dipnoi), (Dipneusti), embryonic development of, 25; modern survivors of, 24; the nose of, 157; Neoceratodus, 25

Luschan, F. v., his work on inheritance, 236

Macaque, embryo of, Fig. 108, 211; external ear of, Fig. 109, 212

"Macula lutea," in man and apes, 199

Malar bone (Jugal), series of skulls showing evolution of, Fig. 51, 81, 83, Fig. 53, 85; joint process of frontal and malar replaces reptilian postorbital, 90

Malleus, human embryo shows origins of, 220; of armadillo, fœtal, Fig. 114, 221; of Cynognathus, Fig. 113, 218; of man, Fig. 103, 203; of man, Fig. 111, 216; of man, fœtal, Fig. 115, 221; of Perameles, fœtal, Fig. 113, 218

Mammals, appear in large numbers at the close of the Age of Reptiles, 52; their condition during the Age of Reptiles, 45; some early m. believed related to Platypus, 47; body temperature of, 40; origin of the, 40; period of dominance of, Fig. 25, 46; type of primitive, Fig. 27, 48; cusps characteristic of cheek teeth of, 145; the ear of, 207, 211; face of, its embryonic development, 166, facial muscles of, their origin, 43, 132; Jacobson's organ in primitive, 158; jaw, embryonic traces of primary upper, 106; jaw, upper, of m., Fig. 50, 80, 87; method of respiration, 119; nasal chamber of, 158; palatal regions of, 119, Fig. 52, 82, Fig. 53, 85; their forerunners from Mongolia, 51; Fig. 29, 50; early placental from New Mexico, 52; tongue of, 123; teeth of triconodont m., 136

"Mammalian joint," see also Interarticular disc, 87, 90; formation of, 39; development of dentary and squamosal bones to form, 108, 109; of Ictidopsis, Fig. 21, 37; of Perameles, fœtal, Fig. 22, 38; of Scymnognathus, Fig. 21, 37; of Thylacinus, Fig. 21, 37

Man, Darwin on the origin of, 65; his debt to the Amphibia, 89; possibility of his existence derives from the Amphibia, 32; unspecialized Amphibia nearest to line of ascent, 115; relation of ganoids to his ancestry, 24; nearer to shark than shark to invertebrates, 14, 102; a hiatus in his

INDEX

Man—(*Continued*)
history in Pliocene, 70; his
ancestors not large ferocious
animals, 20; his ancestors
small, long-snouted, insectivorous - carnivorous mammals, 52; probable carnivorous diet of the earlier ancestors of man, 152; om-
nivorous - carnivorous diet
habits later developed, 70;
derived from frugivorous
proto - anthropoids, 69;
changes in diet of primitive
man, 75; gradual modification
of structure of, 84; structural
changes incident to changes
of habit, 75; bears stamp of
arboreal ancestors and later
bipedal adaptation, 63; compared with chimpanzee and
Notharctus, 65; converges in
past to common source with
anthropoids, 74; date of his
separation from early an-
thropoids, 74; several types
of, in early Pleistocene, 73;
period of dominance, Fig. 25,
46; linear and lateral types
of, Fig. 117, 232; some racial
types compared, 76; source
of the amelioration of his
features, 153; m. and primate,
characters of, 67; development, of, aided by eyes and
ears, 202; branchial skeleton
homologous with primate,
128; "gill slits" of embryo, 126
Ear (of man), external, chimpanzee type of, Fig. 110, 213;
of fœtal m., Fig. 109, 212
Ear (of man), middle, Fig. 111,
216; auditory ossicles, Fig.
115, 221
Ear (of man), internal, Fig. 103,
203; labyrinth of, Fig. 104,
205, Fig. 105, 206
Ear muscles, reduced, 215
Eye (of man), owes development to earliest primates, 90;
anthropoid and human, compared, 195; of shark and man
compared, 192; horizontal
section of, Fig. 100, 193; iris
of, 199

Embryo (of man), Fig. 69, 127,
Fig. 108, 211;
Face (of man)
of Armenian, Fig. 89, facing
170
of Bushman, South Africa,
Fig. 89, facing 170
of Hottentot woman, Fig. 90,
facing 172
of pygmy, African, Fig. 89,
facing 170
of Roman athlete, *frontispiece*
of Nordic Swede, Fig. 90,
facing 172
of Tasmanian, *frontispiece*
of Tyrolese, Fig. 89, facing
170
Facial muscles, origin of the,
Fig. 23, 42
Facial nerve, the Fig. 24, 44
Foot derived from grasping
type, 55
Head, longitudinal section, Fig.
67, 124
Jaws (of man), primary jaws
completely masked by secondary, 106; traces of primary
upper j. in embryo, 106; can
be traced from earliest Amphibia to m., 107; Fig. 50, 80;
Fig. 53, 85; owes plan of
upper and lower j. to mammal-like reptiles and earliest
mammals, 40; lower jaw of,
Fig. 37, 61; origin of zygomatic arch, 89; dominance of
superior maxilla in man, 89;
jaw muscles in, Fig. 61, 103;
muzzle of chimpanzee and
man compared, 142
Nose (of man), Jacobson's
organ lacking or vestigial in,
Fig. 65, 120; kinship of man
and anthropoids as shown by
external nose, 163; nasal
profiles, Fig. 88, 168; development of, 162; of fœtal man,
Fig. 84, 161; development of
nose in fœtal man, 162;
olfactory pit in fœtal man,
Fig. 65, 120; Jacobson's organ
in fœtal man, Fig. 65, 120,
Fig. 82, 159
Palate (of man), comparative
Anatomy of the Human, Fig.

INDEX

Man—(*Continued*)
Palate (of man)—(*Continued*)
66, 121; palatal arch (of white), Fig. 74, 140; development of palatal region in embryo, Fig. 65, 120; in embryo, sixth week, Fig. 66, 121
Skull (of man), side view, Fig. 36, 59, Fig. 48, 78, Fig. 49, 79, Fig. 50, 80, Fig. 51, 81; front view, Fig. 44, 70; longitudinal section, Fig. 83, 160; top view (Cro-Magnon), Fig. 43, 69
Teeth (of man), origin of his dentition, 90; difference between human and anthropoid, 141; traces of derivation of teeth from *Dryopithecus* and *Sivapithecus*, 58; Dentition of, Fig. 78, 148; "*Dryopithecus* pattern" in teeth of, Fig. 80, 151; his teeth and his diet, 57; dental formula of anthropoids and man, 145; development of, in embryo, 134, Fig. 71, 135; fovea anterior and posterior, 149; derived from anthropoids with well-developed canines (Remane), 142; front teeth of, 136; incisors of, 138; incisors, central, of white boy, Fig. 72, 137; incisors, central, of ancient Egyptian, Fig. 72, 137; incisors, three types of, Fig. 73, 139; incisors, upper central, kinship of man and anthropoids as shown by, 139; milk teeth of, Fig. 76, 146; milk teeth of, as derived from anthropoid type, 149; kinship of human and anthropoid lower molars, 146; comparison of molars with those of cynodonts, 145; identity of human and anthropoid molar patterns, 69; molar, lower, of Australian aborigine, Fig. 80, 151; molar, lower, of white man, Fig. 80, 151; history of upper and lower premolars and molars, 146; premolar, lower front, Fig. 75, 144

Cro-Magnon, highbred type of skull of, 73; lower jaw, sectioned, Fig. 45, 71; skull of, side view, Fig. 42, 68; skull of, top view, Fig. 43, 69
Ehringsdorf, *see* Man, Neanderthal (Ehringsdorf)
Heidelberg, chin of, 72; lower jaw of, Fig. 37, 61, Fig. 45, 71; teeth of, 143; lower molar of, Fig. 80, 151
Neanderthal, teeth of, 143
Neanderthal (La Chapelle-aux-Saints), skull of, front view, Fig. 44, 70; skull of, side view, Fig. 42, 68; skull of, top view, Fig. 43, 69
Neanderthal (Ehringsdorf), lower jaw of, Fig. 45, 71; central incisors of, Fig. 72, 137; lower front premolars of, Fig. 75, 144; lower molar of, Fig. 80, 151
Neanderthal (Krapina), "shovel-shaped" incisors of, 138
Neanderthal (Le Moustier), central incisors of, Fig. 72, 137; palatal arch of, Fig. 74, 140; dentition of, Fig. 78, 148; characters of teeth of, Fig. 45, 71, 72
Piltdown, *see* *Eoanthropus*
Rhodesian, skull of, side view, Fig. 42, 68; nose of, 72
Talgai, skull of, side view, Fig. 42, 68; prognathism of, 72
Trinil, *see* *Pithecanthropus*
Marmoset (*Midas*), skull of, Fig. 35, 58
Marsupials, relation to early mammals of, 47, 51; Jacobson's organ in, 159; nasal septum in, 167; skull of, Fig. 53, 85
Mask, bony, of ganoids, 23; Fig. 11, facing 22; of earliest Amphibia, 31; of reptiles, 43; of mammal-like reptiles, 36; of primitive living mammals, 43; starting-point of all cranial bones, 28; covered by facial and jaw muscles, 51
Mastiff, acromegaly and gigantism in, 231

INDEX

Matthew, W. D., contributions to palæontology, 86; *Eodelphis* named by, 47; evidence for conclusions on ancestry of placental mammals, 51

Maxillæ, series of ten skulls showing their evolution, Fig. 50, 80

Rhizodopsis
Palæogyrinus
Seymouria
Mycterosaurus
Scymnognathus
Ictidopsis
Didelphys
Notharctus
Chimpanzee, female
Man

covered with skin in early Amphibia, and reptiles, 130; unite with premaxillæ in anthropoids and man, 87; origin of, in crossopts, 130

of *Baphetes*, Fig. 63, 108
of *Eusthenopteron*, Fig. 63, 108
of *Seymouria*, 32

Maxilla, inferior, development in late mammal-like reptiles, 90; ascending ramus forms mammalian joint with the squamosal, 87

of chimpanzee, Fig. 45, 71
of Cro-Magnon man, Fig. 45, 71
of *Dryopithecus*, Fig. 45, 71
of Heidelberg man, Fig. 45, 71
of Neanderthal man (Ehringsdorf), Fig. 45, 71
of Neanderthal man (Le Moustier), Fig. 45, 71

Maxilla, superior, homologous in crossopts and early Amphibia, 107; evolution of, 87; position of, 107; series showing evolution of, Fig. 53, 85; dominance of, in man, 89; in achondroplasia, 230; of cynodonts, secondary palate derived from, 119; of mammal-like reptiles, Fig. 50, 80; of mammals, Fig. 50, 80, 87

of *Adapis*, Fig. 53, 85
of *Baphetes*, Fig. 53, 85
of *Captorhinus*, Fig. 53, 85
of chimpanzee Fig. 53, 85

of *Cynognathus*, Fig. 53, 85
of *Eusthenopteron*, Fig. 53, 85
of man, Fig. 53, 85
of *Mycterosaurus*, 34
of *Scymnognathus*, Fig. 53, 85
of *Seymouria*, Fig. 53, 85
of *Thylacinus*, Fig. 53, 85

McGregor, J. H., restorations of primitive man by, 143

Meati, nasal, 161, 162

Meckel's cartilage, as primary lower jaw, 102; articular bone develops from, 112; of armadillo, fœtal, Fig. 114, 221; of Devonian crossopts, 110; of shark, Fig. 6, 13, Fig. 7, 17, Fig. 8, 18, 106

Median cartilage (of nose), origin of, 167; growth of, in orang, 169

Megalichthys, lower jaw of, Fig. 64, 111

Meibomian glands, in human eyelid, 194

Melanesians, noses of, 169

Meniscus, of mammalian joint, in *Perameles*, Fig. 22, 38, 39

Mental traits, human and anthropoid agree in basic, 74

Mesethmoid bone, origin of the, 167

Microchœrus, dentition of, Fig. 78, 148

Midas, top view of skull, Fig. 35, 58

Midgets, cause of, 231

Miller, G. S., on hind feet of primates, 54

Mimetic muscles, origin of the, 43, 44

Miocene, Primates began to assume human characters in, 64; anthropoid adaptations during, 91

Molar teeth, identity of human and anthropoid molar patterns, 69; fovea anterior and posterior in upper molars of anthropoids and man, 149; origin of, 90
of cynodonts, 116
of cynodonts and man compared, 145
of fossil man, 143
of primitive man, 76

279

Molars, lower, kinship of human and anthropoid, 146
of chimpanzee, Fig. 79, 150
of *Dryopithecus cautleyi*, Fig. 79, 150
of *D. fontani*, Fig. 79, 150
of *D. frickæ*, Fig. 41, facing 66, Fig. 79, 150
"*Dryopithecus* pattern" in, 149, Fig. 80, 151
of gorilla, Fig. 79, 150
of *Homo heidelbergensis*, Fig. 80, 151
of orang, Fig. 79, 150
Lower (left) *m.*, of *Dryopithecus rhenanus*, Fig. 38, 62
of *Eoanthropus dawsoni*, Fig. 38, 62, Fig. 41, facing 66
of *Homo neanderthalensis* (Le Moustier), Fig. 38, 62
of *Homo sapiens*, Fig. 38, 62
of *Leipsanolestes*, Fig. 38, 62
of *Parapithecus*, Fig. 38, 62
of *Pelycodus*, Fig. 38, 62
of *Propliopithecus*, Fig. 38, 62
Molars, upper, of *Dryopithecus rhenanus*, 149
of *Homo neanderthalensis* (Le Moustier), Fig. 78, 148, 149
Upper (left), of *Dryopithecus rhenanus*, Fig. 38, 62
of *Homo neanderthalensis* (Le Moustier), Fig. 38, 62
of *Homo sapiens*, Fig. 38, 62
of *Indrodon*, Fig. 38, 62
of *Pelycodus*, Fig. 38, 62
of *Propliopithecus* (restored), Fig. 38, 62
Mollusca, development of eye in cephalopod, Fig. 95, 181; paired eyes of higher, 178
Mongolia, Cretaceous mammals from, 51; insectivores from Cretaceous of, Fig. 29, 50
Mongolian face, the, 170
Mongolian nose, its shape, 164, 171
Mongolians, "shovel-shaped" incisors of, 138
Monkeys, catarrhine, external ears of, 214; face of, *frontispiece*, 56, Fig. 34, facing 56; incisors of, 138; nasal chamber of, 161; nose of, 56, 57; orbital axes of, Fig. 35, 58, 196; skull of (*Lasiopyga kolbi*),

Fig. 36, 59; platyrrhine, as offshoot from some primitive tarsioid stock, 56; face of (*Cebus capucinus*), Fig. 34, facing 56; lips of, 56; nose of, 56; orbital axes of *Midas*, Fig. 35, 58, 196
Morton, D. J., on hind feet of primates, 54
Montana, mammalian teeth from Basal Eocene of, 53; *Eodelphis* from Upper Cretaceous of, 47
Mouth, as dominant element of face, 4; conclusions from history of, 152; origin of, uncertain below ostracoderms, 101; nasal sac as outgrowth of, 154
of ancestral prevertebrate forms, 94
of *Amphioxus*, Fig. 54, 92, 129
of annelid worms, 6
of *Cephalaspis* (restoration), Fig. 57, 95
of crossopts, 130
of jellyfish (*Tessera*), 4, Fig. 1, 5
of *Kiaeraspis* (restoration), Fig. 57, 95
of lamprey, adult, 129
of lamprey, larval, 129
of man, fœtal, third week, Fig. 69, 127
of ostracoderms, 129
of *Paramœcium*, Fig. 1, 5
of platypus, 131
of shark, Fig. 5, facing 12
Mouth-legs, of *Orchestia*, Fig. 2, facing 6
of trilobites, 6
Mouth pouches, embryonic, 94
of larval lamprey, longitudinal section, Fig. 56, 94
of rabbit, embryo, Fig. 56, 94
of sharks and embryo vertebrates, supported by cartilaginous bars, 102
Muscles
of accommodation (ciliary), 193
of accommodation, in eyes of *Sepia*, 180
of check and lips, important to new-born mammals, 134; constrictor, of gill arches: jaw muscles of shark derived from, 104

INDEX

Muscles—(*Continued*)
  of the ear, 133
  of the ear, reduced in man, 215
  of the eyeball, in man, Fig. 98,
    190
  of vertebrate eye, 191
  of the eye of shark (*Chlamy-
    doselachus*), Fig. 6, 13, 15
  Facial, origin and development
    of the, 43; origin of, in mam-
    mals, 132
  of gorilla, Fig. 23, 42, 67, 124
  of man, Fig. 23, 42
  geniohyoglossus, of anthropoids,
    126
  of man, Fig. 67, 124, Fig. 68, 125
  of monkey, Fig. 68, 125
  of jaw development associated
    with change of jaw form, 116;
    evolution of the, Fig. 61,
    103
  of fishes, 104
  of shark, their derivation, 104
  of chimpanzee, Fig. 61, 103
  of *Chlamydoselachus*, Fig. 8, 18,
    also Fig. 61, 103
  of *Cynognathus*, Fig. 61, 103
  of *Didelphys*, Fig. 61, 103, *also*
    49
  of *Eryops*, Fig. 61, 103
  of man, Fig. 61, 103
  of *Notharctus*, Fig. 61, 103
  of *Polypterus*, Fig. 61, 103
  of *Scymnognathus*, Fig. 61, 103
  masseter, 116; at corner of
    mouth of some reptiles, 131;
    orbicularis oris, 133; orbi-
    cularis oris of catarrhine
    monkeys, 56; platysma, the
    origin of the, 43; pterygoid,
    116–117; pterygoid, external,
    and mammalian joint, Fig.
    22, 38, 39; sphincter colli,
    43, 132
  of *Echidna*, Fig. 23, 42
  of *Sphenodon*, Fig. 23, 42
  temporal, 116
  of tongue (geniohyoglossus) in
    anthropoids, Fig. 67, 124
Muscle fibres, striped, function of
  the, 19
Mycterosaurus (Permo-Carboniferous), dentition of, Fig. 77,
  147; skull of, Fig. 19, 33,
  Fig. 48, 78

Nares, of crossopts, 24
Naris, internal, series of skulls
  showing evolution of, Fig.
  53, 85
  of *Adapis*
  of *Baphetes*
  of *Captorhinus*
  of chimpanzee
  of *Cynognathus*
  of *Eusthenopteron*
  of man (Australian aboriginal)
  of *Scymnognathus*
  of *Seymouria*
  of *Thylacinus*
Nasal bones, series of skulls showing evolution of, Fig. 49, 79;
  their origin in Amphibia
  30; retained from fish to
  mammals, 86; in advanced
  lemuroids, 60
Nasal chamber, median partition
  of, 158; sinuses and antra of,
  162; of mammal-like reptiles,
  158; of man and monkeys,
  compared, 161
Nasal field, in embryonic development, 166
Nasal meati, 161; connections of
  sinuses with, Fig. 85, 163
Nasal pit of larval lamprey, Fig.
  56, 94
Nasal sac, embryonic origin of,
  154; of embryo sharks and
  mammals, 154
Nasal septum, rates of development of the, 167
Naso-buccal groove, of sharks,
  Fig. 66, 121, 122, 154,
  157
Naso-lacrymal duct, in man,
  194
Naso-pharyngeal passage, 119
Nautilus, eye of, 181
Neanderthal man, *see* Man,
  Neanderthal
Negritos, the nose of, 169
Negro, the iris of, 199; develop-
  ment of the nose in, 167; the
  nose of, 169; Fig. 88, 168;
  the nose of, infant, Fig. 88,
  168
Negro pygmy, nose of the, 164
Nematodes, effect of ultraviolet
  rays on, 174
Neoceratodus, 25

281

Nerve, seventh cranial activates sphincter colli, 43; facial, chief branches of, in man and gorilla, Fig. 24, 44; facial, of *Sphenodon*, Fig. 23, 42; oculomotor, of chimpanzee, 198; olfactory, course and function of, 155; optic, description of, 187, 188; optic, human, function of, 191; optic, of *Sepia*, 180; of semicircular canals, 204, 206

Nerve cells, olfactory, 157

Nervous system of primates, studies of, 63

New Mexico, Notharctidæ from Eocene of, 54; early placental mammals from, 52

Nictitating membrane, vestiges of, in man, 194

Norway, ostracoderms of, 10

Nose, progressive stages in development of, vertebrate, 157; shapes of the human, 164, Fig. 89, facing 170; great diversity of form in the, 172; extreme forms of, Fig. 89, facing 170; factors controlling form of the, 168–171; effect of the bony palate on, 169; effect of premaxillæ on, 168; hereditary factors in 172, 236; development of human, 162; development in fœtal and adult man, 163; varying rates of development of its parts, 167; Prof. Schultz' studies on growth of, 172; embryonic stages of human, Fig. 65, 120, Fig. 82, 159; human, as index of character, 220; shows kinship of man and anthropoids, 163; nasal sinuses of man and anthropoids, 161; septal cartilage of human, Fig. 88, 168; origin of median cartilage in mammalian, 167; olfactory capsules of mammal-like reptiles, 158; naso-buccal groove of shark, Fig. 66, 121, 154, 157; nasal meati, 161; nasal sac, embryonic origin in shark and mammal, 154; embryonic development of mammalian, 166; Jacobson's organ, 158; lateral (or alar) cartilage, 167; primary function of the, 154; essential parts of the, 155; bridge of the, 170; the humped *n.*, cause of, 169; the Mongolian nose, 171; the pug nose, cause of, 169, 171; the wide nose, cause of, 169; shape of, in achondroplasia, 169, 230

in acromegaly, 171

in cretinism, 171

of gorilla, 170

of gorilla, fœtal, Fig. 84, 161

of catarrhine monkey, 56

of shark, 154

of man, fœtal, Fig. 84, 161

of man, infant, 167

of Armenian, Fig. 89, facing 170

of Australian aboriginal, 169

of South African Bushman, Fig. 89, facing 170

of Hittite type, 169; Fig. 89, facing 170

of Melanesian, 169

of Mongolian, 164

of negrito, 169

of negro, 169, Fig. 88, 168

of negro child, Fig. 88, 168

of Papuan, 169

of African pygmy, 164, Fig. 89, facing 170

of Rhodesian man, 72

of Tasmanian, 169

of Tyrolese, Fig. 89, facing 170

of white adult, Fig. 88, 168

of white child, Fig. 88, 168

Nostrils of catarrhine monkeys, 57

Nostrils, internal (choanæ) of early amphibia, Fig. 53, 85, 118

of lung fishes, 157

Notharctidæ, from Eocene of Wyoming and New Mexico, 54; compared with lemurs of Madagascar, 54

Notharctus (Eocene), compared with chimpanzee and man, 65; position of eyes in, Fig. 35, 58, 196; jaw muscles of, Fig. 61, 103; olfactory chamber of, 196; skeleton of *N. osborni*, Fig. 32 facing 54;

INDEX

Notharctus (Eocene)—(*Continued*)
skull of, side view, Fig. 33, 55,
Fig. 36, 59, Fig. 48, 78; skull
of, top view, Fig. 35, 58
Notochord, 21
Nycticebus, external ear of, Fig.
110, 213

Ocellus
of flatworm (*Planaria*), Fig. 2,
facing 6
of jellyfish (*Catablema*), Fig. 91,
175
of jellyfish (*Sarsia*), Fig. 91, 175
of sand flea (*Orchestia*), Fig.
2, facing 6
Octopus, eyes of, 179
Oculomotor nerves, of chimpanzee, 198
Olfactory capsule, its place in the
skull structure, 83; in embryonic development, 167;
the value of double, 156;
in human embryo, 162, Fig.
65, 120
of mammal-like reptiles, 158
of shark, Fig. 6, 13, 14, Fig. 7,
17, 122, 154, Fig. 81, 155
Olfactory chamber
of early amphibia, 118
of *Lemur*, 58
of *Notharctus*, 196
of *Notharctus osborni*, 56
Olfactory membrane, function of
the, 158
Olfactory nerve, course and function of the, 155
Olfactory nerve cells, as specialized cell of skin, 157
Olfactory pit,
in human embryo, Fig. 65, 120
of shark, 122
Olfactory sac, 157
Olfactory sense organs, 155
Oligocene, lower, separation of
man from early anthropoids
in (Osborn), 74
Ontogenetic study of physiognomy, 224
Opercular notch, eardrum formed
in location of, 89
Opercular tract, elimination of
plates of, in early amphibia,
Fig. 17, 30, 114
Opossum, fossil (*Eodelphis*), 47;

skull of, Fig. 48, 78; compared
to that of *Didelphys*, Fig. 27,
48
Opossum, recent (*Didelphys*), most
primitive marsupial of today,
47; with young, Fig. 26,
facing 46; jaw muscles of,
Fig. 61, 103; skull compared
with that of *Eodelphis*, Fig.
27, 48; skull of, Fig. 28, 49
Optic capsule, of shark, Fig. 7, 17
Optic cups, formation of the, Fig.
97, 185, 187; development of
retina from, in vertebrates,
181
Optic nerve, description of the,
188; function of the, 191; of
Sepia, 180
Optic pouch, of the jellyfish, 175
Oral cartilage, of shark and
embryo vertebrates, 102
Orang, pattern of papillæ vallatæ
similar to that in man, 123;
external ear of, Fig. 110, 213,
214; palatal arch of female,
Fig. 74, 140; lacrymal bone
of, 200; nose of, 169; skull of
young, front view, Fig. 102,
197; teeth, lower molar, Fig.
79, 150; tongue of, 123
"Orang type," of human ear,
Fig. 110, 213
Orbicularis oris muscle
of anthropoid apes and man,
133
of catarrhine monkeys, 56
Orbital axes
of lemuroids, Fig. 35, 58, 196
of platyrrhine monkeys, Fig. 35,
58, 196
of catarrhine monkeys, Fig. 35,
58, 196
of anthropoids, Fig. 35, 58, 196
Orbits
of advanced lemuroids, 60
of lower primates, 60
of orang, 169
of *Tarsius*, Fig. 31, facing 53, 60
Orchestia (Sand-flea), Fig. 2, facing 6
Organ of Corti, the, Fig. 103,
203, 204
Organs, lateral line, of fishes, 206
Organ, parapineal, 186; pineal, 186
Ornithorhynchus, mouth of, 131

INDEX

Oronasal groove, *see* nasobuccal groove

Osborn, H. F., evidence for his conclusions on ancestry of placental mammals, 51; view of separation of man and apes from primitive stock, 74

Ossicles, auditory, *see* Ear, auditory ossicles

Osteolepidæ (Crossopterygii) closely related to Amphibia of Carboniferous, 114

Osteolepis (Devonian), skull of, cross section, Fig. 9, facing 20; seen from above, Fig. 11, facing 22; spiracular cleft in, 209

Ostracoderms, probably ancestral to cyclostomes, 186; a modern descendant of the, Fig. 59, 97; their use of cilia for ingestion, 95; ingestion transitional between ciliary and predacious, 97; origin of mouth jaws and teeth uncertain below, 101; mouth of, 129; denticles in skin of, 117; teeth of (*Lanarkia*), 117; Prof. Patten on, 8; Stensiö on cephalaspid o., 94; Anaspida, characters of the order, 96; Fig. 4, 11

Cephalaspis, restoration of, Fig. 4, 11; restoration of head of, Fig. 57, 95

Kiæraspis, restoration of head of, Fig. 57, 95

Lanarkia, shagreen denticles of, 100

Pteraspis, restoration of, Fig. 4, 11

Pterolepis nitidus, restoration of, Fig. 4, 11, *also* Fig. 58, 96

Otic capsule, as a component of the chondrocranium, 83; of shark, Fig. 7, 17, Fig. 81, 155

Otic notch, in early amphibians, 29, 209, Fig. 17, 30

of *Seymouria*, 32, Fig. 19, 33

in reptiles, 209

Otoliths, 206

Palæogyrinus, skull of, showing loss of opercular series, Fig. 17, 30; side view of, Figs. 48–52, 78–82

Palatal arches, reduction in size of teeth, factor in shortening of, 143

of gibbon, female, Fig. 74, 140

of gorilla, male, Fig. 74, 140

of chimpanzee, female, Fig. 74, 140

of orang, female, Fig. 74, 140

of Neanderthal man (Le Moustier), Fig. 74, 140

of modern white man, Fig. 74, 140

Palatal bone, 83

Palatal region

of cynodonts, Fig. 52, 82

of *Scymnognathus*, Fig. 53, 85, 118

progressive changes in, Fig. 53, 85, 118

of mammals, Fig. 53, 85, 119

in human embryo, 120

Palate, bony, its effect on shape of nose, 169; comparative anatomy of human, Fig. 66, 121; cleft, human, 228; cleft palate, in *Felis leo*, Fig. 66, 121; fleshy, possible rudiments in *Scymnognathus*, 119; of lizard, Fig. 66, 121; primitive, formation of, 122; reptilian, 122; secondary, in human embryo, Fig. 66, 162; of cynodonts, Fig. 52, 119; soft, of mammals, 119

Palatine bone, of cynodonts, 119

Palatoquadrate,

of Devonian crossopts, 109

of *Diadectes*, Fig. 62, 105

of shark, Fig. 6, 13, 17, Fig. 7, 17, Fig. 8, 18, 106

Palatoquadrate cartilages, 102

Paleocene of New Mexico, early placental mammals in, 52

Pantotherian, dentition of, Fig. 77, 147

Papillæ vallatæ, of orang similar to those of man, 123

Papuans, noses of, 169

Paramœcium (Slipper animalcule), face of, 4; mouth of, Fig. 1, 5

Parapineal eye, Fig. 97, 185; as directional organ, 200

Parapineal organ, origin of, 187; in pre-chordates, 186

Parapithecus, lower jaw of *P. fraasi*, Fig. 37, 61; left lower molar of, Fig. 38, 62

INDEX

Parasphenoid, of fish, 22; enlargement in amphibians of, 31

Parietal bones, evolution of, Fig. 49, 79; of opossum, 49; as components of dermocranium, 83; among dominant elements of human skull, 87

Parker, G. H., cited on hearing of fishes, 206

Parker, W. K., cited on embryology of sturgeon, 209

Patten, William, theory of derivation of vertebrates, 7, 8, 92, 182; cited on derivation of vertebrate eye, 182

Pecten, eyes of, 178

Pelvic floor, Sir Arthur Keith on the primate, 63

Pelvis, evolution of primate, 63

Pelycodus, lower jaw of, Fig. 37, 61; left lower and upper molars of, Fig. 38, 62

Pen-tailed tree-shrew, Fig. 30, facing 52

Perameles, formation of meniscus in embryo of, Fig. 22, 38, 39

Periotic mass, fusion of squamosal bone with, in mammals, 88

Permian period, labyrinthodonts and stegocephalians of the, 115; *Mycterosaurus*, of the, 34; *Seymouria*, of the, 32

Permocynodon, middle ear of, Fig. 112, 217

Pharynx, function in respiration of, 162
   of *Amphioxus*, 98
   of larval lamprey, 98

Philtrum, of the lip, in man, 133; embryonic development of the, 166

Phototropism, 174

Physiognomy, anthropological method of study of, 224; Aristotle on, 220; the author analyzes his own face, 225–229; clinical method of study of, 224; Darwin's study of, 223; Duchenne's study of (experimental method), 223; embryological study of, 224; evolutionary method of study of, 223; experimental method of study of (Duchenne's), 223; genetic method of study of, 224; origins of modern science of, 222; physiological method of study of, 224; psychiatrist's method of study of, 225; psychoanalyst's method of study of, 225; psychologic method of study of, 224; Sir Charles Bell's study of, 222; study of correlation between crime and types of, 225

Piltdown man (*Eoanthropus*), canine tooth of, 141; characters of, 72, 73; lower jaw of, Fig. 37, 61; Fig. 45, 71, 143; lower molar of, Fig. 38, 62; Fig. 41, facing 66

Pineal eye, Fig. 97, 185, 200

Pineal organ, origin of, 187; in pre-chordates, 186

Pithecanthropus (Trinil man), characters of, 72, 73; skull of (side view), Fig. 42, 68; skull of (top view), Fig. 43, 69

Pituitary glands, effects of diseased, 171

Placental mammals, their forerunners from Mongolia, 51; in Basal Eocene and Paleocene of New Mexico, 52

Planaria, eyes of, as directional organs, Fig. 93, 178; head and tail differentiation of, Fig. 2, facing 6; location of eyes of, Fig. 92, 177

Plant life, origin in Archeozoic era, 27

Plate, L., cited on origin and development of the eye, 174–188; summary of literature on eyes of invertebrates and vertebrates, 174; on eyes of *Amphioxus*, 183, 184; on eye capsules of flatworm, Fig. 93, 178; on human vision, *footnote*, 174; on paired eyes of vertebrates, 178

Platypus, believed related to some mammals of Age of Reptiles, 47; mouth of, 131

Platyrrhine monkeys, see Monkeys, platyrrhine

Platysma muscle, origin of, 43

Pleistocene, lower, already several types of man in, 73

INDEX

Plica semilunaris, of human eye, Fig. 101, 194; as vestige of third eyelid, 194

Pliocene, fossil human record a blank during the, 70, 142; reduction of human canine teeth may have occurred during the, 142

Polyplocodus, teeth of, Fig. 18, following, 30

Polypterus, embryo of, Fig. 14, 26; jaw muscles of, Fig. 61, 103; representative of lobe-finned ganoids, 24

Postfrontal bone, eliminated by time of earliest mammals, 88, 90

Postorbital bone, joint process of frontal and malar replace, 90; eliminated by time of earliest mammals, 88, 90; evolution of, Fig. 51, 81

Postsplenial bone, series of skulls showing evolution of, Fig. 52, 82; reduction of, 88; of *Megalichthys*, Fig. 64, 111; of *Trimerorhachis*, Fig. 64, 111

Posture, its effect upon development of face, Fig. 36, 59, 64, 66; characters of early primates adapted to, 67, 68

Prearticular bone, of *Trimerorhachis*, Fig. 64, 111

Pre-chordates, eyes of, 186

Predaceous habits, organization of primitive vertebrates adapted to, 101

Prefrontal bone, evolution of, Fig. 51, 81; eliminated by time of earliest mammals, 88

Premaxilla, evolution of, Fig. 50, 80; Fig. 53, 85; position of, 107; effect on shape of nose, 168; unites with maxilla in anthropoids and man, 87; of crossopt and early amphibian are homologous, 107; of *Baphetes*, Fig. 63, 108; of *Eusthenopteron*, Fig. 63, 108; covered with skin in early amphibians and reptiles, 130; origin of, in crossopts, 130

Premolars, in primitive man, 76; origin of, 90; of cynodonts, 116; of fossil man, 143; of *Dryopithecus*, *Sivapithecus*, Neanderthal and *Homo sapiens*, Fig. 75, 144; front lower, of anthropoids, 144; nearest affinities of human, 144

Preoperculum, elimination of, Fig. 17, 30, 114

Presphenoid bone, 167

Pre-vertebrates, *see* Chordates

Prevomer bones, evolution of, Fig. 53, 85; of Devonian crossopts, 100

Primates, mammals of Basal Eocene of Montana approach the, 53; family Notharctidæ, 54; hind foot of, always of tree-grasping type, 54; comparison of hands and feet of fossil and recent, 54; arboreal stage passed through by all, 54; skeleton of primitive fossil, Fig. 32, facing 54; skull of primitive fossil, Fig. 33, 55; faces of lower, Fig. 34, facing 56; traces of insectivorous dentition in, 57; ears of the lower, 57; top view of skulls of, Fig. 35, 58; side view of skulls of, Fig. 36, 59; Epitome of Fossil History of, Figs. 37, 38, 61, 62; value of study of fossil and recent, 60; rare as fossils, 60; relation of upper jaws to eyes in, 60; Keith cited on diaphragm, abdomen and pelvic floor of, 63; progressive series presented by brains of, 63; agreement of results of studies on internal and external anatomy and fossil history of, 63; time of assumption of human characters of, 64; enlargement of brain characteristic of, 64; correlated use of eyes, hands and feet in, 64; man derived from Old World, 65; development of eyes of, 65; characters adapted to diet and posture in, 67; characters of man, and 67; man owes

INDEX

Primates—(*Continued*)
development of eyes to early,
90; postorbital bar replaced
by process from frontal and
malar bones in earliest, 90;
character of tongue in, 123;
branchial skeleton of, homologous with human, 128;
salivary glands of, 129; lips
of, 133; Jacobson's organ
lacking or vestigial in higher,
159; nasal septum of, 167;
eyes of primitive, 196; reduced olfactory apparatus in
higher, 196
"Primitive streak," mouth of
Tessera represents, 5
Pro-anthropoids, man derived
from, 69; changes of skull in
arboreal, 91
Protista, supposed rudimentary
eyes of, 174
Protozoa, among earliest marine
invertebrates, 8
Psychiatrist, method of study of
physiognomy by, 225
Psychoanalyst, method of study of
physiognomy by, 225
Psychologic method of study of
physiognomy, 224
Pteraspis, Fig. 4, 11; mouth of, 96
Pterolepis nitidus, Fig. 58, 96
Pterygoid bone, of *Diadectes*, Fig.
62, 105; effect of increase in
size of, 117
Pterygoid muscle, origin of meniscus in, Fig. 22, 38; Gaupp
cited on, 39; influence of its
development on skull, 117
Pulp cavity, in formation of teeth,
134, Fig. 71, 135
Purple, visual (rhodopsin), 189
Pygmy, African, nose of the, 164,
Fig. 89, facing 170

Quadrate bone, 39; evolution of,
Fig. 53, 85; of *Diadectes*, Fig.
62, 105
Quadratojugal bone, evolution of,
Fig. 52, 82; Fig. 53, 85;
reduction of, 88

Rabbit, embryo, mouth pouch of,
Fig. 56, 94; labyrinth of, Fig.
104, 205

Radial symmetry, gives way to
bilateral, 6
Remane, A., cited on incisors of
chimpanzee, 138, 141; study
of anthropoid teeth by, 142;
cited on front lower pre-
molar of man and anthro-
poids, 145
Reptiles, *Seymouria* most primitive, 32; sphincter colli of,
43; period of dominance of,
45, Fig. 25, 46; loss of inter-
and supra-temporals from
skull of early, 89; progressive
changes in teeth of, Fig. 53,
85, 115; naso-buccal channel
of, 122; skin-covered maxillæ,
premaxillæ and dentary of
early, 130; muscle at corner
of mouth of some recent, 131;
Jacobson's organ in, 158;
stage in development of nose
of human embryo like that of,
162; tympanum of, 217; mammal-like, skulls of earlier and
later, Fig. 20, 35; progressive
upgrowth of dentary bone of,
Fig. 21, 37, 108; initial stages
in formation of hair possibly
developed in Triassic, 42;
opossum similar to Triassic,
48, Fig. 28, 49; superior
maxillary of, Fig. 50, 80, 87;
inferior maxillary in, 87;
origin of temporal fossa and
zygomatic arch in early, 89;
development of temporal fossa
in later, 90; palatal region of,
Fig. 53, 85, 118; nasal septum
of, 167; relation of parts of
middle ear in, Fig. 112, 217;
internal ear of advanced, 218;
angular bone of, 218
Reptilian postorbital bar, loss of,
by early mammals, 90
Reptilian stage, in development of
auditory ossicles, Fig. 115, 221
Respiration, origin and function
of the diaphragm, 41; of
early amphibians, 118; of
mammals, 119; of sharks,
Keith cited on, 122; of
dipnoan fishes, Keith cited
on, 122; of air-breathing
fishes and amphibia, 157

Retina, of the squid (*Sepia*), 180; of cephalopods, 181, Fig. 95, 181; of vertebrates, developed from optic cup, 181; formation of the, Fig. 97, 185; of dorsal eyes in pre-chordates, Studnicka cited on, 186, 187; apparently represents inverted patch of epithelium, 187; layers of the, 188; likened to sensitive plate of camera, 189; function of human, 191; of shark, Fig. 99, 192; human, Fig. 100, 193

Rhinarium, of lemur, 56

Rhizodopsis, skull of, Fig. 17, 30; Figs. 48–52, 78–82

Rhodesian man, skull of, Fig. 42, 68, 72

Rhodopsin (visual purple), 189

Ribs, their origin, 21

"Rods," of the primitive eye, 175; in eyes of cephalopods, Fig. 94, 179, 180; in eyes of vertebrates, 180; in organ of Corti, 204

Rods and cones, as layer of retina, 188; of human eye, 190

Rotifers, effect of ultraviolet rays on, 174

Ruge, G., on origin of facial muscles, 44; researches of, show anatomy of facial muscles most like in man and anthropoids, 132, 133; monograph on facial musculature of, shows likeness between ear muscles of chimpanzee and human embryos and children, 215

Sacculus, of inner ear of lower vertebrates, Fig. 104, 205–206

St. Bernard dog, acromegaly and gigantism in, 231

Salamander, skull of fœtal, Fig. 62, 105; embryo of, Fig. 14, 26

Salivary glands, of man and apes, 129

Sand-flea (*Orchestia*), Fig. 2, facing, 6

Sarsia, eye of, Fig. 91, 175

Scales, origin of, in skin of pre-vertebrates, 101; of crossopts,

same nature as covering of primary jaws, 106

Scallop (*Pecten*), eyes of, 178

Schultz, A. H., cited on hind feet of primates, 54; on nose of human fœtus, 164; on development of human nose, 167; studies on human nose, 172

Sclera, of shark, Fig. 99, 192; of human eye, Fig. 100, 193

Sclerotic layer, of eye of vertebrates, 188

Scylacosaurus, dentition of, Fig. 77, 147

Scymnognathus, skull of, Fig. 20, 35; Fig. 21, 37; Figs. 48–53, 78–85; jaw muscles of, Fig. 61, 103

Sea-cucumber, larva of (*Auricularia*), Fig. 55, 93

Sebaceous glands, origin and function of, 41

Semicircular canals, of ear of shark, 16; of human ear, 202, Fig. 103, 203; of primitive fish, 204; nerves of the, 204, 206; of frog, Fig. 106, 208

Sense organs, origin from skin of, 101; mystery of their origin, 156; value of bilateral arrangement of, 156

Sepia (squid), structure of eyes of, Fig. 94, 179, 180

Septal cartilage, in man, Fig. 88, 168

Septum, nasal, origin of, 167; rates of development of, in anthropoid and man, 167

Seymouria, restoration of face of, *frontispiece;* most primitive reptile, 32; otic notch of, 32; skull of, Fig. 19, 33; Figs. 48–53, 78–85; teeth of, 118

Shagreen, of skin, origin of teeth, 19; in primitive sharks, 109

Shagreen denticles, development of, into teeth, Fig. 60, 99; skin of pre-vertebrates gave rise to, 101

Shark, Devonian (Cladoselache), restoration of face of, *frontispiece;* our own face shown in that of, 12; recent (*Chlamydoselachus*), face of, Fig. 5,

INDEX

Shark, Devonian—(*Continued*)
facing 12; instruments of precision in head of, Fig. 6, 13, 14; olfactory capsules of, Fig. 6, 13, 14; Fig. 7, 17, Fig. 81, 155; eye muscles of, Fig. 6, 13, 15; shark nearer to man than to invertebrates, 14, 102; and his prey, 15; taste organs of, 16; "ampullæ" in head of, 16, 204; "internal ears" of, 16; cartilaginous skeleton of head of, Fig. 7, 17; primary jaws of, Figs. 7, 8, 17, 18, Fig. 62, 105; palatoquadrate of, Figs. 7, 8, 17, 18; labial cartilages of, Figs. 7, 8, 17, 18; hyoid of, Fig. 7, 17; hyomandibula of, Figs. 7, 8, 17, 18; jaw muscles of, Fig. 8, 18, Fig. 61, 103; derivation of jaw muscles of, 104; otic capsule of, Fig. 7, 17, Fig. 81, 155; optic capsule of, Fig. 7, 17; skin of the, 19; chemical composition of skeleton of, 23; facial expression of, 19; mouth pouches of embryonic, 94; three stages in development of teeth of, Fig. 60, 99; visceral arches in predecessors of, 104; mouth pouches supported by cartilaginous bars, 104; secondary jaws represented only by skin, 106; development of teeth in typical, 109; less advanced than crossopt, 113; tongue of, 123; dissection of head of, Fig. 81, 155; oronasal groove of, Fig. 66, 121, 154, 157; method of respiration of, 122; mouth of, 130; spiracle of, Fig. 81, 155; eye of, nearer to that of man than to any invertebrate eye, 191; horizontal section of eye of, Fig. 99, 192; labyrinth of, Fig. 104, 205

Shark-like stage, of human eye, 191

Shoulder-girdle, Watson cited on, of fossil amphibians, 28, Fig. 15, 28

Shrew, *see* Tree-shrew

Shylock, and the shark, 12

Silurian and Devonian ostracoderms, 10, Fig. 4, 11; Kiær and Stensiö cited on, 10, 11, 12, 94, 97, 98; *Lanarkia*, 100

"Simian shelf" of Piltdown man, Fig. 45, 71, 143

Sinus, nasal, of man and anthropoids, 161, 162; frontal, connection with nasal meati, Fig. 85, 163; ethmoid, connection with nasal meati, Fig. 85, 163; sphenoid, connection with nasal meati, Fig. 85, 163

Sivapithecus, traces of derivation of human dentition from, 58; lower jaw of, Fig. 37, 61; dental formula of, Fig. 37, 61; front lower premolars of, 144, Fig. 75, 144; upper molars of, 140

Skeleton, of shark, its chemical composition, 23; of *Notharctus*, Fig. 32, facing 54

Skin, of shark, 19; potentialities of, 100; structures derivative from, 101; origin of some sense organs in, 101; origin of teeth in, 101, 109; dentary, maxillæ and premaxillæ of advanced crossopts covered by, 130; on bill of *Platypus*, 131

Skull, heritage of the, 20, 28, 89; structure of the, 21, 83; comparison of lobe-finned ganoid, with early amphibian, 29, 107; simplification of the, 31; formation of mammalian joint of, 39, 90; of some placental mammals approaches that of lowest Primates, 53; dominant elements of human, 87; evolution of human, from fish to man, Figs. 48–53, 78–85; changes in lateral view of, from fish to man, 86–91; factors determining changes in structure of, 88–89; genesis of temporal bone of, 88; loss of bones covering branchial chamber of, 89; changes of, in arboreal pro-anthropoids, 91; attach-

INDEX

Skull—*(Continued)*
    ment of primary upper jaw
    to, 104, Fig. 62, 105; dentary-
    squamosal contact in, 108,
    109; Keith cited on develop-
    ment of, 122; position of
    temporal region of, condi-
    tioned by size of brain, 170;
of achondroplastic dwarf, 230
of *Adapis*, Fig. 53, 85
of *Arctocebus*, top view, Fig. 35,
    58
of *Australopithecus*, Fig. 42, 68,
    72; side view, Fig. 46, facing
    72
of *Baphetes*, under side, Fig. 53,
    85, Fig. 63, 108
of chimpanzee,
    top view, Fig. 35, 58, Fig.
        43, 69
    side view, Fig. 36, 59
    near to human, 65
    front view, Fig. 44, 70
    bones of, Figs. 48-53, 78-85
    longitudinal section, Fig. 83,
        160
    young, front view, Fig. 102,
        197
of Cro-Magnon, side view, Fig.
    42, 68; top view, Fig. 43, 69;
    high-bred, 73
of *Cynognathus*, Fig. 53, 85
of *Deltatheridium*, Fig. 29, 50
of *Diadectes*, Fig. 62, 105
of *Eodelphis*, Fig. 27, 48, Fig.
    48, 78
of *Eusthenopteron*, Fig. 53, 85,
    Fig. 63, 108
of gorilla, young, Fig. 102, 197
of *Hylobates* (gibbon), Fig. 35,
    58
of *Ictidopsis*, Fig. 20, 35, Fig. 21,
    37, Fig. 28, 49, Figs. 48-52,
    78-82
of *Lasiopyga*, side view, Fig.
    36, 59
of *Loxomma allmani*, Fig. 16,
    facing 28
of man, Australian aboriginal,
    Fig. 53, 85; bones of, Figs.
    48-52, 78-82; side view, Fig.
    36, 59; longitudinal section,
    Fig. 83, 160; infant, front
    view, Fig. 102, 197; Modern
    European, Fig. 44, 70

of *Midas* (marmoset), Fig. 35,
    58
of *Mycterosaurus*, Fig. 19, 33;
    bones of, Figs. 48-52, 78-85
of Neanderthal (Chapelle aux
    Saints), side view, Fig. 42, 68;
    top view, Fig. 43, 69; front
    view, Fig. 44, 70
of *Notharctus osborni*, side view,
    Fig. 33, 55, Fig. 36, 59; top
    view, Fig. 35, 58; bones of,
    Figs. 48-52, 78-82
of opossum, recent, Fig. 27, 48,
    Figs. 49-52, 79-82
of orang, young, Fig. 102, 197
of *Osteolepis*, cross-section, Fig.
    9, facing 20; top view, Fig.
    11, facing 22
of *Palæogyrinus*, Fig. 17, 30;
    bones of, Figs. 48-52, 78-82
of Piltdown, Fig. 42, 68, 141
of *Pithecanthropus*, side view,
    Fig. 42, 68; top view, Fig. 43,
    69; ape-like features of, 72
of Primates, showing progres-
    sive shortening of the muzzle,
    Fig. 36, 59
of *Rhizodopsis*, Fig. 17, 30;
    bones of, Figs. 48-52, 78-82
of Rhodesian man, Fig. 42, 68;
    gorilla-like details of nose, 72
of salamander (foetal), Fig. 62,
    105
of *Scymnognathus*, Fig. 20, 35;
    posterior view, Fig. 21, 37;
    bones of, Figs. 48-53, 78-85
of *Seymouria*, Fig. 19, 33; bones
    of, Figs. 48-53, 78-85
of Talgai man, Fig. 42, 68;
    proto-Australoid type of, 72;
    muzzle of, 143
of *Tarsius spectrum*, Fig. 35, 58
of *Thylacinus*, posterior view,
    Fig. 21, 37; under side of, Fig.
    53, 85
of *Zalambdalestes lechei*, Fig. 29,
    50
Slipper animalcule, mouth of, 4,
    Fig. 1, 5
Smelling organs, of shark, 14, 15,
    17, Fig. 81, 155, 154-156
Smell, sense of, not dominant in
    anthropoid apes, 65; sight
    developed at expense of, by
    pro-anthropoids, 91

INDEX

Smith, G. Elliot, cited on evolution
of primate brain, 63
Sonntag, Charles F., work on
facial muscles, 132
Spaniel, King Charles, ateleosis
in, 231
Spectral tarsier (*Tarsius*), Fig. 31,
facing 53
Spinal cord, of *Amphioxus* (sec-
tion), Fig. 96, 183
Sphenoid bone, 83; sinus of the,
162; effect on the face of the,
170
Sphenoid sinus, connection with
nasal meati, Fig. 85, 163
Sphenodon, head of, Fig. 23, 42
Sphenodon, see also Hatteria
Sphincter colli, as origin of facial
muscles, 43, 44; of Echidna,
Fig. 23, 42; of *Sphenodon*,
Fig. 23, 42; migration of, 132
Splenial bone, evolution of, Fig.
52, 82; reduction of, 88; of
Megalichthys, Fig. 64, 111; of
Trimerorhachis, Fig. 64, 111
Spiracle, of shark, Fig. 6, 13, Fig.
81, 155
Squamosal bone, meniscus between dentary and, in embryo
Perameles, Fig. 22, 38; socket
of lower jaw in the, 39;
evolution of, Fig. 52, 82;
contact with ascending ramus
of dentary in mammals, 87,
108, 109; fused with periodic
mass in mammals, 88; only
remnant of temporo-mandi-
bular series in mammals, 88
Squid, eye of, Fig. 94, 179;
comparison of eyes of, with
those of vertebrates, 179,
180
Stapes, of human ear, Fig. 103,
203, Fig. 111, 216; derivation
of the, 215; of frog, Fig. 106,
208; of *Permocynodon*, Fig.
112, 217; of fœtal armadillo,
Fig. 114, 221; of human
embryo, Fig. 115, 221
Starfish (*Bipinnaria*), larva of,
Fig. 55, 93
Stegocephalians, teeth of the, 115
Stensiö, Erik A.: Son, cited on
ostracoderms, 10–12, 94, 97,
98; on cyclostomes, 97, 98

Stereoscopic vision, of anthropoid
apes, 65; of human eye, 189
Stockard, Charles R., studies on
growth, 172, 231, 238; on
abnormal human and animal
types, 230; classification of
human faces, 232; description
of linear and lateral types,
233–236; Fig. 117, 232; Fig.
118, 234; on crossing of
linear and lateral types, 237
Studnička, F. K., evolution of
vertebrate eye figured by,
Fig. 97, 185; cited on embryology of eye in lampreys, 186
Sturgeon, embryo, hyoid gill clefts
in, 209, Fig. 107, 209
Suboperculum, elimination of, Fig.
17, 30, 114
Sudoriparous glands, origin and
function of, 41
Supraoccipital, membranous part
of the, 83
Supratemporal bone, evolution of,
Fig. 49, 79; reduction of, 88;
loss of, by reptiles, 89
Surangular bone, evolution of,
Fig. 52, 82; reduction of, 88;
of *Megalichthys*, Figs. 64, 111;
of *Trimerorhachis*, Fig. 64,
111; of turtle embryo, Fig.
64, 111
Sweat glands (sudoriparous),
origin and function of, 41
Swede, Nordic, face of, Fig. 90,
facing 172
Sylvan life, assisted divergent
evolution of primates, 57
Symmetry, radial, gives way to
bilateral, 6

Tabular bones, evolution of, Fig.
49, 79; disappearance in
mammals of, 86
Talgai man, skull of, Fig. 42, 68,
72; muzzle of, 143
Tarsioid stock, platyrrhine monkeys as offshoot from some
primitive, 56
Tarsius (the Spectral Tarsier),
Fig. 31, facing 53; mammalian
teeth from Basal Eocene of
Montana related to, 53; top
view of skull of, Fig. 35, 58;
eyes and orbits of, 60, 196

INDEX

Tasmanian aborigines, face of, *frontispiece;* noses of, 169

Taste organs, of sharks, 16

Tatusia, foetal auditory ossicles in, Fig. 114, 221

Tear ducts, Fig. 101, 194; glands, 194

Teeth, evolution of mammalian teeth made possible by change in articulation of jaw, 39; anthropoid food and, 57; human diet and, 57; traces of derivation from primitive anthropoid stage of human, 58; diagrammatic history of primate, Fig. 37, 61; evolution of primate, 63; identity of human and anthropoid molar patterns, 69; changes in teeth of primitive man, 76; pro-mammalian reduction of successional teeth to two sets, 90; true teeth lacking in predecessors of vertebrates, 97; of higher vertebrates, origin in shagreen denticles, 100; origin of, uncertain below ostracoderm grade, 101; of herbivores, not ancestral to carnivorous types, 101; labyrinthodont pattern of, Fig. 18, following 30, 112; gradual elimination of, in upper primary jaw, Fig. 53, 85, 115; summary of early history of, 117; embryonic development of, 134; three stages in development of human, Fig. 71, 135; alleged "triconodont" stage in human, 136; differences between human and anthropoid, 141; reduction of front teeth in man foreshadowed in foetal stages, 143; reduction of, factor in shortening palatal arch, 143; effect of civilization on human, 149; numbers of, in man and anthropoids, 145; comparison with those of *Dryopithecus* and *Sivapithecus,* 149; nose form and, Fig. 89, facing 170, 169; incisors, human, 136; three types of upper central, 138, Fig. 73,

139; canines, dog-toothed type of predatory animals, 115; souvenirs of carnivorous ancestry, Fig. 50, 80, 136; "feminized" aspect of human, 141; diminution of human lower, 144; in functional alignment with incisors in man, 144; premolars, front lower, of anthropoids, 144; human, history of, 146; molars, of anthropoids, 57; comparison of human and cynodont, 145; kinship of human and anthropoid, 146; human, history of, 146; fovea anterior of, in anthropoids and primitive man, 149; fovea posterior of, in anthropoids and primitive man, 149; lower, 149; "cruciform pattern" of, Fig. 80, 151; "*Dryopithecus* pattern" of lower, 149, Fig. 79, 150

of amphibians, 31

of Australian aboriginal, Fig. 80, 151

of chimpanzee, Fig. 74, 140; Fig. 79, 150

of crossopts, on dentary, 108; origin of, 109; structure of fossil, Fig. 18, following 30, 112; attachment to derm bones, 112; advance toward higher vertebrates of, 113; origin of larger teeth of, 117

of cyclostomes, 98, Fig. 60, 99

of cynodonts, Fig. 53, 85, 115; mammal-like dentition, 116

of *Cynognathus,* Fig. 77, 147

of *Deltatheridium,* Fig. 77, 147

of *Diademodon,* Fig. 77, 147

of *Didelphodus,* Fig. 77, 147

of *Dryopithecus, rhenanus,* Fig. 38, 62; *fontani,* Fig. 75, 144, Fig. 79, 150; *cautleyi,* Fig. 75, 144, Fig. 79, 150; *frickæ,* Fig. 41, facing 66; Fig. 79, 150

of Ehringsdorf man, *see* Man, Neanderthal

of Egyptian, Fig. 72, 137

of *Eoanthropus,* Fig. 37, 61, Fig. 38, 62, Fig. 41, facing 66, 72,

Teeth—(*Continued*)
141, 143; *see also* Piltdown man
of ganoids, 23, Fig. 18, following 30
of gorilla, Fig. 72, 137, Fig. 74, 140, Fig. 79, 150; of gorilla child, Fig. 76, 146
of Heidelberg man, 143, Fig. 37, 61, Fig. 80, 151
of Hindu, modern, Fig. 80, 151
of *Homo heidelbergensis, see* Heidelberg man
of *Homo neanderthalensis, see* Neanderthal man
of *Homo sapiens*, Fig. 37, 61, Fig. 38, 62, Fig. 72, 137, Fig. 74, 140, Fig. 75, 144, Fig. 76, 146, Fig. 78, 148, Fig. 80, 151
of *Indrodon*, Fig. 38, 62
of lamprey, 98, Fig. 60, 99
of *Leipsanolestes*, Fig. 38, 62
of *Loxomma allmani*, Fig. 18, following 30
of *Michrochoerus*, Fig. 78, 148
of *Mycterosaurus*, Fig. 77, 147
of Neanderthal man (Ehringsdorf), Fig. 72, 137, Fig. 75, 144, Fig. 80, 151
of Neanderthal man (Le Moustier), Fig. 38, 62, Fig. 72, 137, Fig. 74, 140, Fig. 78, 148, Fig. 80, 151
of orang, Fig. 79, 150
of pantotherian (pro-placental,) Fig. 77, 147
of *Parapithecus*, Fig. 37, 61
of *Pelycodus*, Fig. 37, 61
of Piltdown man, 72; canine of, 141, 143; Fig. 37, 61, Fig. 38, 62, Fig. 41, facing 66; *see also Eoanthropus*
of placental mammals, 52, 53
of *Polyplocodus*, Fig. 18, following 30
of *Pronycticebus*, Fig. 78, 148
of *Propliopithecus*, Fig. 37, 61
of *Scylacosaurus*, Fig. 77, 147
of *Seymouria*, 118
of shark, most primitive (*Chlamydoselachus*), Fig. 5, facing 12; origin of, from shagreen, 19; three stages in development of, Fig. 60, 99;
nearer to those of man than to any known teeth of invertebrates, 102; development of, 100; in typical sharks, 109; not separately connected with jaws, 109; manner of replacement of, 117
of *Sivapithecus*, Fig. 37, 61; Fig. 75, 144
of reptiles, Fig. 53, 85; pro-progressive changes in, 115
of triconodont mammals, 136
Temporal bone, socket of lower jaw in, 39; squamous part of, 83; genesis of, in anthropoids and man, 88.
Temporal fossa, foreshadowed in *Mycterosaurus*, 34; first appearance of, Fig. 48, 78, 116; of *Scymnognathus* and *Ictidopsis*, Fig. 20, 35; origin of, 89; later development of, 90
Temporal muscle, relation to development of temporal fossa, Fig. 48, 78, 116; evolution, of, Fig. 61, 103
Temporal region of skull, effect on the face of, 170
Temporo-mandibular articulation, 87
Temporo-mandibular series, reduction of, Fig. 52, 82, 88
Tenrec, of Madagascar, 52.
Tessera, primitive mouth of, Fig. 1, 5
Tetrapods, bony mask of the earliest, 28
Therapsids, *Ictidopsis*, skull of, Fig. 20, 35; *Scymnognathus*, skull of, Fig. 20, 35.
Theromorph reptiles, *see* Reptiles, mammal-like
Thylacinus (Marsupial Wolf), dentary of, Fig. 21, 37; skull of (under side) Fig. 53, 85
Thymus gland, origin in branchial arches of, 126
Thyroid gland, origin in branchial arches of, 126; effects of deficiency in, 171, 237; effect on growth of face of, 232
Tilney, Frederick, on evolution of primate brain, 63
Tongue, possible part in develop-

INDEX

Tongue—(*Continued*)
ment of secondary palate,
119; lacking in *Amphioxus*,
123; of hags and lampreys,
123; of shark, 123; of amphibians, 123; of mammals, 123;
of early and higher primates,
123; papillæ vallatæ of, in
orang and man, 123; figured
by Klaatsch, 124; of young
gorilla, Fig. 67, 124; of man,
Fig. 67, 124; Fig. 68, 125;
of monkey, Fig. 68, 125;
muscles of, in anthropoids
and man, 125; Robinson
cited on, 126; influence of
human, on evolution of lower
jaw, 126; in human embryo,
126
Tonsils, origin in branchial arches,
126
Tooth-bearing plates, primary
jaws in mammals supplanted
by, 104
Tornaria, larva of *Balanoglossus*,
Fig. 55, 93
Tragus, little known of origin of,
211; development of the, 212
Tree-shrew, pen-tailed, Fig. 30,
facing 52; of Indo-Malayan
region, apparent relation to
Basal Eocene mammals of
Montana, 53; (Cretaceous)
Leipsanolestes siegfriedti, jaw
of, Fig. 37, 61; left lower
molar of, Fig. 38, 62; *Indrodon*, left upper molar of,
Fig. 38, 62
Tremataspis, Fig. 4, 11; characteristics of mouth of, 96
Triassic, *Ictidopsis* of, *frontispiece;*
Fig. 28, 49; hair of mammals
possibly developed during,
42; labyrinthodonts and stegocephalians of, 115; mammal-like reptiles of the, 158
Triconodont mammals, teeth of,
136
Trilobites, mouth-legs of, 6
Trimerorhachis, lower jaw of, Fig.
64, 111
Trinil man, *see Pithecanthropus*
Turbinal bones, early structures
resembling, 158; in monkeys
and man, 161

Turtle, lower jaw of embryo, Fig.
64, 111
Tympanic membrane, 202; Fig.
103, 203
Tympanum, formation by amphibians, 89; Fig. 17, 30, 216; of
human ear, 202; Fig. 103,
203; Fig. 111, 216
Tyrolese, nose of, Fig. 89, 170

Ultra-violet rays, injurious effect
on many organisms, 174
Utriculus, of human ear, 202; Fig.
103, 203

Vertebral column, evolution of
primate, 63
Vertebrates, derivation of, 5;
Patten's theory of derivation
of, 7, 92, 182; orthodox
theory of derivation of, 7, 93;
period of origin of, 8; changed
heritage of, 10; antiquity of,
10; predaceous ancestry of, 12;
jaws of earliest landliving,
25; real ancestors of the
higher, 25; inheritance of
framework of face from lower,
91; characters of ancestors of,
93; origin of mouth of, 94,
Fig. 56, 94; organization of,
adapted to predaceous mode
of life, 101; potentialities of
skin in ancestors of, 100, 101;
gill pouches of embryos of
higher, 102; derivation of jaw
muscles of, Fig. 61, 103, 104;
primary upper jaw of, attached to skull, 104, Fig. 62,
105; primary jaws masked by
secondary, 106; secondary
jaws as evidence of unity of
origin of all, 107; branchial
skeleton of, compared with
human, 128; eyes of invertebrate compared with eyes of,
178; origin of paired eyes of,
178; Patten's theory of derivation of eyes of, 182;
evidence of embryology on
origin of eye of, Fig. 97, 185,
186; Eustachian tube in
higher, 208
Viscera, of Primates, results of
study of, 63

294

INDEX

"Visceral arches," architecture of, 104; in predecessors of the sharks, 104

Vision, the mechanism of, 189; binocular, of Old World monkeys, anthropoids and man, 196; binocular, not possible in *Notharctus*, 196; developed by brachiating habit, 198

Visual cortex of brain, 191

Visual purple (rhodopsin), 189

Vitreous humor, of the eye, 188

Vomer, 83

Watson, D. M. S., studies of fossil amphibia, 28; restoration of skeleton of *Eogyrinus* from data of, 28; contributions to palæontology, 86

Weber, Max, evidence for conclusions on ancestry of placental mammals, 51

Williams, J. Leon, cited on three types of central upper incisors, 138, Fig. 73, 139

Williston, S. W., contributions to palæontology, 86

Williston's law, illustrated, Figs. 48–52, 78–82; loss of opercular series, example of, 114

Wolf, marsupial (*Thylacinus*), under side of skull of, Fig. 53, 85; dentary of, Fig. 21, 37

Worm, annelid, head of, 6; flatworm, 6, Fig. 2, facing 6

Wyoming, *Notharctus* found in Eocene formations of, 54

Yerkes, R. M., cited on agreement of mental traits in man and anthropoid, 74; Fig. 39 copied from photograph by, facing 64

Zalambdalestes, skull and restoration of head, Fig. 29, 50

Ziska, Mrs. Helen, drawings made by, 86

Zygomatic arch, foreshadowed in *Mycterosaurus*, 34; origin of human, 89